# DYING WHILE BLACK

# DYING WHILE BLACK

## VERNELLIA R. RANDALL

SEVEN PRINCIPLES PRESS, INC.
DAYTON, OH

Published by
Seven Principles Press, Inc.
408 Red Haw
P.O. Box 60979
Dayton, OH 45406

http://sevenprinciplespress.com

Cover Designed by: Issa Lateef Randall

Publishers Cataloging—in—Publication Data
Randall, Vernellia R., 1948-
  Dying While Black / Vernellia R. Randall
    292 p.
  Includes endnotes, bibliographical references and index.

  ISBN 0-9779160-0-6

1. African Americans -- Health and hygiene 2. African Americans -- Medical care 3. Discrimination in Medical Care -- United States 4. Race discrimination -- Health aspects -- United States 5. Health Status 6. Civil rights 7. United States -- Race relations 8. Racism -- Health aspects -- United States

FOR MY MOTHER AND BROTHER
BOTH WHO DIED YOUNG
VICTIMS OF AMERICAN RACIAL HEALTH INEQUITIES

My Mother
Mary Pauline Hall
Died at age 36

My Brother
James Ernest Randall
Died at age 56.

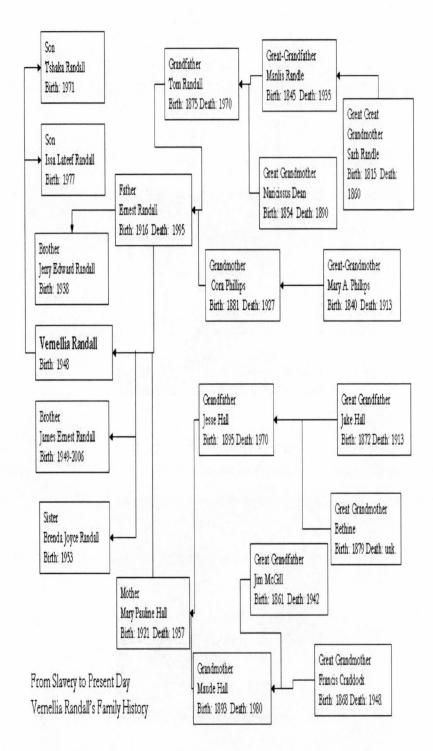

Son
Tshaka Randall
Birth: 1971

Son
Issa Lateef Randall
Birth: 1977

Father
Ernest Randall
Birth: 1916 Death: 1995

Brother
Jerry Edward Randall
Birth: 1938

**Vernellia Randall**
Birth: 1948

Brother
James Ernest Randall
Birth: 1949-2006

Sister
Brenda Joyce Randall
Birth: 1953

Grandfather
Tom Randall
Birth: 1875 Death: 1970

Great-Grandfather
Manlis Randle
Birth: 1845 Death: 1935

Great Great
Grandmother
Sath Randle
Birth: 1815 Death:
1860

Great Grandmother
Narcissus Dean
Birth: 1854 Death: 1890

Grandmother
Cora Phillips
Birth: 1881 Death: 1927

Great-Grandmother
Mary A. Phillips
Birth: 1840 Death: 1913

Grandfather
Jesse Hall
Birth: 1895 Death: 1970

Great Grandfather
Jake Hall
Birth: 1872 Death: 1913

Great Grandmother
Bethine
Birth: 1879 Death: unk.

Great Grandfather
Jim McGill
Birth: 1861 Death: 1942

Mother
Mary Pauline Hall
Birth: 1921 Death: 1957

Grandmother
Maude Hall
Birth: 1893 Death: 1980

Great Grandmother
Francis Craddock
Birth: 1868 Death: 1948

From Slavery to Present Day
Vernellia Randall's Family History

In memory of my brother, James Ernest Randall, the genealogist that did the research that made this chart possible

# My Family

See page 286

For my sons Tshaka and Issa,
my sister Brenda,
my brothers, Jerry and James,
my mother Mary Pauline, my father Ernest
and all my relatives and Ancestors
who suffered or died from
the legacy of
slavery, segregation and racism.

Special Thanks to

# Dr. W. Michael Bryd and Dr. Linda Clayton

For their ground-breaking work:

AN AMERICAN HEALTH DILEMMA: A MEDICAL HISTORY OF AFRICAN AMERICANS AND THE PROBLEM OF RACE, BEGINNINGS TO 1900 (2000).

AN AMERICAN HEALTH DILEMMA: A MEDICAL HISTORY OF AFRICAN AMERICANS AND THE PROBLEM OF RACE – 1900 TO 2000 at 37 (2002).

They coined the term "Slave Health Deficit";
they traced the devastating medical history;
they laid the foundation.

Without their work this book would not exist.

# ACKNOWLEDGEMENTS

I struggled over whether to write specific thanks or general thanks. I did not keep a folder with the names of all the persons who helped me, inspired me and kicked me in the butt to get this book written. I know that I will forget to name someone since over the last 30 years I have stood on the shoulders of many individuals to bring this work to publication. Having said that I want to give my deepest thanks to: my family (Tshaka, Issa, Brenda, Jerry, James Ernest), Kim O'Leary, Andrea Seielstad, Makani Themba Nixon, Stephanie Wildman, Wanda Dillard, Jewel Crawford, Shawn Robinson, Mary Boston and Helen Megson.

For those who I didn't name – please forgive me ---you know you are in my heart.

To all of you I say

Thank you with much love.

# TABLE OF CONTENTS

ILLUSTRATIONS

TABLES

# WHAT LABEL?

The term "African American" and "Black" are used as synonyms for each other and for the terms "colored", "Negro" and "Afro-American". The predicament of Blacks whose history is born out of slavery cannot be overstated. We were captured as members of specific tribes, transformed into African because of the unifying color and continent and were sold as slaves. We were given Anglo names and became property in a very real sense -we had no more legal rights than a horse or a cow. We became their "negroes". After Reconstruction there was a push by Black leaders to give dignity to the name by capitalizing it. So "negro" becomes "Negro". Even still, in 1900 "Colored" competed with Negroes. Many thought that "colored" showed that we were no longer possessions. "Afro-American" was first proposed in 1880, but it never caught on. Through the social unrest of the 1960s we became "Blacks". We wanted respect. We wanted opportunity. We wanted to be proud of our heritage. The 1990s change to "African American" denotes double consciousness and dual cultural heritage.

Each change in label represents a change in attitudes of Blacks toward ourselves and toward others. Ultimately, the changing names of descendants of African slaves represents a continuing struggle by us to gain the power to define ourselves. It represents a struggle to gain social and political power. While powerful groups do not appear to care about how they are labeled (i.e. Americans of British descent), powerless groups frequently try to relabel themselves. Powerful groups who are unwilling to give power often meet these efforts with ridicule and hostility. The power to name is frequently also the power to define. The power to name a group can be the power to position it socially and politically.

# PREFACE

The need to focus on Black health care and health care reform is overwhelming. Not only are Blacks sicker than Whites, they are dying at a significantly higher rate or "Dying While Black." This book explores this problem by making concrete suggestions for eliminating the "Black Health Deficit."

Chapter 1, "Race, Racism and Health', provides the theoretical foundation for understanding the key concepts of race, racism and health. Understanding these concepts are essential to eliminating the Black Health Deficit.

Chapter 2, "From Slave Health Deficit to Black Health Deficit", traces the health deficit of Blacks from slavery through Jim Crow to the twenty-first century. It argues that the deplorable state of Black people's health is directly traceable to slavery. Finally, this chapter argues that "Being Black is Dangerous to Health." It discusses the current health of Blacks. Blacks have disproportionately negative indicators on nearly every health measure, including life expectancy, death rates, infant mortality, low birth weight rates, and disease rates. Blacks are sicker than Whites. Blacks have shorter lives. In short, African Americans are literally dying from being Black

Chapter 3, "Racist Health Care", addresses the racial inequity in the health care system. This inequity exists in access to health care and the quality of treatment received. Racial inequity is manifested in racial barriers that prevent access to hospitals, nursing homes, and physicians and other health care providers. Finally, a shortage of Black health professionals affects both access to health care and minority input into the health care system. The presence of a "racist health care" system is perpetuating the slave health deficit.

However, racial barriers to access are only one aspect of a racialized health care system. The other aspect is racial inequity in the type of services ordered and in the provision of medical treatment. Discrimination in treatment is a substantial factor in inequity in the health of Blacks. It is imperative that the health care system be free of both outright and inadvertent racial discrimination.

Chapter 4, "The Targeting of the Black Community", discusses the targeting of the black community by the tobacco industry. This chapter argues that the tobacco industry's behavior exceeded astute marketing in that they disproportionately flooded the Black community with advertisements and cigarettes. They promoted a more addicting cigarette, and as a result, Blacks are more addicted to nicotine and suffer more from the effects of smoking. The chapter outlines why the national settlement with tobacco companies did not adequately address the needs of the Black community. Specifically, it left the Black community at the mercy of the tobacco companies with little redress for specific harms (addiction and dependency) that had already occurred and will continue to occur.

Chapter 5, " Impact of Managed Care on Blacks" addresses the rationing goal of managed health care organization and its impact on Blacks. Managed care organizations (MCOs) complicate the problem of racially disparate health care because they increase the incentives for providers and facilities to engage in discrimination. MCOs were developed to provide a mechanism of third-party payers and employers to control health care costs. The assumption underlying

MCOs is that reducing the significant over-utilization in the "fee-for-services" system can decrease health care costs. Through "prospective" utilization review and financial risk-shifting (primarily to the providers), MCOs make it easier for both patients and providers to ration health care. Through rationing, managed care may increase the incidence of racially disparate health care treatment by encouraging "unthinking discrimination".

The question of how third-party payers respond to minority communities has remained unanswered. Unfortunately, little is known about how managed care has responded to issues of racial inequity in health services. Yet, without an appropriate response to the needs of Blacks, MCOs are not likely to improve the health of Blacks. In addition, through the inherent force of financial risk-shifting, MCOs may cause providers to increase their "unthinking" discrimination against Blacks. Without careful attention to the problem, managed care will increase the incentives to discriminate based on race.

Chapter 6, "Slavery, Segregation and Racism: It Ain't Always easy to Trust" the Health Care System" discusses the significant distrust towards the health care system in the Black community. This distrust is not just paranoia, it is built on a history of abuses that includes experimentation, the Sickle Cell Screening Initiative, family planning/ involuntary sterilization, and the complicity of the medical system in justifying racism and discrimination. Rebuilding the trust between Blacks and the health care system will be essential if the "Black Health Deficit" is to be eliminated.

Chapter 7, "Health Care in the U.S. as an International Violation of Human Rights" discusses how the combination of racial inequity in health, institutional racism in health care and inadequate legal protection points to serious human rights violations under the International Convention on the Elimination of All Forms of Racial Discrimination (CERD).

Chapter 8, "Reparations: Repairing Black Health" discusses the legitimacy of the demand for reparations, but restructures the call from a compensation request to an equity request. The Slave health deficit-Black Health inequity will be removed only if the United States makes the same significant and sustained commitment that it made to landing on the moon.

In order to eliminate the slave health deficit-Black health inequity, the government will need to do the following: 1. Eliminate racial inequities in disease, illness and deaths, 2. Assure access to quality health care, and 3. Eliminate racial inequities in health care. The burden of a slave health deficit has been a continuous burden and will only be relieved with well-coordinated, aggressive, and comprehensive programs.

Chapter One

# RACE, RACISM AND HEALTH

OVER 100,000 BLACKS DIE EVERY YEAR that would not die if Blacks had the same death rate as Whites. Even when controlling for income and health insurance, Blacks have less access to, and receive a poorer quality of health care than Whites. The current health and health care inequities are directly traceable to slavery. Blacks still suffer from the generational effects of a "slave health deficit", segregation and racism. An organized program of reparations could eliminate the health care gap and repair that health deficit.

In health and in health care, race matters.

## WHAT IS RACE?

As Professor Ian F. Haney Lopez explains, race is a "vast group of people loosely bound together by historically contingent, socially significant elements of their morphology and/or ancestry."[1] Race is not a genetic concept. The notion of genetic differences based on race has been thoroughly refuted.[2] Furthermore, the concept of race has never rested on a firm scientific foundation.[3] Nevertheless, race matters. Race matters because societal privileges and advantages are distributed based on the concept of race. Race is a proxy for that unfairness. Race is an imperfect proxy for marking racism and racial discrimination.

On a genetic basis, there are no races except for the human race. Race is a socially constructed concept, historically constructed around geographically isolated groups and physical characteristics, such as "skin color." Because of this history, some biological and biochemical differences exist among individuals that fall within the socially constructed groups. For example, a study of 853 people with HIV infection found that Central African patients with HIV infection had higher levels of anti-HIV antibodies than did European patients with the HIV infection.[4] In another study, researchers measured blood cotinine levels in 40 Black and 39 White smokers to estimate nicotine uptake while smoking and the rates at which cotinine is eliminated from the body. The researchers found that the nicotine intake per cigarette was 30% greater in Blacks than in Whites, and Blacks eliminated cotinine much more slowly than Whites did.[5] Both studies show that there are biological differences between racial groups. These biological differences may be important in improving quality of health care. However, some use biological difference to argue for the inferiority of Blacks. But in fact, notwithstanding any biological differences, race is primarily a social construction.

19

Race as a social construction of group identity has powerful positive and negative characteristics. As a consequence, a group's identity cannot be readily deconstructed. For instance, race can be compared to geography. The truism that we are one world does nothing to diminish the geopolitical importance of national identity. For example, while in a very real sense, the United States of America is socially constructed; it nevertheless has importance that can not be diminished by saying that we are "one world." Similarly, while it is true that biologically we are only one race, the "socially constructed races" are still of major significance.

If race does not distinguish humans from one another genetically, then why does it matter? "Race" has been shaped by cultural, political, ideological and legal institutions. In other words, "race" is a social construct-something that has meaning only because the society gives it meaning.[6] Such a construct is no less powerful than a biological construct. Once society conveys meaning, that meaning has impact and consequences. Race matters because a core historical American value is intolerance and racism. American society, in short, is racist, and racial discrimination affects health and the access to, and quality of, health care.[7]

Race matters because discrimination based on perceived racial grouping continues to exist. Even though socially constructed, race, like geopolitical constructions, connotes both privilege and deprivation.

My Great-Grandfather's 2nd wife was listed as mulatto in the 1910 census and colored or Negro in later census. My Maternal Grandmother Maude was "enough" Indian that the Bureau of Indian Affairs tried to get her ( and her siblings to enroll). My Grandmother was said to have run them off with a shotgun. My impression was my grandmother's identity was Black. But what both these stories tell me is that racial identity is very much socially constructed, fluid and changing even within a family.

## Race Matters in Health

Inequities in health appear at all income levels.[8] In short, health inequities among Blacks and Whites cannot be attributed to poverty. The current health inequity between Blacks and Whites across economic levels is the cumulative result of both past and current systemic racism in education, housing, employment, and health care.

In general, Blacks have less education and fewer educational opportunities than Whites.[9] Further, Blacks suffer disproportionately from homelessness and have significantly poorer housing options.[10] Blacks also hold a disproportionate percentage of jobs with the lowest pay and the highest health risks. However, even when controlling for income or wealth, racism and racial discrimination continue to exist in health care. The existence of discrimination in all these areas contributes to racism that ultimately affects health. Thus, race is a factor in health.[11]

## Race Matters in Health Care

We live in a world marked by poverty and underdevelopment. Eighty percent of the world's population lives in countries that have access to less than twenty percent of the world's resources, while the other twenty percent of the population consumes more than eighty percent of the resources. Similar inequities in resource distribution occur within the United States. In the United States, race is a major determiner of resource distribution.

Slavery, segregation, and institutional racism resulted in the distribution of resources along racial lines, with whites being privileged and Blacks and other racial and ethnic groups deprived. In fact, race socially constructed all privilege or disadvantage from a past of slavery and colonization and a present built on neo-colonialism, cultural imperialism, and racism.

The legacy of slavery, segregation, and racism have ensured that in most socioeconomic areas, Blacks continue to lag behind Whites. Certainly, poor Blacks have less access to health care than middle-income Blacks, but that is not an appropriate comparison when talking about race and racism. The more appropriate questions are: Do poor Whites have better access to health care than poor Blacks? Do middle-class Whites have a different quality of health care from middle-class Blacks? If so, then it is race, not income that marks the distinction.

Factors affecting health include socioeconomic status, biology, and environment. But in a racist society such as ours, the effect of race is paramount and pervasive. Race also affects the way that health care institutions provide services. Independent of economics, race affects access to and the type and quality of health care that is received. Consequently, to improve the health of Blacks, it is not sufficient merely to remove economic barriers to access. Health care institutions must be more than affordable; they have to be based on equity and distributive justice.[12]

Distributive justice involves the dissemination of social goods. To have distributive justice, not only should similar cases be treated the same, but different cases should be treated differently. However, there must be a morally relevant reason for treating people differently.

A just society is one in which, at a minimum, a person can take advantage of the "normal" range of lifetime opportunities. Individuals must have be healthy to avail themselves of the normal range of opportunities. A just society would assure access to a basic level of services and provide those services in a culturally sensitive and non-discriminatory manner. A just health care system for Blacks must ensure complete access to quality health care and eliminate institutional racism. A just health care system focuses on eliminating the inequities in health care between Blacks and Whites.

## WHAT IS INSTITUTIONAL RACISM?

Any action, intentional or unintentional, that is based on race or skin color and that subordinates an individual or group based on skin color or race is racism. Racism can be enacted individually or institutionally.[13] However, much of the scholarship on racial issues over the last 40 years has focused on individual racism.[14] Nevertheless, institutions are just as capable of being racist. Institutions can behave in ways that are overtly racist (i.e., specifically excluding Blacks from services) or inherently racist (i.e., adopting policies that result in the exclusion of Blacks). Most of the underlying causes for the health inequities are due to institutional racism. As Professor Mary Douglas explains:

> "When individuals disagree on elementary justice, their most insoluble conflict is between institutions . . . . The more severe the conflict, the more useful to understand the institutions that are doing most of the thinking. Exhortation will not help. Passing laws against discrimination will not help. . . . Only changing institutions can help. We should address them, not individuals, and address them continuously, not only in crises."[15]

Institutions can respond to Blacks and Whites differently. Institutional behavior can injure Blacks, and when it does, it is racist in outcome, if not in intent.

Racism is both overt and covert, and it takes three closely related forms: individual, institutional, and systemic. Individual racism consists of overt acts by individuals that cause death, injury, destruction of property, or denial of services or opportunity. Institutional racism is more subtle but no less destructive. Institutional racism involves polices, practices, and procedures of institutions that have a disproportionately negative effect on racial minorities' access to and quality of goods, services, and opportunities. Systemic racism is the basis of individual and institutional racism; it is the value system that is embedded in a society that supports and allows discrimination.

Institutional and systemic racism establishes separate and independent barriers to access and quality of health care. Institutional racism does not have to result from human agency or intention. Thus, racial discrimination can occur in institutions even when the institution does not intend to make distinctions on the basis of race. In fact, institutional discrimination can occur without any awareness that it is happening..[16] Although data on institutional racism in health care is scarce, it does exist.

To understand institutional racism, it is important to understand the interaction between prejudice and discrimination. Prejudice is an attitude that is based on limited information or stereotypes. While prejudice is usually negative, it can also be positive. Both positive and negative prejudices are damaging because they deny the individuality of the person. No one is completely free of prejudices, although they may not have any significant prejudice against a particular group. Oppression is the systematic subjugation of a social group by another social group with access to social power. Power is the ability to control access to resources, the ability to influence others, and access to decision makers. Discrimination is behavior, intentional or not, which negatively treats a person or a group of people based on their racial origins. In the context of racism, *power is a necessary precondition for discrimination.*

Racism depends on the ability to give or withhold social benefits, facilities, services, opportunities etc., from someone who is entitled to them, and is denied on the basis of race, color or national origin. The source of power can be formal or informal, legal or illegal, and is not limited to traditional concepts of power. Intent is irrelevant; the focus is on the result of the behavior.

Given the interaction of prejudice and discrimination, an institution can be a "non-racist", "reformed racist", "reluctant racist", and "overt racist." (Chart 01) Using Blacks as the focal group, a "non-racist" is an institution that has no negative biases or prejudices against Blacks and no discriminatory behaviors. It is very rare that an institution has neither racial bias nor prejudices and engages in no discriminatory behavior. When institutions take the position that they are non-racist, it is possible that the institutions operate in arenas where they have very little contact with Blacks. However, it is more likely that they are in denial about the existence of either prejudices or discrimination.

## Chart 01
## Institutional Racism:
## Distinguishing Prejudice and Discrimination

|  | Presence of Prejudice | |
| --- | --- | --- |
|  | No | Yes |
| No | **Non-Racist**<br>No Prejudice<br>No Discrimination | **Reformed Racist**<br>Prejudice<br>No Discrimination |
| Yes | **Reluctant Racist**<br>No Prejudice<br>Discrimination | **Overt Racist**<br>Prejudice<br>Discrimination |

(Rows labeled by "Presence of Discrimination")

*Based on Robert Merton's formulations

A "reformed racist" institution has definite biases or prejudices against Blacks but does not act on them. For example, an institution could hold a belief that Blacks are more likely to abuse pain medication, but notwithstanding those prejudices, pain medications are prescribed to Blacks equitably. In this situation, the institution makes no difference in health care based on race. This form of racism involves institutions that harbor biases or prejudices but are either too timid to discriminate or who are actively working on not discriminating. The prejudices or biases are still present, but these institutions do not act on them.

An "overt racist" institution has definite bias or prejudice and definite discriminatory behaviors. For example, individuals in an institution could hold a belief that Blacks are more likely to abuse pain medication, and because of those prejudices, pain medications are prescribed to Blacks differently than they would be to Whites. Most people are familiar with this form of racism. Overt racism involves actively and intentionally expressing bias or prejudice and actively discriminating against others in public and private ways. Most discrimination in health care is not overt.

A "reluctant racist" is an institution that purports to have no negative biases or prejudices against Blacks but has definite discriminatory behaviors. For example, an institution could hold no negative beliefs about Blacks but prescribe pain medications differently to Blacks as an indirect result of some other policies. This is the most pervasive form of racism and also the hardest to challenge. Reluctant racism occurs due to mistaken stereotypes, biases or prejudices that are acted out in an unthinking manner or through policies, practices, or procedures of institutions that have a disproportionately negative impact on Blacks.[17] Often, the behavior is motivated by non-race based reasons (e.g. economics). Because of this non-racial motivation, individuals leading and managing institutions often do not believe that their institutions are being racist. Furthermore, it is even more difficult for the institutions to change the behavior. For example, some teaching hospitals do pelvic exams on unconscious female black patients in surgery without the patient's consent in order to train interns, and the hospitals do so without a conscious desire to discriminate. These hospitals would fit into this category of reluctant racist. As Kwame Ture (a.k.a. Stokely Carmichael) and Charles Hamilton explained in their landmark book, "Black Power: The Politics of Liberation":

> "When White terrorists bombed a Black church and killed five Black children, that is an act of individual racism, widely deplored by most segments of the society. But, . . . [when] Black babies die each year because of the lack of proper food, shelter, and medical facilities, and thousands more are destroyed and maimed physically, emotionally, and intellectually because of conditions of poverty and discrimination in the Black community, that is the function of institutional racism."[18]

Once an institution becomes aware of the discriminatory impact of its policies and practices and yet fails to change the policies and practices, then the institution is no longer a "reluctant racist" but an "overt racist".

## WHAT IS HEALTH?

The first step to understanding Black health is understanding the concept of health. Health is difficult to measure.[19] The difficulty in assessing health may result, in part, from a general inability to conceptualize good health. Furthermore, widespread professional disagreement over the meaning of health complicates the search for a definition.

The World Health Organization ("WHO") defines health as "a state of complete physical, mental, and social well-being and not merely the absence of disease or infirmity."[20] However, significant social and cultural barriers prevent Blacks from obtaining the WHO definition of health. The pervasiveness of racism in American society affects Blacks at all economic levels. There cannot be "complete mental and social well-being"[21] for Blacks until the problem of racism has been eliminated.

Health can be defined as a "lifestyle in which an individual attempts to maintain balance and to remain free from physical incapacity while maximizing social capacity."[22] That definition recognizes that an individual's lifestyle affects health and that lifestyle is influenced by social class. It recognizes that Blacks, as a group, surrounded by racism, can never hope to have complete mental well-being.

## Chart 02
## Analyzing Institutional Racism

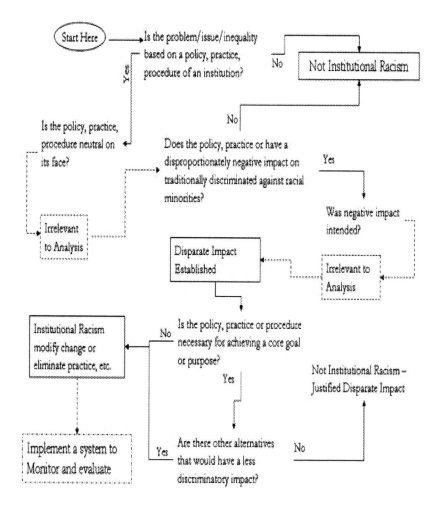

The second definition recognizes that what Blacks must do to maintain balance and remain free from physical and mental incapacity will be different from what is required of Whites. For example, recent discussions of hypertension among Blacks hypothesize that the chronic stress of living in a racist society may be a significant factor in the development of hypertension.[23] If differences in underlying causes of hypertension exist, then the recommended preventive activity for hypertension (a lifestyle of dieting and exercise) might suffice for Whites but may not prevent hypertension in Blacks.

Blacks have shorter life expectancy, more deaths, more illness, more disease, and more disability than Whites. Blacks are sicker than Whites.[24] African Americans are quite literally "Dying While Black." As Louis L. Knowles and Kenneth Prewitt stated:

> "[Blacks] have been subject to victimization in the sense that a system of social relations operates in such a way as to deprive them of a chance to share in the more desirable material and nonmaterial products of a society which is dependent, in part, upon their labor and loyalty. They are 'victimized' also, because they do not have the same degree of access which others have to the attributes needed for rising in the general class system-- money, education, contacts, know-how [and health]."[25]

The lack of good health is perhaps the most significant deprivation caused by racism. While full participation in a society requires money, education, contacts, and know-how, it also requires good health. In fact, health is not only significant in itself, but one's health also affects the availability of choices and the decisions regarding those choices throughout one's life.[26] The lack of prenatal care leads to greater likelihood of infant death, neurological damage, or developmental impairment. Childhood illnesses and unhealthy conditions can reduce learning potential. Adolescent childbearing, substance abuse, and injuries affect long-term health and access to educational and vocational opportunities. Impaired health or chronic disability in adults contributes to low earning capacity and unemployment. Chronic poor health among older adults can lead to premature retirement and loss of independence and self-sufficiency.[27]

Thus, health is an important ingredient in a person's "social position and present and future well-being"[28] especially for Blacks. For people who are born poor, with limited opportunity for quality education and with the burden of racism, health becomes their only tangible asset. When people are subject to racism and discrimination on a daily basis, their health is necessarily compromised regardless of income. Understanding the racist nature of the health care system is critical to appreciating Blacks' health.

## Measuring Health

Being Black in America is dangerous to a person's health. And unlike what most people believe, health is not determined only by socio-economic class. Anyone who thinks that being unhealthy and Black in America is strictly a matter of class or income is wrong. Studies have shown that when controlling for socio-economic class, education, and other indicators of socio-economic status, Blacks are sicker than Whites. Upper-class Blacks, as a group, are sicker than upper-class Whites; Middle-class Blacks, as a group, are sicker than middle-class Whites; and poor Blacks are sicker than poor Whites. Sometimes people want to talk about health inequities by talking about how middle-class Black people are better off than working-class Black people. Of course, that is true, because poverty and class are factors that influence health. However, to understand the impact of race, it is necessary to compare persons of similar economic status. The comparison should be middle-class Blacks to middle-class Whites. When that comparison is made, health and health care inequities between White and Black persist without regard to income.

Several markers are used to determine health: direct observations, records, and self-reporting.[29] Each type of measurement presents its own problems. First, inaccuracies can occur in direct observations due to variations in medical practices and diagnostic labeling. That variation may not only be by geography or region but also by differences among physicians and hospitals.[30]

Second, errors in interpretation can result if researchers misconstrue symptoms and results or when researchers make inaccurate generalizations on the basis of a different time or a more general population group.[31] Finally, failure to consider intra-ethnic differences among Blacks may lead to erroneous conclusions about Black health. Studies should account for the potentially large differences between northern and southern Blacks, urban and rural Blacks, or native and foreign-born Blacks.[32] The overall data on health of Blacks is so significant that these measurement issues are minor.

Many of the articles and books discussing the health of Blacks rely heavily on death rates. The analysis presented here utilizes a broad range of health measurements to give the reader a thorough view of Black health and a strong basis for assessments. Although more comprehensive, this approach presents some challenges. Some of the more subjective measurements, such as discomfort and symptom reporting, appear ambiguous regarding the health of Blacks in comparison to Whites. However, the strong objective data (death rates, disease rates, etc.) clearly indicates that Blacks have poorer health and that more Blacks are dying than Whites. The contradictory results of some subjective measurements do not disprove this. In fact, these apparent discrepancies show subjective reporting differences and the problems that institutions will face if they rely only on subjective data for health analysis.

Whatever the difficulty in measuring health, understanding the full extent of differences in health between Black and Whites is essential to fully appreciating the need for a comprehensive sustained approach to eliminating health inequities. Notwithstanding that the availability of data varies across the time span in question (Pre-slavery to 2000), clear evidence of the Slave deficit exist.

The inequity between Black and White health is demonstrated through life expectancy, death rates, low birth-weight rates, disease and illness rates, disability rates, and discomfort rates.

### Life Expectancy

Life expectancy is defined as the average number of years of life that is expected at birth if current death rates remain constant.[33] Life expectancy is a measure of the general health of a population and is internationally accepted as the gold standard for comparing health between different population groups.[34]

### Death Rate

While health, illness, and morbidity are poorly defined, and the transition from good health to poor health can be gradual, death is definitive. The death rate is the most reliable indicator of the health of a population. However, even this information presents measurement problems. The number of deaths and causes of deaths for Blacks and Whites is obtained from death certificates and autopsy reports. The amount and quality of data on mortality vary and depend on the extent to which the deceased received medical care before death, the degree of familiarity the physicians who certified the death had with the deceased, changes in diagnostic and demographic terminology, frequency of misclassifications, and the accuracy and completeness of the information.[35] Furthermore, comparisons of death statistics for Blacks and Whites may reflect "survivor effects as well as selection by competing causes which can lead to interpretive errors."[36] Nevertheless, death rates for Blacks tell an interesting story, Blacks die younger than Whites.

### Low Birth-Weight Rate

Low birth weight is a common measurement of the potential health of infants. Low birth-weight is defined as a birth-weight less than 2500 grams (or 5.5 pounds). Prior to the 1960s, low birth-weight infants had a very small chance of survival and even as survival rates have improve, underweight babies disproportionately suffer from extensive handicaps, including severe and moderate developmental delays, cerebral palsy, seizure disorders, blindness, hearing defects, and behavioral, learning, and language disorders.[37] Therefore, low birth-weight is an objective measurement of future health.

### Disease and Illness

Health may also be based on the presence of disease and illness. Disease can be divided into acute and chronic conditions. Acute conditions last less than two weeks, and include conditions such as colds and minor injuries.[38] Chronic conditions last two weeks or longer, and include diseases or impairments that are likely to be permanent. Such diseases range from life-threatening conditions such as heart disease to those that can result in considerable debilitation, such as arthritis.[39]

Most researchers determine the presence of disease in a population by reviewing hospital medical records or through self-reporting. When measures of Black health are based on self-reports of acute conditions, Black health appears to be better than that of Whites. Like other records, hospital medical records also have their shortcomings. [40] For example, because not all illnesses are covered in medical records, the records may present an incomplete picture of the illnesses of a population. Moreover, to the extent that Blacks have limited access to non-emergency hospital care, diseases may be under-reported.

## Disability

Disability is defined as the inability to engage in employment or as the short- or long-term reduction of a person's activities because of a health condition.[41] Health researchers use time spent in bed due to disability, work loss days, or restricted activity to report disability rates.[42] Time spent in bed is a measure of the result of disability and doesn't represent people who can work, but can only work in a limited capacity. Work loss days can be assumed to measure disability rates, but there is are many reasons people miss work (eg. illness in the family, individual tolerance towards illness) nor related to disability.[43] Restricted activity days is the most accurate of these three methods of measuring disability rates and despite the risk of interpretive error, restricted activity days are accepted as the best way to measure disability rates and health.[44]

## Dissatisfaction and Discomfort Rates

Dissatisfaction is the degree of discontentment a person has with his or her health.[45] Dissatisfaction information is collected by population surveys, individual and household surveys, and surveys of hospitalized patients. It is assumed that a person in poor health will be more dissatisfied than a person in good health. Because it relies on this self-evaluation, dissatisfaction is the most subjective of the health measurements. In fact, the reasons for dissatisfaction with health vary not only based on an individual's situation, but also on ethnicity, race, and culture. Consequently, it is subject to many potential interpretive errors.[46] Discomfort is the level of aches and pains, fatigue, and sadness.[47] Discomfort information is obtained through self-reporting and is subject to considerable measurement error.[48]

# Chapter Two

---

# SLAVE HEALTH DEFICIT TO BLACK HEALTH INEQUITIES

The health of Blacks is directly traceable to slavery. The enslavement of Africans was inherently dangerous. There were health hazards and high death rates during the African trek, the middle passage, the breaking-in period and the enslavement. Essential to understanding the slave health deficit is understanding the health status of Africans prior to the slave trade. The slave health deficit became black health inequity – a national crisis.

## THE SLAVE HEALTH DEFICIT[1]

To understand "The Slave Health Deficit", it is essential to understand racial stereotypes of Africans. Popular media promotes a vision that the African continent was populated by uncivilized individuals. Today's stereotypes have their roots in legal history. For instance, in 1822 in *United States v. La Jeune Eugenie*, the court held that Africans were incapable of ruling themselves and therefore benefited from slavery.

Never before has the Black race of Central Africa, from the dawn of history to the present day, attained a condition so civilized and so improved, not only physically, but also morally and intellectually. The Honorable Judge Leon Higginbotham, Jr. quoted John C. Calhoun, Speech on the Reception of Abolition Petitions:

> "It [Black race] came among us in a low, degraded, and savage condition, and in the course of a few generations it has grown up under the fostering care of our institutions, reviled as they have been, to its present comparatively civilized condition. This, with the rapid increase of numbers, is conclusive proof of the general happiness of the race, in spite of all the exaggerated tales to the contrary."[1]

---

[1] The term "Slave Health Deficit" was coined by Dr. Michael Bryd and Dr. Linda Clayton in their ground-breaking work: An American Health Dilemma: A Medical History of African Americans and the Problem of Race, Beginnings to 1900 (2000) and An American Health Dilemma: a Medical History of African Americans and the Problem of Race – 1900 to 2000 at 37 (2002)

In reality, Africa was at least as civilized as any other continent.[2] In fact, numerous examples of civilized trading cultures include the great Trading Empires of Ghana (salt and gold), Mali (gold), Timbuktu, Songhai, Luband Luanda (copper, salt), Zimbabwe, and the Kongo kingdom.[3] At the time of enslavement, African people demonstrated a high level of sophistication, as evidenced by the use of currency, the breeding of animals, the smelting of iron, steel, and copper, and establishment of cities with populations as large as thirty thousand.[4]

Like civilizations everywhere, the populace suffered from various health problems.[5] In particular, persons in west and central Africa prior to the slave trade suffered from infectious diseases such as malaria, yellow fever, and sleeping sickness.[6] But they also had immunities to local diseases.[7] In short, Africans had their fair share of illness and death before being captured as slaves, and the African environment was as deadly to Whites as the Americas were to Africans. For instance, during the colonization of Africa, 60% of Whites died within their first eight months on the African continent.[8]

When it came to the health of captive Africans, slave traders were not likely to capture and keep obviously unhealthy persons since such individuals would be more likely to die during the Trans-Atlantic passage. Thus, at the start of the transition from free African to slave, Africans who made it on to the slave ship were probably the healthiest of those captured. The journey affected not only their legal status but also their health. The journey was hazardous, and there were health dangers and high death rates during every phase: (1) the interior trek, (2) the middle passage, (3) the breaking-in period. and (4) the enslavement. The beginning of the "Slave Health Deficit" started with this long journey.

## The Interior Trek

There were numerous health hazards during the slave capture. A common myth is that Africans captured for slavery were only from the "Gold Coast." However, the reality was that of the estimated 20 to 50 million Africans who were enslaved, many were bought or kidnapped from as far away as 1000 miles inland from the coast. For those Africans, in irons and shackles while being whipped, there was a long and arduous trek across the interior. During that trek, persons from many different regions were crowded together and exposed to illness, and of course, there were illnesses caused by the exposure to germs common in Europe but uncommon in Africa. At the end of the trek, Africans were crowded into slave dungeons where they waited for "weeks, months, sometimes as long as a year" before being shipped to the Americas.[9] The death rate for Africans from capture to point of departure is estimated to be about 50%.; and, of the roughly 20 to 50 million who were stolen and kidnapped from their homes and sold into slavery, half never made it out of Africa; they died along the way.[10]

## The Middle Passage

For those who survived, they then faced the infamous Middle Passage, so called because it was the middle leg of a three-part voyage -- a voyage that began and ended in Europe. The first leg carried cargo such as iron, cloth, brandy, firearms, and gunpowder. At Africa's "slave coast", the cargo was exchanged for Africans. For the middle leg, the ships sailed to the Americas where the African slaves were exchanged for products, such as sugar and tobacco.[11] The final leg took the ship back to Europe.

During the middle passage slaves were crowded into decks that held over 400 people.[12] These spaces had little ventilation, and often not even enough space to place buckets for human waste.[13] According to Olaudah Equiano, a slave who wrote and published his autobiography in 1789,

> "The closeness of the place, and the heat of the climate, added to the number in the ship, which was so crowded that each had scarcely room to turn himself, almost suffocated us. This produced copious perspiration, so that the air soon became unfit for respiration, from a variety of loathsome smells, and brought on a sickness among the slaves, of which many died."[14]

While many Africans preferred to die, because of the African's economic values, suicide was not an option that was allowed by the ship masters.[15] An African who tried to starve him or herself was tortured.[16] If torture did not work, the slave was force fed with the help of a contraption called a *speculum orum* which held the mouth open.[17] Nevertheless, middle passage death rates were very high. Space was so crowded that people had to lie in each other's feces, urine, or blood.[18] Africans died from malaria, malnutrition, small pox, yellow fever, scurvy, worms, and typhoid fever.[19] The main killer was "bloody flux" or amebic dysentery.

Furthermore, many Africans were thrown overboard, some in an attempt by the crew to prevent epidemics, but others in an effort to maximize profits.[20] Owners maximized profits by collecting insurance on drowned slaves. Voyages were insured, but the insurance would not pay for sick slaves or even those killed by illness.[21] However, it would cover slaves lost through drowning.[22] Finally, deaths from insurrections were high.[23] As can be expected, Africans were "dejected, depressed and despondent" and as a result took every opportunity to revolt.[24] Alexander Falconbridge noted:

> "As very few of the Negroes can so far brook the loss of their liberty and the hardships they endure, they are ever on the watch to take advantage of the least negligence in their oppressors. Insurrections are frequently the consequence; which are seldom expressed without much bloodshed. Sometimes they are successful and the whole ship's company is cut off." [25]

Thus, the death rates on some ships ran as high as 80%. While it is difficult to determine how many Africans died during the middle passage, estimates place the death rate between 10% and 30%.[26] As a result of the conditions of the slave trade, Black slaves arrived into the Americas less healthy than most other populations.

## The Breaking-in Period

Slaves who survived the middle passage were taken to the Caribbean for a "breaking-in period." This period lasted anywhere from 6 months to 3 years. During this period Africans had to make numerous adjustments. There were adjustments to a cold climate that resulted in many illnesses. But the biggest adjustments were the loss of language, loss of culture and loss of family, all taking a heavy mental health toll resulting in high incidence of depression, anxiety, psychosis and suicide.[27] Finally, Africans continued to be exposed to new germs which resulted in a high incidence of plague, pneumonia, influenza, typhoid and yellow fever.[28] The death rate during this period was 30% to 50%.[29]

## The Enslavement

Blacks in slavery continued to suffer serious deprivation, poverty, mental abuse, and physical abuse. Slaves' houses were cabins with packed dirt floors. These houses were leaky and drafty, and as a consequence, were prime disease producing environments.[30] In addition, slaves often lacked adequate clothing and were unable to keep the clothes clean since they were only able to change and wash their clothes weekly. Thus, their clothing was another disease producing environment.

As to diet, slave owners typically gave slaves a weekly allowance of food. This weekly allowance, while somewhat sufficient in bulk, was generally not nutritionally adequate. For instance, for many slaves, the basic weekly diet consisted of cornmeal and salt pork. Some slave owners allowed their slaves to attempt to supplement their food allocations with fish and game.[31] However, in total, slave diets made the slaves susceptible to nutrition related diseases and malnutrition.[32] In a vain attempt to supplement their diet, some ate dirt (Caehixia Africana).[33] The dietary deficiency diseases included pellagra, beriberi, and scurvy.

While both Whites and Blacks were very vulnerable to epidemic and endemic diseases, the proportion of illness and death was substantially higher for Blacks.[34] (Table 02-01; Table 02-02) Lower living standards, greater exposure, heavier labor, and poorer medical care gave slaves a shorter life expectancy and a higher death rate than Whites.[35] (Table 02-01)

Because of the immunities that they brought from Africa for yellow fever and malaria, slaves suffered fewer fatalities from these diseases than Whites.[36] However, when infected with other diseases, slaves had significantly higher death rates. Common diseases that affected slaves were cholera and pulmonary diseases such as pneumonia and tuberculosis.[37] In Mississippi, one study indicated that 80% of slaves died from tuberculosis.[38] Other diseases that ravaged the slave population were dysentery, diarrhea, measles, mumps, influenza, whooping cough, dengue, scrofula, scarlet fever, rheumatism, typhoid, typhus, smallpox, diphtheria, dropsy, and tetanus.[39] Adult slaves also suffered from mental and nervous disorders.[40] The result of all this disease and death was that slaves had a shorter life expectancy than whites. Estimated longevity at birth for a male slave was 30 years and 32 years for female, at least 5-8 years less than Whites.[41]

With the legal elimination of the Atlantic slave trade in 1807, slave breeding became a necessary component of the slave system.[42] Slave women were "encouraged, cajoled, and coerced" to become pregnant.[43] The growth of slavery, despite the ending of the slave trade, is evidence of deliberate slave breeding. In the United States slavery grew exponentially. In 1619 the United States population included only 20 Blacks, in 1790 the slave population was 757,181, in 1820 there were 1,771,656 slaves, and by the end of the Civil War there were over 4,441,830 slaves.[44]

This desire for more slaves did not translate into better care for slave women, men, or children. Even while pregnant, slave women were over-worked and deprived of proper nutrition. During their pregnancies, slave women received no medical care and as a result, slaves were two to three times more likely than Whites to be sterile, to have spontaneous abortions and stillbirths, and to die during childbirth.[45] Slave women had a greater frequency of irregular and painful menstruation and infections of the uterus and cervix.[46]

Slave children also suffered. They started their lives with poor health from the effects of prenatal malnutrition and shortened periods of breast-feeding. They played in a disease-infested environment and lacked health care.[47] As a consequence, infant slaves had high death rates and low birth weights. (Table 02-02; Table 02-03) The life expectancy at birth for slaves in 1850 was 35.5 years,[48] and slaves at every age died at higher rates than Whites. (Table 02-02; Table 02-03)

Slaves suffered mental and physical illnesses and injuries from the violence that was an inherent part of the slave system.[49] Slaves were whipped, beaten, mutilated, branded, and chained for long periods. Slaves were murdered with impunity.[50] The physical and emotional torture was frequent, unpredictable, gruesome, and indiscriminate of age or gender. Slave women were raped by any white male who wanted them.[51] In fact, some studies indicate that anywhere from 4% to 8% of slave children were the result of rape.[52]

Death from violence was also a result of the high incidence of slave revolt. In 1816, one of the most significant slave revolts took place where 300 Slaves with about 20 American Indian allies held Fort Blount, on Apalachicola Bay, Florida, for several days before it was attacked by United States troops.[53] In 1822, Denmark Vesey led one of the most elaborate enslaved African plots on record, involving thousands of slaves in Charleston, South Carolina, and its vicinity.[54] Authorities arrested 131 slaves and four Whites.[55] Thirty-seven slaves were hung, Vesey and five of his aides were hanged at Blake's Landing, Charleston, South Carolina.

Like most Blacks whose family history is born out of United States slavery, I cannot name all the love ones who made it through the African Trek, the Middle Passage, the Breaking-In Period or most of the Enslavement. But I do know a few.

On my father's side of the family. My Great-Great Grandmother Sarh Randle was born in 1815 and died at age 45. I don't know the cause of her death or any details of her life and while she lived longer than the average female slave, I feel confident that she suffered a lifetime of pain, humiliation and debasement.

At the end of slavery (1865), Great-Grandfather Manlis Randle was 23 years old. Great-Grandfather Manlis is the father of Grandfather Tom. Great-Grandfather Manlis lived significantly longer than average male slave, dying at 81 years old. He outlived Great-Grandmother Narcissa Dean who was 11 years old when slavery ended; 17 years old when they married; and 36 years old when she died. Together they had five children: Clem, Mary Bell, Benny, Tom, Morselle, Estelle, Fozelle and Extra. It is possible that Great-Grandmother Narcissa died during childbirth because she died the same year that Extra was born. Great-Grandfather Manlis married Lou Weaver the same year that Great-Grandmother Narcissa died and was divorced 10 years later. They had no children. He married Emma (last name unknown) in 1909. Interestingly she is identified as mulatto in both the 1910 and the 1920 census. Great-Grandfather Manlis did well after slavery. According to the 1910 census, at age 65 he was a retail merchant, a land-owner with a mortgage free house. Grandfather Tom Randall was born 1875. Grandfather Tom changed the spelling of the family name from Randle to Randall because a white man told him he was spelling it wrong. Given that it was a slave name I don't see that it mattered, but it mattered to Grandfather Tom. Great-Grandmother Mary Phillips was 25 years old at the end of slavery and lived to be 73 years old. Again, she lived longer than average black person of her generation. Great-Grandmother Mary was the mother of Grandmother Cora Phillips.

On my mother's side of the family. Great-Grandfather Jim McGill was 4 years old at the end of slavery. Great-Grandfather Jim was the father of Grandmother Maude McGill Hall.

In 1829, race riots in Cincinnati, Ohio (a free state), were so serious that more than 1,000 Blacks left the city for Canada.[57] In 1831, Nat Turner led a revolt in Southampton County, Virginia that resulted in some 60 Whites being killed. Nat Turner was eventually captured and hung.[56] In 1859, John Brown attacked Harpers Ferry, Va. with five slaves and 13 Whites.[57] Two slaves were killed, 2 captured, and one escaped..[58] All of these examples point to the long-term impact of violence on the health of enslaved Africans and their descendants.

## Summary

During slavery, Blacks suffered demoralizing physical and mental conditions, lack of health care, and emotional and physical violence, not to mention neglect. It should be no surprise that at the end of slavery, significant health inequities between Whites and Blacks existed.

# BLACK HEALTH INEQUITIES

Africans arrived in the United States after surviving a highly lethal journey that killed over half of those captured. The process of transforming Africans into property harmed both their mental and physical health. As slaves, they were sicker and lived shorter lives. The inequity in health that existed during slavery continued through the Civil War and reconstruction, the Jim Crow era, the Civil Rights era, and the Racial Re-entrenchment period.

## Civil War and Reconstruction: 1861 to 1879

The Civil War started not over slavery but over the secession of the southern states from the Union. Two nations were established: the United States of America (also known as the Union or the North) and the Confederate States of America (also known as the South or the Rebels). The two nations fought the Civil War over the issue of secession. A byproduct of the Civil War was the freeing of the slaves. The end of slavery did not occur until after the end of the Civil War and the passage of the 13th amendment in 1865. After the end of slavery, the South entered a period that has been called Reconstruction. During both periods (the Civil War and the Reconstruction), the United States made no progress in closing the "Black Health Inequities."

### The Civil War: 1861-1865

When discussing the health of Blacks during this period, it is important to focus on both Blacks in the military and Black civilians. For both groups, the Civil War extended the health deficit. At the start of the Civil War, federal law barred Blacks from serving in the military. However, several states enrolled slaves in state militias. For instance, Missouri and South Carolina emancipated slaves in their military regions and permitted them to enlist. By the middle of 1862, the Federal government withdrew the ban on Blacks serving in the military because of the escalating number of former slaves, the declining number of White volunteers, and the increasingly pressing personnel needs of the Union Army. With the passage of the Second Confiscation and Militia Act, Congress provided freedom for slaves whose owners were in the Confederate Army and allowed for the enlistment of those freed slaves and other free Blacks. [59] By the end of the Civil War, 179,000 Black men had served in the Union Army (approximately 10% of the army) and another 19,000 had served in the Navy. Nearly 68,000 Black soldiers died during the war, but more than 3/4 of the deaths were from disease.[60] While death during the Civil War was high for both Blacks and Whites, Blacks had a disproportionately high number.

As the South suffered social disorganization and chaos, the slaves' situation deteriorated. Death rates and suffering from disease and malnutrition worsened. Furthermore, as White men went to war, slaves were used in unfamiliar industrial labor that resulted in a significant increase in occupational injuries.[61] The health situation for the Black civilian population (free Blacks and slaves) deteriorated during the Civil War.

## Reconstruction: 1865-1879

During this period, the Black health inequity increased.[62] Epidemic levels of small pox, yellow fever, and cholera existed throughout the South, Washington, D.C., and some Northern communities.[63] While the epidemic affected both Black and White communities, Black communities were disproportionately impacted.[64] For example, Black death rates from tuberculosis were four times higher than those experienced by Whites.[65]

Violence also increased against the Black population. Between 1866 and 1879, over 3,500 Blacks were murdered.[66] The Reconstruction period, which should have been one of reparations and reconstruction of the Black community, turned out to be just another period of deprivation and extreme neglect. The health inequity between Whites and Blacks continued.

During civil war and reconstruction (1861 through 1879) on my father's side of the family, Grandfather Tom Randle (Randall) was born in 1875. Grandfather Tom lived to 95 years, much older than most Blacks of his generation.

On my mother's side of the family, Great-Grandfather Jake Hall was born in 1872. Great- Grandmother Bethine was born in 1879. Great-Grandfather Jake and Great-Grandmother Bethine were the parents of Grandfather Jesse Hall. Great-Grandmother Francis Craddock was born in 1868 and she lived 60 years. Great-Grandmother Francis was the mother of Grandmother Maude McGill Hall.

## The Jim Crow Era: 1880 to 1954

Jim Crow was not a person. Rather, the Jim Crow era took its name from a popular 19th-century minstrel song that stereotyped Blacks. Jim Crow came to personify the system of legally-sanctioned racial oppression and segregation in the United States. Health-wise, the period can be divided into three periods: Early Years (1880 to 1900), Middle Years (1901 through 1929), and Final Years (1930 to 1954).

### The Early Years: 1880 through 1900

The census conducted in 1890 showed that Black birth rates were lower than White birth rates for the first time.[67] Black death rates, however, increased between 1870-1890.[68] In 1900, the estimated life expectancy for Blacks was 32.5 years for males and 33.5 years for females.[69] Life expectancy for Black males was 14.1 years less than White males, and Black females was 15.2 years less than White females.[70] (Table 02-04, Table 02-05) Anti-Black violence escalated during this period, and the lynching of Blacks peaked with over 74 deaths per year being recorded.[71]

---

During the early years (1880 through 1900), Grandmother Cora Phillips Randall was born in 1881; and, she lived 44 years. Grandfather Tom's first wife (name unknown) was killed at 18 years old in a horse and buggy accident.

---

### The Middle Years: 1901-1929

Since a standard registry for deaths was not established until 1933, it is difficult to accurately determine death rates before this time.[72] However, examination of historical and statistical records does provide some information.[75] Throughout the period of 1901-1929, Blacks continued to experience infant death rates at twice the rate of Whites.[73] Deaths due to complications of childbirth, such as infection and hemorrhage, were common throughout the South where few Black women had access to physician-assisted birth.[74]

The 1920's Black death rate in Harlem was 42% higher than the death rate of Whites in New York City.[75] Black death rates from syphilis, heart disease, rickets, and cancer exceeded White death rates.[76] For example, in Chicago, the Black death rates were twice those of Whites even though Chicago boasted the lowest death rate for large cities.[77]

Blacks began to see an improvement in health around 1910 Death rates declined, longevity increased, and the infant mortality rate decreased, but the improvement in health in the Black community did not keep pace with improvements seen by Whites.[78] Further, Blacks were victimized in large numbers by involuntary sterilization after the Supreme Court upheld such practices in 1927 in *Buck v. Bell*.[79]

## The Final Years: 1930 to 1954

Excess death is the number of deaths that occur each year per 100,000 population, that would not have occurred if Blacks had the same death rate as Whites. For instance, in 1950, there were 266 excess or preventable deaths among Black men per 100,000 population

---

During the middle years (1901 through 1929), on father's side of family, Grandfather Tom and Grandmother Cora was married in 1904. They had 9 children: Ora (1903), Elbert (1905), Mary (1907), James Calvin (1909), Ola B (1911), Elmer (1914), Ernest (1916), Exa Charlesetta (1919) Arthur Leon (1921). Two of the children died in childhood: Elbert (age 1 year) and Exa (age 12 years).

Grandmother Cora died in 1927 at age 46 of dropsy (swelling from excessive accumulation of serous fluid in tissue). My Father (Ernest) was 11 years old when his mother died and he remembers being sent outside regularly to get a switch (a slender flexible rod, stick, or twig, especially one used for whipping) and then having to whip her leg so the fluid could leak out. This was Grandmother Cora's primary treatment.

On mother's side of family, Grandfather Jessie and grandmother Maudie were married in 1918. They had eight children: Arlee, Mary Pauline, Matthew, Teresa, Red, John, Barbara and Betty. Of those children Pauline, Teresa, Red and John all died in young adulthood. Pauline was my mother and she died at 36 years old.

---

Although Blacks gained an average of twenty years to their expected life span between 1900-1940, the death rate of Blacks remained higher than that of Whites.[80] Much of the improvement can be credited to better sanitation, malaria prevention, and some improvement in the Black lifestyle.[81] By 1940, the number of children dying before the age of 5 declined 66%[82] However, significant inequity between Blacks and Whites continued.[83]

In 1950, Black males had an estimated life expectancy of 59.1 years and Black females had a life expectancy of 62.9 years. This meant that Black males lived 7.4 years less than White males, and Black females lived 9.3 years less than White females.[84] (Table02-04, Table 02-05) The excess death rate (311.3) was one of the lowest in the last 70 years. Fetal death rate was slightly less than 2.0 per 1000 live births. (Table 02-06) In 1950s, Black children led very fragile lives. For instance, the death rate for Black females and Black males aged 1-4 years was 10 times the death rate of White children of the same age. (Table 02-07; Table 02-08) In the period between 1945-1954, Black health still lagged behind that of Whites, but the gap had begun to close.[85]

In 1950, the age-adjusted death rate from all causes for Black males was 1,909.1 per 100,000 population and 1,642.5 for White males. There were 266.6 excess deaths per 100,000 population. Black males had excess deaths in every age group except 75 years and older. (Table 02-07 to Table 02-10) The age-adjusted death rate for Black females from all causes was 1,545.5, and 1,198 for White females. The excess deaths were 347.5 per 100,000 population. Black females had excess deaths in every age group except 75 years and older. (Table 02-07 to Table 02-10)

In the 1930s, tuberculosis and pneumonia continued to be deadly diseases for Blacks, causing one fifth of adult deaths.[86] However, by 1950, the primary causes of death were cerebro-vascular disease, influenza, pneumonia, and homicide. [87] In fact, Blacks had excess deaths from every cause except cancer (malignant neoplasms), chronic liver disease and cirrhosis, and suicide. [88] (Table 02-11)

## The Civil Rights Era: 1954 to 1980

The Supreme Court's 1954 decision in *Brown vs Board of Education* declared the concept of "separate but equal" – the basis of Jim Crow segregation - as unconstitutional and marked the beginning of the Civil Rights era. Furthermore, in 1964, Congress passed Civil Rights statutes intended to prevent discrimination based on race. But although there were significant advances made in civil rights during this period, the progress in eliminating the slave health deficit and the Black health inequities was uneven.

For Black men, this period marked a decreasing life expectancy and a widening of the gap between Black males and White males. In 1960, the estimated life expectancy for Black men was 61.1 compared to White men's 67.4. That represented a 6.3 difference and a 1.1 decrease from 1950. By 1970, Black men's life expectancy had decreased to 60 years while White men's life expectancy increased to 68, representing an 8-year gap. By the 1980's, Black men's life expectancy increased to 63.8 and White men's to 70.7. This represented a 1.2 year decrease in the racial gap.[89] (Table 02-04)

Black women, on the other hand, continued to experience a decrease in life expectancy over the entire 26-year period. In 1960, the estimated life expectancy for Black women was 66.3 compared to White women's 74.1. That represented a 7.8 year difference and a 1.5 year decrease from 1950. In 1970, the life expectancy for Black women continued to increased to 68.3 years, while White women's life expectancy increased to 75.6 resulting in a 7.3 year difference and a .5 year decrease from 1960.[90] (Table 02-05) By the 1980's, the life expectancy gap had decreased by 1.7 years. (Table 02-05)

Notwithstanding this overall decrease in the life expectancy gap, Black women remained 4.1 times more likely than White women to die from complications of pregnancy, childbirth, and postpartum complications.[91] (Table 02-16) This difference increased to 4.5 by 1970 and dropped to 3.7 by 1980. (Table 02-16) The infant death rate declined significantly between 1965-1980 for both Whites and Blacks, declining by over 50%.[92]

In 1965, Black infant deaths occurring between birth and the first twenty eight days of life were 1.58 times higher then that of White infants.[93] However, the extremely high death rate for children ages 1 to 4 in 1950 was reduced by 1980 to only 1.7 times the White rate. (Table 02-14, Table 02-15) Similarly, Black women were twice as likely as White women to have low birth weight babies in the 1960's.[94]

From 1950 to 1970, the excess Black death rate increased from 311.3 to 324. This means that despite the increase in life expectancy, the number of preventable deaths increased. In 1980, the age-adjusted death rate from all causes for Black males was 1,697.8 and 1,317.6 for White males per 100000 population. The excess deaths were 380.2 per 100,000 population. Thus, the excess deaths for Black males increased from 266 to 380 from 1950 to 1980. Black males had excess deaths in every age group except 75 years and older. (Table 02-08) The age-adjusted death rate for Black females from all causes was 1,545.5 and 1,198 for White females. The excess deaths were 347.5 per 100,000 population. Black females had excess deaths in every age group except 75 years and older. (Table 02-07).

Blacks continue to lag behind in important health indicators. Far more needs to be done to erase the health inequities that exist between Blacks and Whites. During the Civil Rights period, integration of medical facilities, increased numbers of minority health professionals, and government intervention to create access for more people could not overcome the legacy of need.[95]

## Racial Re-Entrenchment: 1981 to 1997

There has been a legal and social retreat from the civil rights achievements of the previous period. From 1981 to 1997, along with that retreat, came a slowing down of the improvement --and in some cases, a worsening—of Black health.

Between 1980 and 1990, Black men's life expectancy increased from 63.8 to 64.5 (.7 years) and Black women's increased from 72.5 to 73.6 (1.1 years). However, the inequities between Black and White life expectancy increased from 6.9 years difference to 8.2 years for Black men and from 5.6 to 5.8 years for Black women (Table 02-04, Table 02-05, Table 02-17, Table 02-18). In fact, overall between 1980 and 1996, Whites experienced an increase in annual death rate of almost 15 percent.[96] However, during this same period Blacks experienced an increase in their annual death rate of almost 21 percent.[97] The Black gain in life expectancy that exceeded Whites in the 1965-1980 period was reversed. The excess deaths for Blacks increased by 20,000 per year from 1980 to 1990. (Table 02-13) While both the Black and White death rates decreased from 1983, the ratio of Black infant deaths increased from 2.1 Black infant deaths for every White death in 1983 to 2.3 in 1990. .

In 1990, the ratio of deaths of Black women to deaths of White women doubled in the age groups 25-34 years, 35-44 years, and 45-44years. (Table 02-07) Similarly, for Black men, the ratio doubled compared to White men in the age groups 25-34 years, 35-44 years, and 45-44years. (Table 02-08). The causes of the most excess deaths for Blacks are diseases of the heart (74.5), cancer (67.9), homicide (30.8), cerebrovascular disease (28.8), diabetes (21.7), and HIV/AIDS

(18.4). (Table 02-11) Maternal excess deaths decreased from 18.2 to 16.6 in 1990. (Table 02-16)

Between 1980 and 1990, the percentage of Black babies born with low birth weight increased from 12.69% to 13.25%, and decreased for Whites: 5.72% to 5.70%. When looking at low weight babies by education level, not only does the inequity exist at every level, the greatest difference between Blacks and Whites is for babies born of mothers that had 13 years or more of education. (Table 02-20)

Each year, Blacks died who would not have died if Blacks had the same death rate as Whites. This number has steadily increased from 46,000 a year in 1950, to a high of over 100,000 per year in the 1990's. In 1997, the issue of eliminating the health inequities became a national priority.

# Eliminating Health Inequities: 1997 through 2005

Change has been exceedingly slow. The "slave health deficit" that evolved into "Black Health Inequities" continues. In fact, what the excess death and illness points to is, notwithstanding, a need to focus on eliminating the inequities the gap continues.

## Life Expectancy

The difference in life expectancy at birth between Blacks and Whites continues to decrease. In 1900, there was a 14.1 year difference in life expectancy for males and a 15.2 year difference for females at birth.[100] In 2002, at birth, the difference in life expectancy was 6.3 years for males and 4.7 years for females.[98] (Table 02.04, Table 02-05 ) Thus, even though both Blacks and Whites are living longer, Whites still have longer lives than Blacks.

Men in Barbados, Mexico and Cuba have a longer life expectancy than Black men in the United States, (Table 02-21). Women in Barbados, Chile, and Cuba, have a longer life expectancy than Black women in the United States (Table 02-22).[99] Shockingly, women and men in some poor, so called "third world" countries, have better health than Black women and Black men from the so-called richest, most powerful nation in the world – the United States of America.

## Death

The death rate for all Americans in 2000 was 1121.4 per 100,000.[100] The overall death rate has decreased since 1950 (from 1721.1 to 1121.4).[101] However, the excess death rates between Whites and Blacks fluctuated significantly between 1950 through 1990. In 1950, there were 311.3 excess deaths per 100,000 in the Black population. This means that for every white death, 1.221 Blacks died.[102] In 1990, there were 1.374 Black deaths for every White death.[103] In 2000, the death ratio fell to 1.320.[104] (Table 02-07; Table 02-08) However, this change may have been largely due to a change in how the United States Department of Health and Human Services reported race and calculated death rates.

As Professor Joe Feagin has noted:

"Wounded, [racism] retreated to more subtle expressions from its most deeply entrenched bunker. . . [F]orms of sophisticated racism attached to economic opportunities unfortunately can still be found today *nowhere is that better exemplified than in the rate of excess death among Blacks.*"[105] [Emphasis added.].

## Black Male Deaths

In 2002, White males had age-adjusted death rates of 1012.8. Black males had age adjusted death rates of 1375.0.[106] Black men had 35.8 % more deaths than White men. However, like Black women, the difference in death rates varies significantly by age.[107] For example, other than infants (see supra), men between the ages of 25 and 34 have the highest excess death ratio (1.971).[108] That is, for every White male death in the 25-34 year age cohort, Black men in the same group experience .971 more deaths. The very elderly (85 years and older) is the only age group where Black male deaths did not exceed white male deaths. As with Black women, the lowest ratio for Black men was for the most elderly (85 years and older).[109] In that age group, for every White male death, Blacks experience only 0.964 deaths.

In 2002, the top four causes of death for Black men were cardiac disease, cancer, accident, and stroke. When compared to the death rate among White males, the causes of death with the largest differences based on race were acquired immune deficiency disease (AIDS), homicide, cerebrovascular disease, cancer, and cardiac disease. [110]

## Black Female Deaths

White females have age- adjusted death rates of 713.5 per 100,000 population. Black females have age-adjusted death rates of 912.5 per 100,000.[111] Thus, Black women have 27.89% more deaths than White women. However, the differences in death rates vary significantly by age.[112] For instance, other than infants, Black women between the ages of 35 and 44 have the highest excess death ratio (2.061).[113] That is, for every White female death in the 34-44 age cohort, 2.061 Black women in the same cohort die.[114] The lowest rate was for the most elderly (85 years and older).119 In that age group, for every White female death, Blacks experience only .944 deaths.[115] (Table 02-17) In 2002, for each White female death per 100,000 population, there were 1.29 Black female deaths, a statistic that is the same as 1950. (See Table 02-07)[116]

The top five causes of death among Black women are cardiac disease, cancer, cerebro-vascular disease, diabetes, and renal failure.[117] Among White females, the leading causes of death are AIDS, homicide, and death during childbirth. An area of particular concern to women is breast cancer. Although the incidence of age-adjusted breast cancer among White women has been 12-29% higher than for Black women, Black women are 32.3 percent more likely to die from breast cancer than White women.[118] Mortality from breast cancer among Black women in the United States ranked highest among 31 developed countries.[119] The breast cancer mortality rate among U.S. Black women was higher that of women in New Zealand, Netherlands, Denmark, and the United Kingdom.[120]

## Maternal Deaths

It is important to take a specific look at maternal mortality, deaths related to complications of pregnancy, childbirth and the purpureum.[121] We tend to think of this childbirth and the period immediately following childbirth as fairly safe and not to associate it with death. Yet, the increased risk of maternal death among black women compared to White women is one of the largest health-related inequities.[122] Black women have a higher risk of dying from every pregnancy and childbirth-related condition, including hemorrhage, embolism, and hypertension.[123] This increase is evident in every age group and without regard to the level of prenatal care received.[124] In 2002, for each death from maternal mortality among White women, there were 4.8 such deaths among black women. (Table 02-16)

## Black Infant Deaths

In 2002, based on the race of the mother, in the first year of life, Blacks (14.1 per 1000 births) have more infant deaths than Whites (5.8 per 1000 births).[125] (Table 02-12, Table 02-23) In other words, for every White infant death, there are 1.69 Black infant deaths. In 2000, the U.S. Black infant mortality rate was higher than the infant mortality rates of Chile, Cuba. Bahamas, Mexico and Barbados.[126]

One counter argument is that the difference in infant mortality rates is related to poverty, but this does not seem to be true. A comparison of similarly situated Blacks and Whites shows that the inequity persists. In some instances, the difference in inequity is even greater. For example, the death ratio for Black babies born to mothers with 13 years or more of education is 2.76. That is, for every White infant that dies, 2.76 Black infants die. The ratio for mothers with less than 12 years of education is 1.63. (Table 02-20) This presents clear evidence that health status difference is not merely class difference but a racial difference.

## Summary.

Professor Joe Feagin argues that the theory of internal colonialism continues to view Blacks as slaves. In fact, the history of Blacks in North America from the 1600s until today shows that his theory has merit. The legacy of slavery persisted until the 1960s and then assumed the form of institutionalized racism.[127] Since the civil rights and voting rights laws of the early 1960s, the United States has seen significant changes in the status of Blacks. However, it is arguable whether "apartheid-U.S. ... or whether economic segregation and the perpetuation of our essentially feudal status amount to its continuation, in fact, if not in law."[128] Thus, death rate statistics seem to suggest that the feudal status of Blacks has not only continued, but is killing Blacks.

## Low Birth Weight

In 2002, Whites had a low birth weight rate of 6.91, while Blacks had a low birth weight rate of 13.13.[129] Therefore, for every White baby born with low birth weight, 1.94 Black infants suffered from low birth weight and its accompanying handicaps. (Table 02-24, Table 02-25)

## Disease and Illness

For the age group under 18, 36.3% fewer Blacks than Whites reported acute health conditions; for the 18-44 age group, 15.9% fewer Blacks than Whites reported acute conditions, such as colds, pneumonia; and, for people 45 and above, 10.1% reported fewer conditions.[130] Blacks under 18 had fewer acute conditions (183 per 100 persons per year) than Whites (283 per 100 persons per year), resulting in an excess disease rate (acute conditions) of -36.3%.[131]

Despite the seemingly lower incidence of acute diseases, Blacks have a higher mortality rate from acute conditions than Whites.[132] For instance, Black males have 58% more deaths from pneumonia than White males. Black females have 26% more deaths from pneumonia than White females.[133] The lower incidence of reported acute disease could be related to Blacks having less access to health care and as a result they present to doctors with more serious illnesses.

The percentage calculated for limitations in activity due to chronic diseases is higher in Blacks than in Whites for all age groups.[134] For instance, for the under-18 age group, 20% more Blacks than Whites reported limitations in activity because of chronic disease; for the 18-44 age group, 22.5% more Blacks than Whites reported limitations; in the 45-64 age group, 34.8% more Blacks than Whites reported limitations; and in the 65-69 age group, 31.6% more Blacks reported limitations than Whites. Finally, in the 70 and-over age group, 23.8% more Blacks than Whites reported limitations.[135] Therefore, while Blacks report fewer acute conditions, they tend to report more limitations based on chronic conditions.

## Disability

Using the number of days of restricted activity per year, Blacks under age five have no extraordinary disability. This outcome is entirely predictable since a child under five neither goes to work nor to school. What is not predictable is the 22.8% fewer restricted activity days for Blacks in the 5-17 age group.[136] However, when looking at the number of school-loss days associated with acute conditions per 100 youths aged 5-17, Black-Americans had 427.2 days whereas Whites had 322.[137] Given the higher death rate and disease rate of Blacks in this age group, it is likely that this difference is either an interpretation or a reporting error.

The 5-17 year old age group could have more illness but fewer restricted days because of cultural differences. Black culture tends to encourage individuals not to let illness interfere with normal activities, especially for children, since many parents may not be able to afford to take the child to the doctor or take off work to stay at home with a sick child. Thus, many Black children are actually encouraged to continue their activities even when they are ill. This assessment of error seems particularly true since Blacks in the 18-and-over age group reported 37.5% more days of activity restriction per year than Whites reported.[138]

## Dissatisfaction and Discomfort

The inequity in perception of health status is present in all age groups. The percentage of Blacks between the age of 5 and 17 who described their health status as fair or poor was 4.2%, while the percentage of Whites in the same age range making the same assessment was only 2.1%.

Nevertheless, 17% of Blacks describe their health as fair or poor, compared to 9% of Whites.[139] Similarly, 12% of Blacks, compared to 8% of Whites, report "some, little, or no satisfaction" with their health. Thus, approximately 50% more Blacks than Whites report having some, little, or no satisfaction with their health and physical condition.[140] Notwithstanding interpretive errors, these figures reflect a significant difference between Blacks' and Whites' dissatisfaction with their health.

Measuring health status by the results of reported discomfort surveys present interesting results. One such result is that Blacks under 45 years of age actually reported fewer symptoms than Whites.[141] There are several ways to view this result. The most obvious is that the Black age group, in fact, had fewer and less severe symptoms. However, that interpretation would be at odds with results based on death rates. A second interpretation of this result is that Blacks under-report, particularly more serious symptoms.

There are numerous reasons why Blacks might under-report symptoms. First, in a culture that has limited access to health care, it might be viewed as futile to complain. Second, Black-Americans may actually accept some "aches and pains" as normal, not as a sign of illness. Third, Blacks may be reluctant to discuss their health with a stranger. While all these reasons can be articulated by subgroups in other populations, given the impact of racism, Blacks may be more reluctant to complain about their health and/or to seek help. The theory that Blacks under-report symptoms is strengthened by evidence that once they are in the health care system, they require more visits than their White counterparts.[142] Thus, it is more likely that the under-reporting of symptoms contributes to an inaccurate reflection of health status.

# CONCLUSION

The picture that emerges from these health measurements is one of significant health inequity between Black Americans and White Americans.[143] While there are some age group variations in the more subjective health measurements (e.g., dissatisfaction), the most objective health measurement (death) clearly indicates that Black Americans are sicker than White Americans.[144]

Since Black-Americans are sicker, partly as a result of differential treatment in the health care system, they are victims of a racist health care system.[145] Without good health, it is nearly impossible for Black Americans to have access to the American economic system. Therefore, when Black-Americans are sick and poor, they are still enslaved because illness and poverty are forms of enslavement. Even the health of middle-class Black Americans is affected by the racist nature of the health care system resulting in too many Blacks of all socio-economic backgrounds "Dying While Black".

# TABLES

### Table 02-01

Death Rates for Whites and Slaves, 1850-1858,
per 10,000 population

| Year | Slaves | Whites | Ratio |
|------|--------|--------|-------|
| 1850 | 178 | 111 | 1.6 |
| 1853 | 172 | 111 | 1.55 |
| 1855 | 151 | 105 | 1.43 |
| 1857 | 152 | 97 | 1.57 |
| 1858 | 146 | 95 | 1.54 |

Source: Todd L. Savitt, Medicine and Slavery: The Diseases and Health Care of Blacks in Antebellum Virginia 140-141 (2002).

### Table 02-02

Child Death Rates and Ratio
per 1000 population

| Age | Male | | | Female | | |
|-----|------|---|---|--------|---|---|
| | Slaves | Whites | Ratio | Slaves | Whites | Ratio |
| Less 1 yr | 159 | 94 | 1.7 | 137 | 71 | 1.9 |
| 1-4 yr | 29 | 21 | 1.4 | 26 | 17 | 1.5 |
| 5-9 yrs | 7 | 5 | 1.4 | 9 | 5 | 1.8 |
| 10-14 yrs | 5 | 2 | 2.5 | 6 | 3 | 2 |

Source: Todd L. Savitt, Medicine and Slavery: The Diseases and Health Care of Blacks in Antebellum Virginia 140-141 (2002).

## Table 02-03

Disease Specific Infant Death
per 100,000 population

|  | Slaves | Whites | Ratio |
|---|---|---|---|
| Acute Respiratory Infections | 2412.2 | 1520.4 | 1.6 |
| Acute Diarrheal Diseases | 827.3 | 986.2 | 0.8 |
| Malarial Infections | 322 | 503 | 0.6 |
| Gastrointestinal Complaints | 252.6 | 135.9 | 1.9 |
| Tetanus | 1611.1 | 624.3 | 2.6 |
| Intestinal Worms | 69.7 | 17.3 | 4 |

Source: Todd L. Savitt, Medicine and Slavery: The Diseases and
Health Care of Blacks in Antebellum Virginia (2002).

## Table 02-04

Life Expectancy (1900-2002)
at Birth - Males

|  | Black | White | Difference |
|---|---|---|---|
| 1900 | 32.5 | 46.6 | -14.1 |
| 1950 | 59.1 | 66.5 | -7.4 |
| 1960 | 61.1 | 67.4 | -6.3 |
| 1970 | 60 | 68 | -8 |
| 1980 | 63.8 | 70.7 | -6.9 |
| 1990 | 64.5 | 72.7 | -8.2 |
| 2000 | 68.3 | 74.9 | -6.6 |
| 2002 | 68.8 | 75.1 | -6.3 |

Table 27. Life expectancy at birth, at 65 years of age, and at 75 years
of age, according to race and sex: United States, selected years 1900-
2002, Health United States 2004 at 143.

### Table 02-05

Life Expectancy (1900-2002)
at Birth- Females

|      | Black | White | Difference |
|------|-------|-------|------------|
| 1900 | 33.5  | 48.7  | -15.2      |
| 1950 | 62.9  | 72.2  | -9.3       |
| 1960 | 66.3  | 74.1  | -7.8       |
| 1970 | 68.3  | 75.6  | -7.3       |
| 1980 | 72.5  | 78.1  | -5.6       |
| 1990 | 73.6  | 79.4  | -5.8       |
| 2000 | 75.2  | 80.1  | -4.9       |
| 2002 | 75.6  | 80.3  | -4.7       |

Table 27. Life expectancy at birth, at 65 years of age, and at 75 years of age, according to race and sex: United States, selected years 1900-2002, Health United States 2004 at 143.

### Table 02-06

Fetal Death Rate and Ratio, Black and White,
per 1000 live births (1950 – 2002)

| Year | Black | White | Ratio* |
|------|-------|-------|--------|
| 1950 | 32.1  | 16.6  | 1.9    |
| 1970 | 23.2  | 12.3  | 1.9    |
| 1980 | 14.7  | 8.1   | 1.8    |
| 1990 | 13.3  | 6.4   | 2.1    |
| 2000 | 12.4  | 5.6   | 2.2    |
| 2002 | 11.9  | 5.5   | 2.2    |

*Number of fetal deaths of 20 weeks or more gestation per 1,000 live births plus fetal deaths.

Source: Table 22. Infant mortality rates, fetal mortality rates, and perinatal mortality rates, according to Race: United States, selected years 1950-2002, HEALTH UNITED STATES, 2004 at 135.

## Table 02-07

Age- Adjusted Death Ratio by Age,
for Black Females to White Females, Selected Years

| Years | 1950 | 1960 | 1970 | 1980 | 1990 | 2000 | 2002 |
|---|---|---|---|---|---|---|---|
| All Ages | 1.29 | 1.27 | 1.3 | 1.3 | 1.34 | 1.3 | 1.29 |
| Under 1 | | 2.07 | 2.09 | 2.21 | 2.52 | 2.32 | 2.26 |
| 1-4 | 10.15 | 2.03 | 1.96 | 1.71 | 1.87 | 1.78 | 1.6 |
| 5 - 15 | 1.61 | 1.55 | 1.46 | 1.33 | 1.54 | 1.42 | 1.45 |
| 15-24 | 2.98 | 1.96 | 1.82 | 1.27 | 1.5 | 1.42 | 1.28 |
| 25-34 | 3.49 | 3.21 | 2.75 | 2.29 | 2.59 | 2.21 | 2.05 |
| 35-44 | 3.22 | 2.97 | 2.76 | 2.34 | 2.54 | 2.16 | 2.04 |
| 45-54 | 2.89 | 2.57 | 2.26 | 2.06 | 2.07 | 2.09 | 2.02 |
| 55-64 | 2.39 | 2.33 | 1.96 | 1.78 | 1.77 | 1.68 | 1.69 |
| 65-74 | 1.23 | 1.46 | 1.56 | 1.48 | 1.49 | 1.44 | 1.4 |
| 75-84 | 0.98 | 0.87 | 1 | 1.15 | 1.18 | 1.19 | 1.18 |
| 85and over | 0 | 0.67 | 0.67 | 0.83 | 0.92 | 0.94 | 0.95 |

Source: Table 28, Age-adjusted death rates, selected years, HEALTH, UNITED STATES 2004 at 144 (2004).

## Table 02 -08

Age- Adjusted Death Ratio by age,
Black Males to White Males, Selected Years

| Years | 1950 | 1960 | 1970 | 1980 | 1990 | 2000 | 2002 |
|---|---|---|---|---|---|---|---|
| All Ages | 1.16 | 1.14 | 1.24 | 1.29 | 1.41 | 1.36 | 1.35 |
| Under 1 | | 1.97 | 2.03 | 2.1 | 2.36 | 2.35 | 2.08 |
| 1 – 4 | 10.43 | 1.99 | 1.8 | 1.67 | 1.87 | 1.67 | 1.73 |
| 5 – 14 | 1.42 | 1.43 | 1.4 | 1.35 | 1.56 | 1.42 | 1.57 |
| 15-24 | 1.9 | 1.48 | 1.88 | 1.25 | 1.92 | 1.71 | 1.57 |
| 25-34 | 2.72 | 2.47 | 3.17 | 2.38 | 2.45 | 2.1 | 2.06 |
| 35-44 | 2.31 | 2.29 | 2.78 | 2.68 | 2.61 | 1.94 | 1.82 |
| 45-54 | 1.93 | 1.74 | 2.01 | 2.12 | 2.3 | 2.05 | 1.94 |
| 55-64 | 1.64 | 1.49 | 1.48 | 1.66 | 1.78 | 1.79 | 1.82 |
| 65-74 | 1.09 | 1.2 | 1.21 | 1.27 | 1.46 | 1.46 | 1.44 |
| 75-84 | 0.96 | 0.84 | 0.94 | 1.05 | 1.16 | 1.22 | 1.21 |
| 85and over | | 0.68 | 0.66 | 0.84 | 0.93 | 0.95 | 0.95 |

Source: Table 28, Age-adjusted death rates, selected years, HEALTH, UNITED STATES 2004 at 144 (2004).

**Table 02-09**

1950 Death Rates, Ratio, Excess Deaths for all causes,
Female, Black and White, selected years
Per 100,000 population

|  | Black | White | Ratio | Excess Deaths |
|---|---|---|---|---|
| All ages, age adjusted | 1,545.50 | 1,198.00 | 1.3 | 347.5 |
| Under 1 year | --- | 2,566.80 | | |
| 1-4 years | 1,139.30 | 112.2 | 10.2 | 1,027.10 |
| 5-14 years | 72.8 | 45.1 | 1.6 | 27.7 |
| 15-24 years | 213.1 | 71.5 | 3 | 141.6 |
| 25-34 years | 393.3 | 112.8 | 3.5 | 280.5 |
| 35-44 years | 758.1 | 235.8 | 3.2 | 522.3 |
| 45-54 years | 1,576.40 | 546.4 | 2.9 | 1,030.00 |
| 55-64 years | 3,089.40 | 1,293.80 | 2.4 | 1,795.60 |
| 65-74 years | 4,000.20 | 3,242.80 | 1.2 | 757.4 |
| 75-84 years | 8,347.00 | 8,481.50 | 1 | -134.5 |
| 85 years and over | --- | 19,679.50 | | |

Source: Table 35 Death rates for all causes, according to sex, race, Hispanic origin, and age: United States, selected years 1950–2002 HEALTH, UNITED STATES 2004 at 165-168 (2004).

**Table 02-10**

1950 Death Rates, Ratio and Excess Deaths Rates for all causes,
Male, Black and White, selected years Per 100,000 population

|  | Black | White | Ratio | Excess Deaths |
|---|---|---|---|---|
| All ages, age adjusted | 1,909.10 | 1,642.50 | 1.2 | 266.6 |
| Under 1 year | --- | 3,400.50 | | |
| 1-4 years | 1,412.60 | 135.5 | 10.4 | 1277.1 |
| 5-14 years | 95.1 | 67.2 | 1.4 | 27.9 |
| 15-24 years | 289.7 | 152.4 | 1.9 | 137.3 |
| 25-34 years | 503.5 | 185.3 | 2.7 | 318.2 |
| 35-44 years | 878.1 | 380.9 | 2.3 | 497.2 |
| 45-54 years | 1,905.00 | 984.5 | 1.9 | 920.5 |
| 55-64 years | 3,773.20 | 2,304.40 | 1.6 | 1468.8 |
| 65-74 years | 5,310.30 | 4,864.90 | 1.1 | 445.4 |
| 75-84 years | 10,101.90 | 10,526.30 | 1 | -424.4 |
| 85 years and over | --- | 22,116.30 | | |

Source: Table 35 Death rates for all causes, according to sex, race, Hispanic origin, and age: United States, selected years 1950–2002 HEALTH, UNITED STATES 2004 at 165-168 (2004).

**Table 02-11**

Excess Black Death Rates for selected Causes and Selected Years
Black and White Difference Per 100,000 Black population

|  | 1950 | 1970 | 1990 | 2000 |
|---|---|---|---|---|
| All causes | 311.3 | 324.8 | 340.5 | 271.6 |
| Diseases of heart | 1.9 | 19.8 | 74.5 | 71.4 |
| Cerebrovascular diseases | 58.1 | 53.6 | 28.8 | 23.1 |
| Malignant neoplasms | -18.2 | 28.6 | 67.9 | 51.3 |
| Prostate | 2.5 | 21.1 | 41.5 | 40.3 |
| Breast | -7.1 | -3.6 | 4.9 | 8.2 |
| Influenza and pneumonia | 31.9 | 17.4 | 3 | 2.1 |
| Chronic liver disease and cirrhosis | -2.5 | 11.5 | 6 | -0.2 |
| Diabetes mellitus | 0.6 | 15.9 | 21.7 | 26.7 |
| Human immunodeficiency virus disease |  |  | 18.4 | 20.5 |
| Unintentional injuries | 2.9 | 20.5 | 8.3 | 22.1 |
| Motor vehicle-related injuries | 1.6 | 4 | 0.3 | 0.1 |
| Suicide | -9.4 | -7.6 | -6.3 | -5.8 |
| Homicide | 25.7 | 39.3 | 30.8 | 16.9 |

Source: Table 29. Age-adjusted death rates for selected causes of death,
according to sex, race, and Hispanic origin: United States, selected years
1950-2002; HEALTH, UNITED STATES 2004 at 146 (2004).

**Table 02-12**

Infant Death Rate and Excess Deaths, Selected Years
per 1000 Live Births

| Race of Child | Death Rate | | Excess Death Rate |
|---|---|---|---|
|  | Black | White | |
| 1950 | 43.9 | 26.8 | 17.1 |
| 1960 | 44.3 | 22.9 | 21.4 |
| 1970 | 32.6 | 17.8 | 14.8 |
| 1980 | 21.4 | 11 | 10.4 |
| Race of Mother | Death Rate | | Excess Death Rate |
|  | Black | White | |
| 1980 | 22.2 | 10.9 | 11.3 |
| 1990 | 18.0 | 7.6 | 10.4 |
| 2000 | 14.1 | 5.7 | 8.4 |
| 2002 | 14.1 | 5.8 | 8.3 |

Source: Table 22. Infant mortality rates, fetal mortality rates, and
perinatal mortality rates, according to Race: United States, selected
years 1950–2002, HEALTH, UNITED STATES 2004 at 135 (2004).

**Table 02-13**

Excess Death and Death Rate, Blacks, 1950-2002

| | Population | Rate | Number |
|---|---|---|---|
| 1950 | 15,044,598 | 311.3 | 46834 |
| 1960 | 18,872,000 | 266.2 | 50237 |
| 1970 | 22,580,289 | 324.8 | 73341 |
| 1980 | 26,630,517 | 302.1 | 80451 |
| 1990 | 30,483,281 | 340.5 | 103796 |
| 2000 | 36,594,309 | 271.6 | 99390 |
| 2002 | 37,747,692 | 254.3 | 95992 |

Source: Table 1. Resident population, according to age, sex, race, and Hispanic origin: United States, selected years 1950-2002; Table 29. Age-adjusted death rates for selected causes of death, according to sex, race, and Hispanic origin: United States, selected years 1950-2002; HEALTH, UNITED STATES 2004 at 105, 146 (2004).

**Table 02-14**

Death Rates, Ratio, Excess Deaths for all causes,

Female, Black and White, selected years Per 100,000 population

| | 1980 | | | |
|---|---|---|---|---|
| | Black | White | Ratio | Excess Deaths |
| All ages, age adjusted | 1,033.30 | 796.1 | 1.3 | 237.2 |
| Under 1 year. | 2,123.70 | 962.5 | 2.2 | 1,161.20 |
| 1-4 years | 84.4 | 49.3 | 1.7 | 35.1 |
| 5-14 years | 30.5 | 22.9 | 1.3 | 7.6 |
| 15-24 years | 70.5 | 55.5 | 1.3 | 15 |
| 25-34 years | 150 | 65.4 | 2.3 | 84.6 |
| 35-44 years | 323.9 | 138.2 | 2.3 | 185.7 |
| 45-54 years | 768.2 | 372.7 | 2.1 | 395.5 |
| 55-64 years | 1,561.00 | 876.2 | 1.8 | 684.8 |
| 65-74 years | 3,057.40 | 2,066.60 | 1.5 | 990.8 |
| 75-84 years | 6,212.10 | 5,401.70 | 1.2 | 810.4 |
| 85 years and over | 12,367.20 | 14,979.60 | 0.8 | -2,612.40 |

Source: Table 35 Death rates for all causes, according to sex, race, Hispanic origin, and age: United States, selected years 1950–2002 HEALTH, UNITED STATES 2004 at 165-168 (2004).

**Table 02-15**

1980 Death Rates, Ratio and Excess Deaths for all causes,
Male, Black and White, Per 100,000 population

|  | Black | White | Ratio | Excess Deaths |
|---|---|---|---|---|
| All ages, age adjusted | 1,697.80 | 1,317.60 | 1.3 | 380.2 |
| Under 1 year | 2,586.70 | 1,230.30 | 2.1 | 1356.4 |
| 1-4 years4 | 110.5 | 66.1 | 1.7 | 44.4 |
| 5-14 years | 47.4 | 35 | 1.4 | 12.4 |
| 15-24 years | 209.1 | 167 | 1.3 | 42.1 |
| 25-34 years | 407.3 | 171.3 | 2.4 | 236 |
| 35-44 years | 689.8 | 257.4 | 2.7 | 432.4 |
| 45-54 years | 1,479.90 | 698.9 | 2.1 | 781 |
| 55-64 years | 2,873.00 | 1,728.50 | 1.7 | 1144.5 |
| 65-74 years | 5,131.10 | 4,035.70 | 1.3 | 1095.4 |
| 75-84 years5 | 9,231.60 | 8,829.80 | 1 | 401.8 |
| 85 years and over | 16,098.80 | 19,097.30 | 0.8 | -2998.5 |

Source: Table 35 Death rates for all causes, according to sex, race, Hispanic origin, and age: United States, selected years 1950–2002 HEALTH, UNITED STATES 2004 at 165-168 (2004).

**Table 02-16**

Maternal Death Rates and Excess Black deaths (1950-2002)
per 100,000 population

|  | Black | White | Ratio | Excess Deaths |
|---|---|---|---|---|
| 1950 | --- | 53.1 |  |  |
| 1960 | 92 | 22.4 | 4.1 | 69.6 |
| 1970 | 65.5 | 14.4 | 4.5 | 51.1 |
| 1980 | 24.9 | 6.7 | 3.7 | 18.2 |
| 1990 | 21.7 | 5.1 | 4.3 | 16.6 |
| 2000 | 20.1 | 6.2 | 3.2 | 13.9 |
| 2002 | 22.9 | 4.8 | 4.8 | 18.1 |

Source: Table 43. Maternal mortality for complications of pregnancy, childbirth, and the puerperium, according to race, Hispanic origin, and age: United States, selected years 1950-2002, HEALTH, UNITED STATES, 2004 at 189.

## Table 02-17

1990 Death rates, Ratio, Excess Deaths for all causes,
Female, Black and White, selected years Per 100,000 population

|  | Black | White | Ratio | Excess |
|---|---|---|---|---|
| All ages, age adjusted | 975.1 | 728.8 | 1.3 | 246.3 |
| Under 1 year | 1,735.50 | 690 | 2.5 | 1,045.50 |
| 1-4 years | 67.6 | 36.1 | 1.9 | 31.5 |
| 5-14 years | 27.5 | 17.9 | 1.5 | 9.6 |
| 15-24 years | 68.7 | 45.9 | 1.5 | 22.8 |
| 25-34 years | 159.5 | 61.5 | 2.6 | 98 |
| 35-44 years | 298.6 | 117.4 | 2.5 | 181.2 |
| 45-54 years | 639.4 | 309.3 | 2.1 | 330.1 |
| 55-64 years | 1,452.60 | 822.7 | 1.8 | 629.9 |
| 65-74 years | 2,865.70 | 1,923.50 | 1.5 | 942.2 |
| 75-84 years | 5,688.30 | 4,839.10 | 1.2 | 849.2 |
| 85 years and over | 13,309.50 | 14,400.60 | 0.9 | 1,091.10 |

Source: Table 35 Death rates for all causes, according to sex, race, Hispanic origin, and age: United States, selected years 1950–2002 HEALTH, UNITED STATES 2004 at 165-168 (2004).

## Table 02-18

1990 Death rates and Ratio for all causes,
Male, Black and White, selected years
Per 100,000 population

|  | Black | White | Ratio | Excess |
|---|---|---|---|---|
| All ages, age adjusted | 1,644.50 | 1,165.90 | 1.4 | 478.6 |
| Under 1 year | 2,112.40 | 896.1 | 2.4 | 1216.3 |
| 1-4 years | 85.8 | 45.9 | 1.9 | 39.9 |
| 5-14 years | 41.2 | 26.4 | 1.6 | 14.8 |
| 15-24 years | 252.2 | 131.3 | 1.9 | 120.9 |
| 25-34 years | 430.8 | 176.1 | 2.4 | 254.7 |
| 35-44 years | 699.6 | 268.2 | 2.6 | 431.4 |
| 45-54 years | 1,261.00 | 548.7 | 2.3 | 712.3 |
| 55-64 years | 2,618.40 | 1,467.20 | 1.8 | 1151.2 |
| 65-74 years | 4,946.10 | 3,397.70 | 1.5 | 1548.4 |
| 75-84 years | 9,129.50 | 7,844.90 | 1.2 | 1284.6 |
| 85 years and over | 16,954.90 | 18,268.30 | 0.9 | -1313.4 |

Source: Table 35 Death rates for all causes, according to sex, race, Hispanic origin, and age: United States, selected years 1950–2002 HEALTH, UNITED STATES 2004 at 165-168 (2004).

**Table 02-19**

Infant Mortality Rate, Deaths per 1000 Live Births
International Comparison

| Country | Rate | Country | Rate |
|---|---|---|---|
| Singapore | 2 | Bahrain | 7 |
| Japan | 3 | Chile | 7 |
| Czech Republic | 4 | Cuba | 7 |
| France | 4 | Bahamas | 8 |
| Germany | 4 | Paraguay | 10 |
| Australia | 5 | Costa Rica | 11 |
| Canada | 5 | El Salvador | 11 |
| Israel | 5 | Mexico | 13 |
| Switzerland | 5 | Panama | 14 |
| United Kingdom | 5 | Uruguay | 14 |
| Jamaica | 6 | Barbados | 14 |
| **White Americans** | 6 | **Black Americans** | 14 |

Source: World Health Organization, Child and Adolescent Health and
Development, Morality Rates 2000, http://www.who.int/child-
adolescenthealth/OVERVIEW/CHILD_HEALTH/Mortality_Rates_03.pd
f (Last Visited: Dec. 30, 2005)

**Table - 02-20**

Infant Mortality Rate and Years of Education
Per 1000 live Births, 2000

|  | Black | White | Difference |
|---|---|---|---|
| Less than 12 years of education | 15.0 | 9.2 | 5.8 |
| 12 years of education | 13.5 | 6.3 | 7.2 |
| 13 years or more of education | 11.5 | 4.2 | 7.3 |

Table 20 Infant mortality rates for mothers 20 years of age and over, according to
mother's education, detailed race, and Hispanic origin: United States, selected years
1983-2002; Health United States, 2004 at 133.

## Table 02-21
Life Expectancy, at Birth
Males, International Comparisons

| Rank | Country | Years | Rank | Country | Years |
|------|---------|-------|------|---------|-------|
| 1 | Iceland | 78.4 | 21 | United Kingdom | 75.8 |
| 2 | Japan | 78.4 | 27 | Cuba | 75.0 |
| 3 | Sweden | 78.0 | 29 | Costa Rica | 74.8 |
| 4 | Australia | 77.9 | 36 | Chile | 73.4 |
| 5 | Monaco | 77.8 | 37 | Panama | 72.8 |
| 6 | Switzerland | 77.7 | 41 | Republic of Korea | 71.8 |
| 7 | Singapore | 77.4 | 42 | Mexico | 71.7 |
| 8 | Israel | 77.3 | 46 | Dominica | 71.0 |
| 9 | Canada | 77.2 | 49 | Venezuela | 71.0 |
| 10 | San Marino | 77.2 | 52 | Barbados | 70.5 |
| 12 | Italy | 76.8 | 55 | Saint Lucia | 69.8 |
| 18 | France | 76.0 | 58 | China | 69.6 |
| 19 | Netherlands | 76.0 | 61 | Bahamas | 69.4 |
| **20** | **White Americans** | **75.1** | **68** | **Black Americans** | **68.8** |

SOURCE: Annex 1: Basic Indicators, THE WORLD HEALTH REPORT 2004: CHANGING HISTORY. Geneva, World Health Organization, 2004. (http://www.who.int/whr/2004/en/report04_en.pdf) (Last Visited: February, 2005).

**Table 02-22**

Life Expectancy, at Birth, Females, International Comparisons

| Rank | Country | Years | Rank | Country | Years |
|---|---|---|---|---|---|
| 1 | Japan | 85.3 | 28 | Chile | 80 |
| 2 | Monaco | 84.5 | 33 | Republic of Korea | 79.4 |
| 5 | France | 83.6 | 34 | Cuba | 79.3 |
| 6 | Switzerland | 83.3 | 35 | Uruguay | 79.3 |
| 7 | Australia | 83 | 37 | Czech Republic | 79 |
| 8 | Spain | 83 | 39 | Croatia | 78.6 |
| 9 | Sweden | 82.6 | 41 | Panama | 78.2 |
| 10 | Italy | 82.5 | 42 | Argentina | 78.1 |
| 11 | Canada | 82.3 | 43 | Barbados | 77.9 |
| 20 | Israel | 81.4 | 50 | Venezuela | 76.8 |
| 24 | Greece | 81.1 | 54 | Colombia | 76.3 |
| 25 | United Kingdom | 80.5 | 55 | Dominica | 75.8 |
| 27 | Slovenia | 80.5 | 57 | Bahamas | 75.7 |
| **28** | **White Americans** | **80.3** | **58** | **Black Americans** | **75.6** |

SOURCE: Annex 1: Basic Indicators, THE WORLD HEALTH REPORT 2004: CHANGING HISTORY. Geneva, World Health Organization, 2004. (http://www.who.int/whr/2004/en/report04_en.pdf) (Last Visited: February, 2005).

**Table 02-23**

Infant, Neonatal and Post-neonatal Death Rates
per 1000 live births

| | | 1983 | 1990 | 2000 | 2002 |
|---|---|---|---|---|---|
| Infant Deaths (under 1 year of age) | Black | 19.2 | 16.9 | 13.5 | 13.8 |
| | White | 9.3 | 7.3 | 5.7 | 5.8 |
| | Ratio | 2.1 | 2.3 | 2.4 | 2.4 |
| Neonatal deaths (under 28 days) | Black | 12.5 | 11.1 | 9.1 | 9.3 |
| | White | 6.1 | 4.6 | 3.8 | 3.9 |
| | Ratio | 2 | 2.4 | 2.4 | 2.4 |
| Postneonatal deaths (28 days-11 months). | Black | 6.7 | 5.9 | 4.3 | 4.5 |
| | White | 3.2 | 2.7 | 1.9 | 1.9 |
| | Ratio | 2.1 | 2.2 | 2.3 | 2.4 |

Source: Table 19. Infant, neonatal, and postneonatal mortality rates, according to detailed race and Hispanic origin of mother: United States, selected years 1983-2002 HEALTH, UNITED STATES 2004 at 131.

## Table 02-24

Low-birth weight live births, according to mother's detailed race, Selected Years

|      | Black | White | Ratio |
|------|-------|-------|-------|
| 1970 | 13.9  | 6.85  | 2.03  |
| 1975 | 13.19 | 6.27  | 2.1   |
| 1980 | 12.71 | 5.67  | 2.24  |
| 1985 | 12.61 | 5.6   | 2.25  |
| 1990 | 13.32 | 5.61  | 2.37  |
| 1995 | 13.21 | 6.2   | 2.13  |
| 2000 | 13.13 | 6.6   | 1.99  |
| 2002 | 13.39 | 6.91  | 1.94  |

Source: Table 12. Low-birth weight live births, according to mother's detailed race, Hispanic origin, and smoking status: United States, selected years 1970-2002, Health, United States 2005.

\

**Table 02-25**

Low Birth weight Rate

% of live births weighing less than 2500 by education and race

| Total | 1970 | 1980 | 1990 | 2000 | 2002 |
|---|---|---|---|---|---|
| Black | 13.9 | 12.69 | 13.25 | 12.99 | 13.29 |
| White | 6.85 | 5.72 | 5.7 | 6.55 | 6.8 |
| Less than 12 years of education | | | | | |
| Black | | | 16.5 | 14.8 | 15 |
| White | | | 7 | 7.1 | 7.1 |
| 12 years of education | | | | | |
| Black | | | 13.1 | 13 | 13.4 |
| White | | | 5.8 | 6.8 | 7 |
| 13 years or more of education | | | | | |
| Black | | | 11.1 | 11.6 | 12 |
| White | | | 4.6 | 5.8 | 6.2 |
| % based on live births with known birthweight. | | | | | |

Source: Table 13. Low-birthweight live births among mothers 20 years of age and over, by mother's detailed race, Hispanic origin, and education: United States, selected years 1989-2002, Health, United States, 2004.

# Chapter Three

---

# RACIST HEALTH CARE

Knowing that Black Americans are sicker than White Americans does not explain why they are sicker. It certainly does not indicate the presence of institutional racism and discrimination in the health care system. Furthermore, it does not necessarily prove that discrimination in health care impacts health status. Understanding the role of institutional racism on health status requires an understanding of how health status is determined.

Many factors influence health status. A person's personal lifestyle choices affect health status because they affect his or her personal behavior and emotional or mental health, which affects his or her physical health. Physical environment and biology also affect health status. Health care institutions affect health status because both personal behavior and human biology are affected by an individual's access to health care and by the quality of health care he or she receives from health care institutions.[1]

But what about socioeconomic status? Class theory maintains that poverty is a major factor in determining individual health, and there is truth to this assertion. Certainly, poverty is a major factor in health. The poor are unable to afford the food, housing, clothing, and education which would allow them to be equal participants in American society. Certainly, access to health care services is limited by a person's ability to pay, and ability to pay is related to access to health insurance. It is estimated that over 45 million Americans are uninsured.[2] In fact, the amount of care an individual receives is related to whether the individual has health insurance.[3] The spiraling costs of health care and health insurance mean that many people cannot afford to get sick. Consequently, many policy makers are suggesting health care reform proposals designed to minimize the effect of ability to pay as a barrier to access to health care.

The class theory, however, completely ignores the independent role of racism in American society.[5] Black Americans with hypertension, regardless of their socioeconomic status, report less frequent visits to physicians, more difficulties in accessing the health care system, and greater dissatisfaction with both the availability and the quality of health care.[6] Racism influences not only life-style, personal behavior, psycho-social behavior, physical environment, and biology, but also socioeconomic status. Racism has a dual influence. Racism in America erects barriers to health care institutions and to health care. Those who advocate for the class theory alone ignore the fact that removing economic barriers does not remove racial barriers. Making the health care system better for everyone will not necessarily remove all inequities in health care. A generalized approach such as "health for all people" will continue to maintain differences unless specific attention to eliminating the health care inequities.

Racial barriers to health care appear in two areas. First, institutional policies, practices, and procedures prevent Black Americans from having access to quality health care. Second, some practitioners tend to provide different medical treatment to Black Americans based on their race not merely their socioeconomic class.[7]

The "Slave Health Deficit" has been compounded by racial discrimination, and by institutional racism in health care that has affected both access to and the quality of health care.[8] Despite efforts to eliminate discrimination and segregation over the past 40 years, there has been little change in the quality of, or access to, health care for Black Americans. According to the United States Commission on Civil Rights, "Despite the existence of civil rights legislation, equal treatment and equal access are not a reality for racial/ethnic minorities and women in the current climate of the health care industry. Many barriers limit both the quality of health care and utilization for these groups, including discrimination."[9] Racial discrimination in health care delivery, funding, and research continues to exist, and racial barriers to quality health care continue to manifest themselves. Little has changed since Gunnar Myrdal made the following observation over 60 years ago:

> "Discrimination increases [Black] sickness and death both directly and indirectly and manifests itself both consciously and unconsciously. Discrimination is involved when hospitals will not take in [Black] patients; or when, if they do permit [Black] patients, they restrict their numbers, give them the poorest quarters, and refuse to hire [Black] doctors and nurses to attend them.... [poor] health reduces the chance of economic advancement, which in turn operates to reduce the chance of getting adequate medical facilities or knowledge necessary for personal care."[10]

# HISTORICAL BASIS FOR RACIALIZED HEALTH CARE

Discrimination in health care has its foundation in the historical relationship between Black Americans and southern medical institutions.

## Slave Health Care

As slaves, Black Americans were considered to be property. "Slavery in North America was one of the "harshest form[s] of social relations ever to exist."[11] Unlike slavery in many other areas, American slaves had no rights and received no protections from society.[12] The slave owner had absolute power over the slave.[13] While some slave owners protected their investments by providing minimal health care, most left ill slaves to live or die on their own.

Although slaves were property, some courts recognized their humanity. By 1860, the Southern legal system had begun to see slaves simultaneously as property and as persons.[14] This dual status of slaves as valuable property and as persons with rights may have encouraged some slave owners to provide a minimal standard of health care.[15] In fact, the high cost of slaves led some settlers to treat their slaves as subordinates, as property with inherent value.[16] Also by 1860, the Southern legal system had begun to accept an implicit duality of the slaves as both property and person.[17]

Nevertheless, the slave owner had power of life and death over the slave. Health care varied from some very exceptional plantations that had slave hospitals and "contract physicians" to those that had no health care. In fact, most slaves had no access to physicians or hospitals. Sometimes doctors would be called in as a last resort. However, to the extent that health care was available, it was most often provided by Blacks themselves ("conjure men, slave nurses, midwives and root doctors").[18]

A significant contributor to inequitable health treatment of Black slaves was the medical profession's scientific support of the concept of racial superiority and inferiority.[19] Physicians defined slaves as biologically different, in part by inventing "slave diseases." Physicians helped to frame the difference in terms of White superiority and Black inferiority. In fact, the medical profession was heavily involved in the promotion and promulgation of scientific racism.[20] It was physicians who assigned social meanings to the perceived differences of people of African descent and who gave those assignments scientific legitimacy. For instance, supposedly,

- slaves had larger penises, breasts and "butts" than Whites taken as signs of their "indecent and unbridled sexuality;"[21]
- slaves were similar to apes because slaves tolerated pain better than Whites;[22]
- slave women had less copious menstruation which similar to apes;"[23] and,
- slaves had a stronger body odor because they sweated less;[24]
- slaves had a deficiency of red blood which made them biologically distinctly different from Whites[25]

In fact, the medical profession developed an entire lexicon of "Negro diseases"[26]:

- Cachexia Africana was a disease that caused slaves to eat dirt.[27]
- Difficult Parturition was a disease of pain caused by heavy burdens and kicks of the masters.[28]
- Drapomania Disease caused slaves to run away.[29]
- Dysaethesia Aethipis was a disease that resulted in mental lethargy or dullness of the mind and stupid sensibility of the body.[30]
- Furor Sexualis described Black men's sexuality resembling bulls and elephants.[31]
- Struma Africana was "Negro consumption", or pulmonary tuberculosis.[32]
- Typhoid Pneumonia was a severe form of pneumonia peculiar to slaves.[33]

Being Black was seen as a specific medical condition: "Negritude".[34] Dr. Benjamin Rush was the first to describe *Negritude*.[35] Dr. Rush was *a* signer of the Declaration of Independence, Dean of the Medical School at the University of Pennsylvania and the "Father of American Psychiatry. According to him, Negritude was a mild form of leprosy which included symptoms such as Blackening of the skin, big lips, flat nose, wooly hair, and smell.[36] Of course, the cure for Negritude was to become White.[37] Something that could never be achieved. Thus, modern medicine's foundation is based on a view of Blackness as a pathological incurable medical condition. This view continues to be evidenced in the significant health care inequity in how physicians treat Black patients.[38] It is an inequity that is not based on differences in insurance status, income, age, or severity of condition.[39]

## Civil War and Reconstruction: 1861 to 1879

The Civil War and Reconstruction did not bring an improvement in Black health; Black solders continued to receive inferior care and be used as a source of experimentation. Consequently, Black health continued to deteriorate during the Civil War and Reconstruction.[40]

In 1865, the Federal government dealt with the problems of the emancipated slaves by creating the Freedman's Bureau.[41] The Bureau's programs provided educational opportunities, aid for the impoverished, and enforced the Thirteenth, Fourteenth, and Fifteenth Amendments.[42] The Bureau also built a network of hospitals across the South, especially in urban areas, to provide care for Black Americans who were ill with contagious diseases .[43] Although the hospitals were often under-funded, rundown, and understaffed, they saved many lives.[44] Unfortunately, the hospital and clinic system was ended in 1869, and with the exception of one hospital in Washington, D.C., the Bureau was completely shut down by 1872. The effort was too brief to have a lasting effect on the lives of Black Americans.[45]

Making matters worse was the assassination of President Abraham Lincoln in April, 1865.[46] Following the death of Lincoln, the leadership of the country passed to Vice-President Andrew Johnson.[47] Johnson, a Southerner, clashed with the Northern-dominated Congress and a Southern resistance grew.[48] Government promises of farm land ("40 Acres and a mule") for the emancipated slaves were never kept.[49] As a result, many Black farmers were forced to work as tenant farmers or sharecroppers for their former owners, forming a *de facto* slave system.[50] Blacks were charged excessive rents by the landowners, cheated out of profits, and forced to struggle to provide for their families.[51]

"Landless Blacks were thrown into a criminal and immoral cycle of debt that was protected by a corrupt legal system and a system of racial etiquette that demanded the most abhorrent obsequiousness under the threat of losing one's livelihood or even being lynched."[52]

Under Reconstruction, the health of Black Americans was worse than it had ever been.[53] In fact, throughout the period of Reconstruction, attempts were made by many Whites to thwart the advancement toward "racial democracy."[54] The trauma of war and racism, dislocation, scarce food and health resources, poor nutrition, and unsanitary living conditions combined to make Black Americans unhealthy.[55] The government did very little to improve Black American health until the 1960's. During the post-Reconstruction era, Black Americans were excluded from health care either by prohibition or discrimination.[56] As noted by Randy Finley, *In War's Wake: Health Care and Arkansas Freedmen*, 1863-1868:

> "[Even] where segregation and discrimination [were] not required by law they became deeply ingrained in the mores. Such behavior became part of the American Way of Life."[57]

The end of the Freedman's Bureau medical programs, and a shift to reliance on the private sector to provide health care for Black Americans and the poor, institutionalized a racially separate and inadequate system for the next 100 years.[58]

## The Jim Crow Era: 1880 through 1954

### Early Years: 1880 through 1900

The years from 1870 to 1890 were known as the Gilded Age. This period was marked by a return to a more traditional conservative political agenda and attitude towards public policy.[59] In 1875, Congress passed the Civil Rights Act, which made it a crime for a person to deny any citizen equal access to accommodations in inns, public conveyances, theaters, and other places of amusement.[60] In 1877, Rutherford Hayes won the presidency through a political bargain known as the Hayes-Tilden Compromise.[61] The compromise provided for the removal of Union troops from the South.[62] The removal of the troops, coupled with the government's ambivalence toward Blacks, left Southern Blacks with no one to enforce their newly won civil rights or to ensure their safety.[63] Hayes' presidency marked the end of government sympathy for the plight of Southern Blacks and a return of Southern influence to the political arena.[64] Hayes' presidency also led to the appointment of several Southerners to the Supreme Court. The new justices were responsible for the landmark decision in *Plessy v. Ferguson* (1896) condoning the doctrine of separate but equal.[65] Homer Adolph Plessy challenged the Louisiana Separate Railway Act of 1890, which required separate traveling cars for Blacks and Whites. In *Plessy v. Ferguson*, the Supreme Court majority declared the following:

"[T]he enforced separation of the races, as applied to the internal commerce of the state, neither abridges the privileges or immunities of the colored man, deprives him of his property without due process of law, nor denies him the equal protection of the laws, within the meaning of the Fourteenth Amendment."[66]

In 1883, the Supreme Court declared the Civil Rights Act of 1875 unconstitutional.[67] In 1896, the Court ruled that segregated facilities for Black Americans and White Americans did not violate the Thirteenth or Fourteenth Amendments. Setting the pattern for race relations for more than three decades, *Plessy v. Ferguson* declared:

"Legislation is powerless to eradicate racial instincts, or to abolish distinctions based upon physical differences, and the attempt to do so can only result in accentuating the difficulties of the present situation. If the civil and political rights of both races be equal, one cannot be inferior to the other civilly or politically. If one race be inferior to the other socially, the constitution of the United States cannot put them upon the same plane."[68]

The racially segregated health system begun during Reconstruction was "institutionalized during the Gilded Age, a period of economic expansion between the 1870s and the early 1900s."[69] Opportunities to create an integrated health infrastructure were ignored and, instead, a segregated system was created that would worsen health inequities between Blacks and Whites.[70]

The year 1890 ushered in the so-called "Progressive Era" and a worsening situation for Blacks.[71] Voting rights were stripped away from Blacks in Mississippi (1890) and South Carolina (1895).[72] Democrats gained greater political power, while Northern influence in the South waned.[73]

These turbulent times saw some progress. Black health professionals were trained.[74] By 1900, there was more than 1,000 Black physicians in the United States and eight Black medical schools.[75] Additionally, nursing, dental, and pharmacy programs provided the Black American community with health professionals.[76] The National Medical Association, an association of Black physicians, was formed in 1895 after the American Medical Association refused to admit Black physicians to its ranks.[77] These advances brought a slight improvement to the health status of Blacks, but could not erase the decades of health deficits.[78]

## The Middle Years: 1901-1929

For White America, the early 1900s was the progressive era. It was marked by industrial growth, accumulated wealth by White corporate America, expanding markets, and increased immigration.[79] America was shifting from an agricultural economy toward one of "mass production, corporate entities, and monopoly capitalism."[80] The period also saw the rise of labor unions, new political groups, and farmers' cooperatives, almost all of whom discriminated against or excluded Black Americans.[81] Racism kept Blacks on the margins of the American economy and society.[82] Lynching continued to be a daily occurrence, and life for Blacks reached a new low point.[83]

During World War I, a boll weevil infestation and large floods in the South sent thousands of Blacks migrating to cities in the North.[84] World War I led to limits on immigration between 1915-1917 and thus opened job opportunities in a market that had expanded market to meet war time demands.[85] The concentration of Blacks in urban areas resulted in white flight and discrimination in housing and education, which created ghettos.[86] "Bombings, mob violence, police brutality, restrictive covenants (agreements between realtors not to rent or sell to Blacks), and the like were used by Whites to limit the areas where Blacks could live."[87] As a result, Blacks were "compressed in large contiguous neighborhoods" that were often slum-like.[88]

Following the war, many Black factory workers lost their jobs, and racial tensions increased.[89] Between 1917 and 1921, race riots erupted in Houston, Philadelphia, Chicago, East St. Louis, and Tulsa. [90] The Ku Klux Klan grew to a "membership high of four million" in 1924.[91] Fundamentalist religious beliefs also re-emerged following the war with much of the justification for their beliefs stemming from biological or biomedical research.[92] These religious fundamentalist beliefs influence health conditions for Blacks because it helped to foster scientific racism. Scientific racism taught that criminality and intelligence were biologically determined.[93] These beliefs were seen as justification for racist policies and social structures that affected the health care industry.[94]

Developing medical education policies, which focused on a shift in medical education from hospital based education to university-based education, led to the closing of several hospital-based Black medical schools. By 1923, only Howard and Meharry Medical Schools (both university based schools) survived.[95] With very few doctors to care for the black population, the closing of medical schools led to even more chronic shortages and less access to health care for Blacks.[96]

While the number of medical schools was decreasing, the number of hospitals that treated only Black patients was rising. In 1906, there were approximately 50 Black hospitals in the United States, and that number would approach 75 in the 1920's.[97] Racist policies kept Black physicians from training and working in White hospitals.[98] Black hospitals were constructed in small communities and staffed by Black physicians.[99] However, huge increases in costs and technology, coupled with limited funding, made Black hospitals a risky investment.[100]

## The Final Years: 1930 to 1954

The crash of the stock market in October, 1929 ushered America into the Great Depression.[101] Although Blacks had been excluded from the economic prosperity of the previous decade, they were now subject to even greater levels of unemployment, malnutrition, and disease.[102] By 1932, unemployment levels for Blacks would reach a staggering 25% and would not drop below 15% until 1940.[103]

Franklin Delano Roosevelt was elected President in 1932.[104] Roosevelt introduced his New Deal legislation for major social reform.[105] The government assumed responsibility for providing health care to the elderly, the disabled, and to poor children. Health insurance as a right of employment became a means of paying for health services.[106] The result was that the racial discrimination, which existed in employment opportunities was translated into racial discrimination in access to health care.[107]

In December 1941, the Japanese bombed Pearl Harbor, and the United States was once again involved in a World War.[108] World War II created a labor shortage in the United States, and Black Americans were put to work.[109] While President Lincoln integrated the military during the Civil War, President Wilson re-segregated it during World War I. It was integrated for a second time by President Truman. However, segregation remained, and only small segments of the military were integrated. [110]

World War II ended in 1945 and ushered in a period of unrest among minority groups, particularly Black Americans who having fought for freedom on foreign land was unwilling to accept to accept the shackles of Jim Crow discrimination..[111] Unfortunately, while the war had brought America out of the Great Depression and into a period of unprecedented economic growth, this was not being experienced by Black Americans.[112] Thus, Black Americans having fought for freedom gained the inspiration to begin the civil rights movement in earnest, and health care was part of the agenda.[113]

Anti-communist paranoia made civil rights efforts difficult during the 1950's.[114] The mood and political atmosphere of the time was very conservative and any challenge to the status quo was viewed suspiciously. Witch hunts, like those conducted by Senator Joseph McCarthy, not only kept many Black leaders from pursuing progressive platforms that appeared radical to their opponents, but many Black leaders joined in the hunt.[115] Even so, in 1948, President Truman integrated all branches of the armed forces, and the 1954 landmark decision in *Brown v. Board of Education* overturned the doctrine of separate but equal education, desegregating the school system.[116] In a unanimous decision, the court found that legally sanctioned racial segregation usually implied racial inferiority and adversely affected the educational development of Black children. "Any language in *Plessy v. Ferguson* contrary to this finding is rejected."[117]

These gains were followed by violent responses from Southern resistance groups and led to a new wave of lynches, bombings and other kinds of violence.[118] Black civil rights leaders organized the famous Montgomery bus boycott and other peaceful protests.[119] Following the civil rights movement, the Medical Committee for Human Rights was formed in 1964 with a goal of making health care a civil rights issue.[120] Despite these commendable attempts to establish equity in health care for Blacks, this entire period can be characterized as separate and unequal.

## The Civil Rights Era: 1954 to 1980

While *Brown v. Board of Education* was a milestone in civil rights, Jim Crow segregation remained until the Civil Rights Movement of the 1960's.[121] That movement culminated in the Civil Rights Acts of 1964 and the Voting Rights Act of 1965, which eliminated legally sanctioned signs of discrimination.[122] On the heels of civil rights legislation and political gains of the early 1960's, Blacks experienced unprecedented health gains. However, the government's earlier commitment to social programs would soon be eroded by the effects of war, inflation, and economic recession. The end of the 1960's would see a return to conservative leadership and the deterioration of the social programs born of the civil rights era. Furthermore, health care institutions that traditionally served the Black communities all but disappeared. Even so, Blacks, like Whites had an improved health status even though significant health inequities between White and Black persisted.

The improved health status of Blacks and Whites was largely due to President Lyndon Johnson's administration expanding government funding of his "Great Society" programs.[123] President Johnson created the Office of Economic Opportunity, Medicare, Medicaid, Community Action Agencies, and the Department of Housing and Urban Development.[124] These programs were aimed at race or class- based discrimination in employment, access to health care, and political and voting rights, and were designed to improve the quality of life for Blacks and other minority groups.[125] Of all the programs created under the Great Society, "those devoted to health care receive[d] the largest and most rapidly growing share of budget resources."[126]

In 1957 when I was 8 years old, my mother died of cancer. The last time I saw my mother, my father took us up into the hospital through a back stair way into a dark room that smelled funny. It was a women's ward and while Pennsylvania did not have Jim Crow laws all the patients "just happened to be black." It was my first experience with discrimination in the health care system it would not be my last.

One of the most significant events during this time was the creation of Medicare and Medicaid in 1966. These programs brought many segments of the Black and poor populations in to the health care system. First, Medicare and Medicaid provided medical insurance coverage to people who had been unable to afford health care in the traditional fee-for-service format and who did not have health coverage because they were unemployed or under-employed. For example, in 1964, people in the lowest income group had contact with a physician 3.9 times a year, in contrast to those in the highest income group who had 5.2 contacts a year.[127] Over the next thirty years this pattern would reverse itself. The lowest income group would have 7.6 physician contacts in 1994, and the highest income group would have only 6.0.[128] Medicaid was an important factor in this change.

The impact of Medicare and Medicaid on hospital use by low- income groups was even more dramatic, leading to an age-adjusted hospital stay rate that was three times that of the highest income group.[129]

Second, Medicare and Medicaid paved the way for desegregation of the nation's hospitals.[130] Medicare provided financial support for hospitals that offered medical care to the elderly. [131] Most of this care had previously been uncompensated. However, if hospitals wanted to receive government support they would have to comply with Title VI of the Civil Rights Act which prohibits discrimination by any institution receiving federal money.[132] The passage of Medicare legislation prompted many hospitals to desegregate in order to be eligible for the program.

In June of 1968 some 8,000 hospitals were cleared for participation in Medicare. Of these, more than 3,000 had revised traditional practices in order to obtain Medicare clearance. There were approximately 250 hospitals, most of them in the South, which refused to comply with Title VI of the Civil Rights Act and hence could not receive Federal assistance. [133]

Although President Johnson's administration improved the lives of Blacks in the 1960s, the gains were offset by the effects of the Vietnam War.[134] The war had a disproportionate impact on the Black community. Blacks were placed in combat units in greater numbers than their White counterparts and thus ran a far greater risk of death.[135] From January to November of 1966, 22.4% percent of all the casualties in the Army were Black soldiers [136]

The costs of the war in Vietnam drove the inflation rate up and forced the government to cut programs that largely affected the poor, in general, and Blacks in particular.[137] The Great Society had improved the lives of Blacks, but the economic repercussions of the war led to a six billion dollar reduction in funds that had been earmarked for Great Society programs.[138] President Johnson declared that he would not seek a second term, and the White House passed to right wing conservatives.[139]

Richard Nixon replaced Lyndon Johnson in 1968 and began a period of "tax hikes and relentless program cuts."[140] Just three years after the enactment of Medicare and Medicaid, President Nixon cited spiraling costs and declared a health care crisis in 1969.[141] The crisis, however, ran deeper than escalating costs.

Access to health care was a staggering problem across the United States. Middle class families complained that health care costs were unaffordable.[142] People living in poverty found that access to physicians was restricted by the shortage of doctors practicing in low-income neighborhoods.[143] "The City of Beverly Hills...had one doctor for every 225 people. Meanwhile, the Negro ghetto of Watts, 20 miles away, had but one doctor for every 2,700 people."[144] Adding to the problem was the emergence of "Medicaid mills" in low-income areas, something which disproportionately impacted Blacks.[145] Doctors opened offices in these areas, they treated hundreds of patients each day, but offered little personal attention or an acceptable quality of care.[146]

Medicare and Medicaid opened the doors of health care to many people in the 1960's and 1970's.[147] Medicare provided insurance coverage for almost all people over age sixty-five. The program's structure allowed deductibles and co-insurance balances that imposed a heavy burden upon lower income citizens.[148] Medicaid assisted the indigent in obtaining health care; its very low reimbursement rates caused many doctors to refuse to accept Medicaid patients, thus increasing the problem of finding health care in lower income neighborhoods, particularly in Black communities.[149]

In an attempt to train more Black American medical professionals, Black medical schools initiated aggressive recruitment programs between 1965 and 1970.[150] As a result of these efforts, 75% of Blacks who applied to these medical schools were accepted in 1969. A return to more conservative times in the 1970s quickly eroded these initial gains.[151] Attacks on affirmative action programs by the United States Supreme Court, in decisions such as *The Regents of the University of California v. Bakke*, which held that enrollment quotas were unconstitutional, made finding a solution to the shortage more difficult.[152] Challenging affirmative action affect Black enrollment because as the nation moved toward "color-blindness" both historically white schools and historically black schools matriculated fewer black students.

The devastating loss in Vietnam, President Nixon's resignation in 1974 in the wake of the Watergate scandal, followed by President Ford's presidential pardon, increased racial tensions. Trying economic times led to further general distrust of government in the late 1960s and 1970s.[153] This distrust was compounded for Blacks in 1972 with the revelations of the Tuskegee syphilis experiment.[154]

The involuntary sterilization of people who were poor or Black contributed to Blacks' general distrust of health care institutions. Throughout the 1960s and 1970s, Black women and men were coerced or forced to undergo sterilization procedures.[155] The belief that women who lived on welfare and had several children were not intelligent enough to use contraception was commonplace amongst some segment of the medical community in this period.[156] A 1972 Planned Parenthood survey reported that between 30% and 52% of doctors polled in the urban and rural areas of the United States believed that welfare mothers who became pregnant again should be forced to undergo sterilization in order to continue receiving benefits.[157] In July, 1973, two Black women in South Carolina sued their doctor for withholding prenatal and obstetrical care unless they agreed to sterilization.[158] The doctor was the only physician serving that South Carolina county who accepted Medicaid.[159]

## Racial Re-entrenchment: 1980 to 1997

Under President Reagan's administration the advancements seen in the previous fifteen years abruptly came to an end. President Reagan's economic philosophy, often termed "Reaganomics", claimed that the economy suffered from "excessive taxation and over-regulation of the free market."[160] President Reagan slashed taxes, and to make up for the lost revenue, he eliminated $40 billion dollars from the Federal budget.[161] The tax cuts benefited the wealthiest, while the budget cuts disproportionately affected Blacks and the poor, especially in the area of health care.[162] The nation found itself deep in a recession in 1982.[163]

Inflation was rampant and caused a decrease in tax revenues in many of the nation's cities.[164] This affected the health of Blacks and the poor who were the main clientele of public clinics and county hospitals that depended on this type of funding.[165]

The standard of living for Blacks declined under the Reagan administration.[166] "In 1983, the median White family had eleven times the wealth of the median non-White family. By 1989, this ratio had grown to twenty."[167] In addition, President Reagan reduced funding for food stamps, low-income housing, student loans, and other forms of federal assistance to states and cities.[168] These budget cuts threatened the progress that Blacks had made in health over the last two decades.[169]

Health care in the 1980s was dominated by huge health care corporations that eliminated not-for-profit medical services.[170] Managed care was key to this system.[171] This shift was caused by the concentration of the control and ownership of health care services in regional and national markets, and by single entities, such as HMOs, taking over multiple layers of care.[172] The evolution of this approach to health care by big business raised serious issues for disadvantaged populations when the focus ceased to be on delivering a high quality care but became the generating of a profit and making shareholders happy.[173]

The transformation to a managed health care system imposed additional burdens on the poor, the elderly, and Blacks. Low-income families faced problems that large corporate-based managed care did not solve.[174] For instance, many low-income families lived in urban or rural areas where few "network" providers were available and transportation was a significant problem.[175] Also, low-income families' health problems were often complex and may include cultural and language barriers.[176]

The 1990s brought enormous profits to health insurance companies, drug companies, and many health care providers, while Americans experienced a 22% decrease in insurance coverage and a growing dissatisfaction with the system.[177] Some of the defects in the system as it existed in the 1990s included 1) the lack of universal coverage with growing numbers of uninsured, 2) the lack of comprehensive care, which raised out-of-pocket expenses, 3) the lack of security prompted by self insurance plans that could eliminate coverage if a patient's expenses were too high, 4) the lack of a graduated system for premiums, and 5) wasteful spending on administrative costs.[178]

Hospitals did not escape the perils of corporate-dominated health care. The hospitals most threatened by the shift to a competitive, profit-driven market were "rural hospitals, Black hospitals, inner-city hospitals, public and city hospitals, and teaching hospitals."[179] Due to the larger base of sicker, under-insured, or uninsured patients served by these institutions, the hospitals' very survival was at-risk.[180] The charity care and bad debt burdens of these hospitals made it increasingly difficult for them to compete in a commercial environment and threatened the already limited health care options available to Black Americans.[181] Many hospitals serving the poor and disadvantaged were forced to close, with a disproportionate number of hospital closings occurring in Black communities. Much of the hospital expansion took place in already over-saturated markets far from the urban centers and rural locations where they were needed.[182]

Following a period of declining health for Black Americans and a period of intense dissatisfaction, the Clinton Administration promised to reform health care.[183] President Clinton's task force to analyze the health care problem did not include a representative number of disadvantaged, Black, or underserved community representatives.[184] A group of 150 Black and civil rights groups banded together to create their own task force, known as "Summit '93."[185] This group formulated policy suggestions and plans aimed at helping the disadvantaged and minority communities.[186] In 1993, after the President's Task Force had completed much of its work and the health care policy was almost completely formed, Summit '93 was invited to join the task force and share its suggestions.[187] The group's recommendation that a universal single-payer system be established was rejected, although some minor points were adopted.[188] In the end, Congress rejected President Clinton's health plan, and the corporate, managed care system continued.[189] Congress has been unwilling to contain the managed care industry although costs continue to rise.[190]

## Eliminating Health Care Inequities: 1997 through 2005

Starting in 1997, a concentrated effort was placed on eliminating health and health care inequities. President Clinton addressed racial inequities in health care in 1998 when he committed the Nation to a goal of eliminating racial and ethnic disparities in six areas of health status by the year 2010.[191] In 2000, President Clinton signed the *Minority Heath and Health Disparities Research and Education Act*.[192] The Act provided $150 million to establish a National Institutes of Health center to study disparities affecting minority populations.[193] Several bills were introduced in the 108th and the 109th Sessions of Congress to address health care inequities, But notwithstanding those efforts, institutional racism in health care continued to exist.

Institutional racism is the disproportionate negative impact of institutional policies, practices, and procedures on a racial or ethnic minority. Institutional racism can be based on intentional conduct, or it can be based on conduct that is not intentional but nevertheless results in a disproportionate negative impact on people of a different racial group. Over the last 40 years, racism has moved from intentional conduct to unintentional conduct. While this classification may offer a distinction when assigning fault or culpability, the classification makes little difference to the Black s who suffer the adverse effects of discrimination.

In short, the legacy of a racist health care system persists. Blacks are sicker than Whites and continue to experience a racialized health care system. This racialized system is evidenced by the following: 1) lack of economic access to health care, 2) non-economic barriers to hospitals and health care institutions, 3) barriers to physicians and other providers, 4) barriers to long-term care, 5) racial inequities in medical treatment, 6) discriminatory policies and practices, 7) lack of language and culturally competent care, and 8) disparate impact of the intersection of race and gender.

## Lack of Economic Access to Health Care

More than 45 million Americans were uninsured in 2003.[194] A disproportionate number of the uninsured are racial minorities.[195] A higher percentage of Black s are uninsured (21%) than Whites (13%).[196] Only about half of all Blacks have private health insurance, one in five has Medicaid or Medicare, and one in five has no health insurance coverage.[197] Since access to health insurance in the United States is most often tied to employment, racial stratification of the economy due to other forms of discrimination has concentrated Blacks in low wage jobs. These jobs rarely come with insurance benefits.[198] As a result, disproportionate numbers of the uninsured are Black s.[199]

Recent changes in the so-called "safety net" have only worsened these problems. In 1996, welfare reform changed the structure of public assistance, and this had a disproportionate impact on women and minorities.[200] One of the direct effects of welfare reform has been a reduction in the use of Medicaid by those who qualify. People who are eligible are unaware of the requirements, a situation that has increased the number of uninsured.[201] A second effect is that the subsequent increase in poverty among those in need of assistance has caused a worsening of health status and an increase in the demand for health care services.[202] In fact, a disproportionate number of racial minorities have no insurance, are unemployed, are employed in jobs that do not provide health care insurance, do not qualify for government assistance programs, or fail to participate because of administrative barriers. Gaps in health status and the absence of relevant health information are directly related to access to health care.[203]

*A Case in Point: The Idaho Child Health Insurance Program*

The discrimination in the Idaho Child Health Insurance Program (CHIP) Program is an excellent case in point. The Idaho Community Action Network (ICAN), a grassroots, member- based organization, received numerous complaints from its members about the application process for the federal Child Health Insurance Program. ICAN took testimony from members and found that although nearly all applicants were treated poorly, there was a clear pattern of discrimination that merited further investigation. ICAN developed a project that tested the accessibility of the program in three Idaho cities. White and Latino families were sent to apply for the CHIP and ICAN documented how the people were treated. The testing program uncovered clear evidence of discrimination. There were a lack of translators, intrusive questions by eligibility and caseworkers, requirements of proof of citizenship for Latino applicants, and unduly long processing time for all applicants- especially for Black and Latino applicants. Mounting a publicity and organizing campaign, ICAN forced the state to standardize application procedures and reduce the written application form for both Medicaid and CHIP from twelve pages to four.[204]

## Barriers to Hospitals and Health Care Institutions

The institutional and structural racism in hospitals and health care institutions manifests itself in the 1) adoption, administration, and implementation of policies that restrict admission,[205] 2) the closure, relocation, or privatization of hospitals that primarily serve the minority community;[206] and 3) the continued transfer of unwanted patients (known as "patient dumping") by hospitals and institutions.[207] Nearly one in three minority doctors reported that they could not obtain hospital admissions for their patients. An estimated one in four White physicians reported this problem.[208] Similarly, 210 hospitals that closed between 1937 and 1977 were located in neighborhoods where Blacks comprised at least 60% of the population.[209]

Finally, a study of 467 transfers to Cook County Hospital in Chicago showed that 89% were Blacks or Latinos. The study concluded that most of the patients were transferred for economic reasons and the transfers were made without their consent.[210] Such practices have a disproportionate effect on racial minorities, banishing them to overburdened institutions or denying them any care at all.[211]

### Admission Restrictions

Many hospitals discriminate by using restrictive patient referral and acceptance standards. These practices disproportionately bar Blacks from admission to hospitals.[212] Discriminatory admission practices have included the following:

- Laying off recently hired Black physicians who admit most of the Black patients served by the hospital;[213]
- Failing to have physicians on staff who will accept Medicaid patients with a disproportionate percentage of Medicaid patients who are black;[214]
- Requiring pre-admission deposits as a condition of obtaining care;[215]
- Refusing to participate in programs to finance care for low-income patients who are ineligible for Medicaid; [216] and,
- Accepting patients only from physicians with staff privileges when these physicians do not reflect the racial composition of the local community.[217]

Such practices have a devastating effect on Blacks. These practices may banish Blacks to distinctly overburdened institutions that are under-funded and treating mostly minority groups. They may completely prevent care where Black s have no access to other sources of care.

### Community Availability

Racial barriers to health care access are based on the unavailability of community services. Hospitals that serve the Black community are closing, relocating, or privatizing. In a study done between 1937-1977, researchers found that the likelihood of a hospital's closing was directly related to the percentage of Black s in the surrounding population.[218] For instance, 210 hospitals either closed or relocated during the period studied. While the articulated reason for closing was financial viability, hospital closings were related more to the race of the community than the income of the community. Thus, a disproportionate number of the hospitals that closed or relocated were located in predominantly Black communities.

Throughout the 1980's, many hospitals relocated from Black communities to predominantly White suburban communities.[219] These closures were met with ineffective resistance. For instance, in *NAACP v. Wilmington*, the National Association for the Advancement of Colored People (NAACP) fought a proposal that was intended to reduce the number of urban facilities which served minorities in order to construct a new suburban facility.[220] In *Bryan v Koch*, the community fought the closure of a New York City hospital whose patients were 98% minorities.[221] However, these efforts were unsuccessful and this loss of services resulted in reduced access to health care for Blacks.

Geographical availability and proximity are important determinants of finding timely health care services. If Blacks fail to seek early health care, they are more likely to be sicker when they do enter the system, and the cost for the patient to receive service and for the system to provide services is likely to be higher. Therefore, not only does the loss of services significantly increase health care costs to Blacks, but it also increases health care costs for society in general.[222]

Another devastating trend is the privatization of non-profit and public hospitals. Hundreds of public and non-profit hospitals have elected to restructure as private, for-profit corporations. As public hospitals, under the Hill-Burton Act, they had been obligated to provide uncompensated care.[223] One goal of the Hill-Burton Act was to assure that hospitals would provide medical services to the residents in their communities, including those who were indigent.[224] As private hospitals, these institutions are most likely to discontinue general health services to the indigent [225] and essential primary health care services to Blacks. For example, in *NAACP v. Medical Center*, the NAACP attempted to stop a medical center from closing high-risk obstetrical care, inpatient pediatric care, and gerontology services.[226]

Specifically, hospitals which receive funds under the Hill-Burton Act are obligated to meet a community service requirement.[227] In order to comply with this requirement, Subpart G of the regulation requires that recipient health facilities be made available to all residents and prohibits exclusion of anyone in the area served by the hospital on the basis of any factor unrelated to need.[228]

The Hill-Burton community services requirement was ignored for thirty years. Privately initiated civil lawsuits during the 1970's resulted in regulation changes in 1972.[229] These regulations outlined a program for monitoring compliance by Hill-Burton facilities that relied on state agencies for implementation. Unfortunately, the 1972 regulations did not amend or define the meaning of community service.[230] It was not until 1975 that the Department of Health, Education, and Welfare, under court order, finally issued regulations interpreting the community service requirement.[231] Henceforth, recipient facilities had to participate in Medicare and Medicaid and take "such steps as necessary" to ensure that Medicare and Medicaid patients were admitted without discrimination.[232] These regulations stopped short of imposing explicit standards for assessing compliance with the substantive requirement. In addition, evaluation and enforcement of the community service obligation was primarily done by state agencies, and a twenty-year limitation was placed on the community service obligation.[233] This limitation was later invalidated.

In 1978, the Department of Health, Education, and Welfare proposed new charity care regulations.[234] These new regulations, adopted in 1979, were intended to clarify the community service obligation, federalize the enforcement and monitoring of responsibilities[235,], and spell out the obligation of Hill-Burton recipients with regard to people who rely on Medicare or Medicaid. [236] The 1979 regulations also prohibited the pre-admission deposits and the required referrals to staff physicians, both of which excluded otherwise eligible patients.[237] Under Hill-Burton, a hospital is released from the uncompensated care requirement under the statutory buy-out provision.[238]

The problem of limited resources has plagued the Black community since slavery. Historically, Black communities dealt with the problem by opening their own hospitals.

By the 1940's, there were more than 200 hospitals in Black communities. Blacks relied on these institutions to "heal and save their lives."[239] Now, these institutions have lost the battle for their survival. By the 1960s, only 90 hospitals were located in majority Black communities. Between 1961 and 1988, 57 hospitals serving Black communities closed and 14 others either merged, converted to for-profit or consolidated. By 1991, only 12 hospitals that served the Black community continued to "struggle daily just to keep their doors open."[240] As a result of closures, relocations and privatization, many Blacks were left with limited, if any, access to hospitals.

### Patient Dumping

A Black seeking care at a private hospital faces the possibility of being "dumped", that is, transferred to a different facility.[241] The transfer is medically justified only when the care required is not available at the transferring hospital. However, many transfers are made for economic reasons, i.e., the patient was either uninsured or unable to pay the admission deposits.[242] Blacks are disproportionately affected by "dumping."[243]

In 1986, Congress passed the Emergency Medical Treatment and Active Labor Act which became effective as Section 9121 of the Consolidated Omnibus Reconciliation Act (COBRA).[244] The Act provides a right for an individual to sue hospitals that "dump" patients from their emergency rooms who have emergency conditions or who "dump" pregnant patients in active labor.[245]

Under COBRA, a hospital is required to provide appropriate medical screening examinations within its capabilities. If a person has an emergency or is in active labor, the hospital must stabilize the patient, provide treatment for labor, or transfer under certain conditions. There can be no transfer until the patient has been stabilized, unless the patient requests otherwise, if it is medically necessary, or if another facility is better equipped to treat the patient. A transfer is appropriate if the receiving facility has available space, qualified personnel, and equipment. Enforcement of illegal transfers is through termination of the hospital's Medicare provider agreement, monetary penalties, and civil action for personal injury or financial loss.[246]

Several states have made "patient dumping" illegal. Arizona limits transfers to three situations: when no hospital exists, when the transferring hospital is overcrowded, or when the transferring hospital does not provide the necessary services.[247] California requires exams, evaluations, and emergency treatment prior to the transfer of a patient. To transfer a patient, the following requirements must be met: the transfer may not create a medical hazard, the admitting hospital must have an available bed, and the information, personnel, and equipment necessary for treatment must be given to the receiving hospital.[248] Many other states that have made patient dumping illegal including Delaware, Florida, Idaho, Illinois, Massachusetts, North Carolina, Pennsylvania, Tennessee, Texas, and Washington.[249]

However, limited enforcement of these laws makes patient dumping an ongoing problem. By October 30, 1990, only 530 facilities had been investigated,[250] 139 facilities were found in violation of the statute,[251] but only five actually lost their Medicare contracts.[252] Because a high percentage of Black s are uninsured or under-insured, patient dumping continues to plague Blacks. Furthermore, hospitals have developed methods to circumvent the statute. The statute requires that hospitals receiving federal funding must accept any patient who "comes to an emergency room." If hospitals re-route the patient before the patient arrives, then the statute does not apply.[253]

In one case, *Johnson v. University Hospital*, a mother called the paramedics after her baby went into cardiac arrest.[254] The paramedics contacted the University of Chicago hospital which was five blocks away.[255] The hospital told the paramedics to take the child to another hospital.[256] The child was taken to a hospital without a pediatric intensive care unit and had to be transferred to a third hospital, where the child subsequently died.[257] The plaintiff sued, the trial court dismissed the case, and the appeals court upheld the dismissal. The Seventh Circuit noted that, "In accordance with the plain meaning of the statutory language, we do not believe that the infant ever 'came to' the hospital or its emergency department."[258] The court went on to acknowledge that a "... hospital could conceivably use a telemetry system to dump patients"; nevertheless, the court held that the "statute does not expressly address the question of liability in such a situation."[259] Thus, the Seventh Circuit left the door open for other hospitals to continue dumping patients, making it more than likely a disproportionate number will be Blacks.

## Barriers to Physicians and Other Providers.

The existence of hospitals and physicians is not enough. People need access to health care, and for various reasons, this has been a problem for the Black community. Areas that are heavily populated tend to be medically under-served.[273] According to one study of ten cities, the number of office-based primary care physicians in poor, inner city areas declined 45% from 1963 to 1980, while there was only a 27% decline of these services in non-poverty areas.[274] Disproportionately few White physicians have opened practices in Black communities.[275] Part of the answer to the problem might be to train more Black physicians; Black medical schools such as Howard University and Meharry

Medical School have done that, and this has proven to be effective. Black physicians are significantly more likely to practice in Black communities, making the health education and training of Black physicians extremely important.[276] For instance, poor, urban areas of the U.S. with a high proportion of their population that is Black or Hispanic have only 24 physicians per 100,000 people, compared to a national average of nearly 200 physicians per 100,000 people.[277] In fact, nearly 40% of all minority medical school graduates will practice medicine in under-served areas, compared to 10% of their non-minority colleagues.[278] Furthermore, Black health professionals tend to engage in the general practice of medicine and primary care specialties.[271] Access to health care among Blacks could be substantially improved by increasing the number of Black health care professionals.[272]

But the Black medical schools cannot provide all the physicians that the Black community needs; Black students in white medical schools are a necessity. However, there has been a long history of segregation in medical schools.[261] Thefirst Black did not receive a medical degree from an American medical school until 1847. Although nine White medical schools admitted Blacks prior to the Civil War, most did not. As late as 1971, 21 medical schools out of 85 still had no Black students. Even with the admission of Black As to predominantly White schools, the Black medical schools – Howard University and Meharry Medical School – still train 75% of the Black physicians. [263]

The result is that although 13% of the population is Black, Black physicians are under-represented in the health care professions. Only 3% of the physicians in the United States are Black, [264] and only 2.5% of all dentists[265] and 3.6% of all pharmacists are Black.[266] While this lack of representation is particularly significant for Black communities, it also affects all the communities. For instance, because of the lack of physicians, Black patients have long waits at county-run facilities.[267] In fact, one study showed that 75% of all Black physicians were practicing in or near shortage areas, 90% had patient case loads that were minorities, two-thirds had 70% minority case loads, and one-third had a case load that was 90% minority.[268]

The shortage of Black professionals affects the availability of health care by limiting Black input into the health care system.[280] While the distribution of health care is ultimately in the hands of the individual physician, that control is influenced and limited by law, hospital practices and policies, and medical organizations. With so few Black health care professionals, the control of the health care system lies almost exclusively in White hands. The result is inadequate attention to Black health care. Therefore, Whites are ignorant of the health concerns of Blacks.

The shortage of Black health professionals affects not only access to health care but also access to the power and resources to structure the health care system.[281] The result is an inadequate, ineffective, and marginalized voice on Black health care issues. When health care issues are defined, the policy makers' ignorance results in neglect of Blacks' health concerns which results in institutional racism.

## Barriers to Long Term Care

Nursing homes are the most segregated publicly licensed health care facilities in the United States. "Nursing home" is a generic term used to describe Intermediate Care Facilities (ICF) and Skilled Nursing Care Facilities (SNF).[282] The former provide institutional, health-related services above the level of room and board, but at a level of care below that of SNF care.[283] Skilled Nursing Facilities provide institutional care above the level of ICF services but below the level of a hospital.[284] Racial discrimination is the major factor explaining segregation in long-term care.[285]

---

Right before my father died he used to shuffle through the house as if he carried the weight of the world on his shoulders. Often he would make noises that I never understood. Sometimes he would say . . . . "Lordy . . . Lordy . . .Lordy" and shake his head. When I would ask him what was wrong, his eyes would tear up a bit and he would say nothing. Once I asked him "Daddy, why do you say "Lordy. . .Lordy. . . Lordy". He looked from those deep well of eyes, with that expression that I remember from childhood. That expression that said, that he didn't expect me to understand because I was too young. He shook his head a little and said: "Nell, you think being black is hard." Try being Black and old. I am just sick and tired. . . of being sick and tired." I remember this comment often and writing about it can capture the sag in my father's should, the sadness in his eyes, the tiredness in his body or the anger in his voice.

---

It has been suggested that any differences in Black American use of nursing homes can be explained by cultural biases against using nursing homes for disabled or aged family members. But in *Linton v. Carey*, the Supreme Court rejected the defendants' assertion that "self-selection preferences" of the minorities, based upon traditional reliance upon the extended family, lack of transportation, and fear of institutional care adequately explain the disparate impact.[286] However, in Delaware and Detroit, Black Americans make up a higher portion of nursing home residents than White Americans. This suggests that Black Americans do not consistently decide against nursing homes.[287] For instance, although Black Americans often rely on family and friends for long term care, the rate of use of nursing homes is rising faster for Black Americans than for White Americans.[288] Furthermore, even where racially neutral policies exist, institutional racism is still a factor. For instance, evidence about the use of nursing homes under Medicaid demonstrates that institutional racism has an impact even without regard to economic class.[289]

An individual's eligibility for Medicaid is based on need, age, disability, and indigence. Indigence is measured by state and Federal standards. To obtain Medicaid coverage for nursing home care, the patient must first establish financial eligibility and then demonstrate eligibility for ICF or SNF services. The medical requirements are established by the state to guard against unnecessary treatment. In order to determine a patient's medical eligibility, states generally require that each Medicaid recipient's need for admission to a nursing home be evaluated prior to the recipient's admission, or if the patient has already been admitted, prior to an authorization of Medicaid reimbursement. This process is referred to as the preadmission evaluation (PAE) process. Once a patient has been admitted to a nursing home, his or her continued need for ICF or SNF care is annually reviewed by state Medicaid officials pursuant to a process referred to as utilization review.[290] Particularly difficult for black elders are the barriers to long-term care.

Although Black Americans constitute only 12% of the nation's population, the Black American poverty rate (31%) is three times greater than the White American poverty rate (10%).[291] However, Black Americans constitute only 29% of the Medicaid population and 23% of the elderly poor.[292] Medicaid expenditures for Black Americans are only 18% of total expenditures.[293] In part, this inequity in expenditure is based on the limited access that Black Americans on Medicaid have to nursing homes.[294] This limited access is partly caused by the state and federal regulations. For instance, Federal law authorizes state agencies to certify facilities for either SNF or ICF reimbursement. Such certification may be of a "distinct part of an institution."[295] A "distinct part " SNF or ICF must be a separately identifiable unit and all bed in that unit must be reservd for patients that need the care that provided by an SNF or an ICF. A distinct part SNF or ICF unit is paid as an entity separate from the rest of the institution.[296] Consequently, facilities limit the number of beds that they have available by certifying only part of their facility. Because of these rules, White middle class women are disproportionately represented on Medicaid.

Only 10% of Medicaid intermediate care patients are Black Americans.[297] Similarly, only 9% of Medicaid skilled nursing care facilities' patients are Black Americans.[298] Nevertheless, if Black Americans are sicker, then Medicaid expenditures for Black Americans should at least be equal to, if not greater than, the percentage of Medicaid's Black American population. It is this combination of under-representation and under-spending in Medicaid that suggests racism. For the Black elderly, neither Medicaid nor Medicare removes the racial barrier to long-term care facilities.

Long-term care policy should examine the impact it will have on elderly Black Americans. First, even color-blind policy can have an unintended negative consequence. Second, the life of the Black American elderly has been affected by racism. That impact is likely to continue. Finally, racialized policies and practices have resulted in conditions in which older minorities generally have poorer health, lower incomes, and more difficult living conditions than older Whites.

For the long-term care industry to meet the needs of the Black American elderly, specific actions need to be taken. First, good public policy would assure universal access to long-term care. In the interim, there has to be a more equitable selection of patients to fill Medicaid beds. Second, while Title VI of the Civil Rights Act of 1964 could be made more effective, a truly effective anti-discrimination effort will require specific legislation. One essential component to eliminating racial discrimination is data. Data must be collected by race, provider, and facility. Third, organizational, administrative, and cultural barriers to long-term care use must be eliminated. It is clear that economic access is not the only barrier to the use of long-term care. There needs to be integration of referral systems and health care facilities in order to eliminate discontinuities in care due to jurisdictional boundaries and to increase the number of Black American-owned and operated nursing homes.

Real differences in long-term care will occur over the next fifty years because of the changing face of the elderly. Clearly, long-term care will need to market itself to Black Americans, to treat health problems that may be different in type and certainly different in severity. Long-term care will have to adapt to increased involvement of family members in health choices and assure culturally competent care. Finally, Black American elderly must receive a fair share of long-term care resources.

## Racial Discrimination in Medical Treatment

Racial barriers to access are only one aspect of institutional racism. Other aspects include the racial inequities in types of services ordered and in the provision of medical treatment itself; this has been well-documented in studies of cardiology, cardiac surgery, kidney disease, organ transplantation, internal medicine, and obstetrics. One wonders how much of the inequity in treatment is a legacy of the racist mindset during slevery era when "...doctors frequently complained that they were unable to administer treatment because the slaves were not amenable to the same medical treatment as White patients."[299]

*Racial inequities exist when a gap in medical treatment continues even after other factors (such as income, insurance, age, illness status) are controlled.* Racial inequities exist even where similarly situated individuals are compared. Racial inequities in treatment have been demonstrated in many studies in the following areas: asthma, cancer, cerebrovascular disease, children health, diabetes, HIV/AIDS, hospital/clinical services, cancer, kidney disease and kidney transplantation, maternal/child health services, mental health, pain management, and rehabilitation services. (See Table 02). These inequities are discrimination and should be called such.

---

My cousin died from breast cancer. She is not the first woman in my maternal family to die of cancer. My mother died at 36. My aunt died at 42. Another cousin died at 35. My grandmother died at 75. I have another aunt who is a breast cancer survivor. . . and yet, my cousin's doctor when finding a lump told her to wait.

She waited.

She died at 42

Often, when confronted with the above statistics, people will try to explain them in terms of socioeconomic class. However, race plays an independent role.[300] There are marked differences in time spent with physicians, quality of care, and quantity of doctor's office visits between Whites and Blacks.[301] Whites are more likely to receive more thorough diagnostic work-up, better treatment, and better care than Black Americans.[302] Differences also exist in the number of doctor's office visits between Whites and Blacks, even when controlling for income, education, and insurance.[303]

`In 1990, I received an urgent call on a Saturday in October. Daddy had been admitted to the hospital and they were going to do open heart surgery on him the following Monday. I dropped everything and rush to my father's side. When I arrived in Portland, I found my Dad looking in fairly good health. I asked him if I could review his chart. I went to the nurse's station, told them I was nurse practitioner and attorney and I wanted to review my father's chart. Almost immediately, things begin to happened. Different doctors came to exam my father. By noon on Sunday, the powers that be decided that instead of resident #16 doing the surgery, it would be resident #3. By Sunday night it was resident # 1 and by Monday Morning the surgery had been cancelled – the chief of surgery had decided that my father had not had a sufficient try of medical treatment. They started my father on medicines and he never had the surgery. And when he died 5 years later it was from cancer. Some times the inequity is unnecessary care for the purpose of teaching.

Researchers have concluded that doctors are less aggressive when treating Black American patients.[304] In fact, at least one study indicated a combined effect of race and gender resulting in significantly different health care for Black American women.[305] Thus, the most favored patient is a "White male between the ages of 25 to 44."

Whether these differences are based on individual prejudices or medical school training, it is compelling evidence of institutional racism that cannot be tolerated. Any patient seeking care from a physician should be confident of receiving the most appropriate medical treatment available. Regardless of race, each of us should trust our physician to act in our best interest. Every person should be assured that the physician will not let personal or medical prejudice compromise the quality of medical treatment. Black Americans do not have those assurances.

## Chart 03
## Results of Selected Studies on Health Care Inequities

In each of the instances below, the comparison group is similarly situated Whites, that is whites of similar socio-economic, educational, insurance and health status.

### Asthma[337]
- Blacks are more likely to receive treatment for asthma in emergency rooms
- Blacks are more likely to use inhaled bronchodilator medications than inhaled corticosteroids
- Blacks are less likely to be seen by an asthma specialist
- Blacks are more likely to use oral corticosteroids
- Blacks are less likely to be prescribed inhaled anti-cholinergic medications

### Cancer[338]
- Blacks are diagnosed at later stages of cancer progression than Whites
- Blacks are less likely to be treated by an experienced board-certified physician
- Black women with breast cancer are less likely to receive progesterone receptor assays (a prognostic test), radiation therapy in combination with radical/modified mastectomy, and to receive rehabilitation support services following mastectomy
- Black men aged 50 to 69 years with prostate cancer are less likely to undergo prostatectomy
- Black men with prostate cancer are twice as likely as to received no treatment
- Blacks with colon cancer are more likely to receive a barium enema only, less likely to receive a combination of barium enema and sigmoidoscopy, and less likely to undergo colonoscopy
- Black cancer patients are less likely to receive follow-up treatment
- Black women with cervical cancer are more likely to receive neither radiation therapy nor surgery
- Blacks are more likely to not have any treatment recommended
- Blacks with colorectal cancer are less likely to receive a major procedure for treatment of colorectal cancer
- Blacks with metastasis are less likely to receive a major treatment such as surgery

### Cardiovascular Care[339]
- Blacks are less likely to receive revascularization procedures within 90 days of admission
- Blacks are less likely to be considered for future catheterization
- Black Veteran's Administration hospital patients are less likely to receive cardiovascular procedures
- Blacks are more than twice as likely to not receive invasive procedures
- Black patients with a heart attack are less likely to receive thrombolytic therapy and bypass surgery
- Blacks are nearly three times less likely to receive catheterization, angioplasty, or coronary artery bypass graft
- Whites use some clinical services at higher rates than minorities, even when not necessarily indicated

## Cerebro-vascular Disease[340]
- Blacks have lower rates of diagnostic and therapeutic procedures
- Blacks are half as likely to receive carotid imaging;
- Blacks are less likely to be assessed as appropriate candidates for surgery
- Blacks are less likely to receive noninvasive cerebrovascular testing
- Blacks are less likely to receive anticoagulant therapy
- Blacks are less likely to receive care from a neurologist

## Child Health[341]
- Blacks are less likely to be activated on the kidney transplant wait list
- Blacks are less likely to receive prescription medication when the see a physician
- Blacks received the fewest number of medications
- Blacks are less likely to receive psychotropic prescriptions

## Diabetes[342]
- Black non-insulin dependent diabetes patients are more likely to be treated with insulin
- Blacks have lower rates for visits to specialists for diabetes complications, testing and screening
- While Blacks are more likely to receive patient education, the median number of hours of instruction are was lower

## HIV/AIDS[343]
- Blacks are less likely to receive anti-retroviral therapy, prophylaxis for pneumocystic pneumonia, and protease inhibitors
- Blacks are less likely to receive protease inhibitors or nonnucleoside reverse transcriptase inhibitors at initial assessment
- Blacks waited longer to receive appropriate medications

## Hospital/Clinical Services[344]
- Blacks are less likely to have an admitting diagnosis of myocardial infarction (MI), are less likely to have a history of coronary artery disease, but have a higher severity of illness
- Blacks with glaucoma, are nearly half as likely to receive surgery
- Blacks diagnosed with gall bladder or biliary disease, who underwent cholecystectomy are less likely to undergo the laparoscopic procedure
- Blacks with congestive heart failure are more likely to received a lower overall quality of care
- Blacks are less likely to receive major therapeutic procedures for 37 of 77 conditions
- Blacks admitted to intensive care have a shorter length of stay and lower resource use in the first seven days
- Blacks with osteoarthritis are less likely to receive total knee arthroplasty
- Black patients are less likely to use long-term care services, particularly prescription medications and physician services
- Blacks are less likely to have a primary care specialist as a regular provider
- Blacks are more likely to report long waiting periods before seeing their care provider
- Blacks are more likely to undergo amputation than White patients

## Kidney Disease and Kidney Transplantation[345]
- Blacks with end stage renal disease are less likely to receive a kidney transplant
- Blacks are less likely to be referred for transplantation

- Blacks are less likely to appear on waiting lists within the first year of Medicare eligibility
- Blacks' average waiting time for kidney transplantation is almost twice as long
- Blacks are less likely to be judged as appropriate for transplantation, to appear on transplantation waiting lists, and to undergo transplantation procedures, even after controlling for patients' insurance status and other factors
- Among patients considered appropriate for transplantation, Black patients are less likely to be referred for evaluation, to be placed on a waiting list, and to ultimately undergo transplantation
- Black patients are less likely to be placed on waiting lists before initiating maintenance dialysis
- Blacks are half as likely as White patients to be initially treated with peritoneal dialysis
- Black patients are much less likely to be referred to a transplant center for evaluation
- Blacks are much less likely to be placed on a waiting list or to have received a transplant within 18 months after initiating dialysis

### Maternal/Infant Health[346]
- Blacks are more likely to receive cesarean delivery;
- Pregnant Black women are less likely to have an amniocentesis
- Blacks are less likely to undergo an ultrasonography
- Black women with single births are only slightly more likely to receive tocolysis although the risk of idiopathic pre-term delivery is estimated to be three times higher in Black women
- Black women are less likely to report receiving advice for alcohol and smoking cessation
- Black s are less likely to be given advice about breast-feeding
- Black single women are less likely to receive advice on drug cessation

### Mental Health[347]
- In emergency rooms, Blacks are given significantly higher 24-hour dosage of anti-psychotic medications
- Blacks who are depressed are less likely to received antidepressant treatment within 30 days of the first indicator of depression

### Pain Management and Analgesia[348]
- Blacks with long-bone fractures seen in emergency rooms are less likely to receive analgesia
- Black elderly nursing home residents with cancer are more likely to receive no pain medication
- Black cancer patients are more likely to receive inadequate pain medication.
- Male physicians are more likely to prescribe lower doses of pain treatment to Black patients

### Rehabilitation Services.[349]
- Black patients are more likely to receive a lower intensity of physical or occupational therapy
- Black patients are less likely to receive acute physical therapy only
- Blacks are less likely to receive therapy in both acute care and skilled nursing facilities
- Blacks are more likely to receive no physical therapy at all

## Discriminatory Policies and Practices

Discriminatory policies and practices can take the form of medical redlining, excessive wait times, unequal access to emergency care, deposit requirements as a prerequisite to care, and lack of continuity of care, all of which have a negative effect on the type of care received.[306] Discriminatory policies are often racially neutral and difficult to detect but collectively have a more adverse effect on black patients. There are many examples of policies and practices that disproportionately affect Black Americans, such as the refusal to admiet patients whose physicians do not have admitting privileges at that hospital, exclusion of Medicaid patients, and failure to provide translators and interpretations of printed material.[307]

One significant example is a "racially neutral" federal Medicaid policy that limits the number of beds a nursing home can allocate to Medicaid recipients. In *Linton v. Carney*, the court noted that "Tennessee, at the provider's instructions, certified a limited number of beds in a facility which provides the same ICF level of care in all beds."[308] The policy encourages these facilities to move existing patients who have spent down their assets and are now eligible for Medicaid into "Medicaid beds" as they become available. It is mostly White women who can afford long- term care without Medicaid and live long enough to exhaust their financial assets. The effect of this policy is that fewer Medicaid resources are spent on Black American populations for nursing home care, even though they represent a larger portion of the Medicaid population and have more illness.[309] The combination of Black American over-representation and government under-spending in Medicaid is yet another example of the kind of structural and institutional racial discrimination that persists in many areas of the health care system.

Another example[310] is the Bush administration's policy to permit Medicare plus Choice organizations to identify their service areas on a sub-county basis. This policy has been linked explicitly to an effort to allow the organizations to hold on to a market. Unfortunately, the policy is likely to have a disproportionately negative impact on Blacks because it would allow Medicare organizations to exclude Black communities with poorer health and higher cost.[311] Thus, through an apparently neutral policy, Medicare continues to allow the insurance industry to link race, poor health, and high cost.[312]

## Lack of Language and Culturally Competent Care

A key challenge has been to persuade the government to establish clear standards for culturally competent health care. Culturally competent care is sensitive to issues related to culture, race, gender, and sexual orientation. Cultural competency involves ensuring that all health care providers can function effectively in a culturally diverse setting, and it involves understanding and respecting cultural differences.[313] In addition to recognizing the inequities in health status between White Americans and Black Americans, we must recognize differences within groups.[314] Black American communities include groups with multiple histories, languages, cultures, religions, beliefs, and traditions. This diversity should be reflected in the health care they receive and their experiences with the health care industry.[315] That is, without understanding and incorporating these subgroup differences, health care cannot be culturally competent.[316]

One study noted that the "prevalence of negative stereotypes about Black and Hispanic groups…[has] resulted in discriminatory practices in health care service delivery."[317] Nonetheless, there has been relatively little research done on the differences in accessing quality health care by subgroups of the Black American community. In addition, there is evidence that health care providers come to the practice with cultural biases that may undermine their delivery of care.[318]

According to one researcher, the doctor apparently arrives at the patient's bedside with preconceived notions about the patient's needs for pain medication, notions that are tied to ethnicity and not to the illness. What is worse is that there are no data to suggest that such perceptions are accurate, nor are physicians even aware of their behavior.[319] Furthermore, racial bias "may represent overt prejudice on the part of physicians or, more likely, could be the result of subconscious perceptions rather than deliberate actions or thoughts."[320]

Another example of institutional barriers to culturally competent care is the prevalence of linguistic barriers.[321] This has become a serious problem for the Black community because immigration from Africa and South America has resulted in a growing number of Blacks who do not speak English or who speak it as a second language. The failure of the health care industry to use bilingual, professionally and culturally competent, and ethnically matched staff in patient/client contact positions results in lack of access, miscommunication, and mistreatment because of limited proficiency in English.[322] This failure includes not providing education or information at the appropriate literacy level. Furthermore, "English only" laws that restrict access of public services to those with proficiency in English also have an acute and racially disproportionate impact on immigrant Blacks.[323] The lack of an official government infrastructure (from the Federal to the local level) to ensure standards of culturally competent care and equal access to services is a critical issue affecting health care delivery.

## Disparate Impact of the Intersection of Race and Gender

The unique experiences of Black American women have been ignored by the health care system.[324] Black American women share many of the problems experienced by Black American men, and women as a whole. However, racial discrimination and gender discrimination often intersect to magnify the difficulties Black American women face in acquiring equal access to quality health care.[325] Some barriers to care predominantly affect Black American women. There are also gender differences in medical use, provision of treatments, and inclusion in research.[326] This is partly the result of the different expectations of men and women of medical care and of gender bias among health care providers.[327] Furthermore, the difficulty that Black American women face in obtaining health care is not limited to illnesses that affect both male and female populations. Rather, there is evidence that Black American women often find it difficult to find quality health care related to gender-specific illnesses, such as breast cancer.[328]

> When it comes to the law of discrimination and to health care, it often seems as if "all women are white, all blacks are men." If Black women problems are not white women problems often it is not seen as a gender issue. If Black women problems are not Black men problem often it is not seen as a race problem. But there is compounding effect of race and gender – making Black women's experience of gender different from white women and the experience of race different from Black men.

An additional indication of gender bias in the health care system is the way in which Black American women's medical concerns are not taken as seriously as Black American men's. Women's complaints are often dismissed as emotional distress or as a psychosomatic condition. Further, some health issues, such as domestic violence, have been largely ignored by the medical community, which sees this violence as a social issue rather than as a health issue. The medical professions have historically lacked a female perspective, in much the same way that they lack a Black American perspective.[329]

Policies and practices that increase government oversight and control of Black American women are also a key factor in health status. In the case of domestic violence, Black American women are less likely to receive sympathetic intervention by law enforcement.[330] Black American women who, after calling upon police for help in such cases, are often victims of both domestic violence and police neglect.

Family planning is another area where public policy has harmed the health status and life choices of Black American women.[331] Black American women do not have equal access to preventive medicine or the full range of birth control. Barriers include lack of family planning services or facilities in their communities, lack of coverage of reproductive counseling services, medications or procedures by Medicaid or other publicly funded health insurance programs, and disproportionately higher prescription of medically risky or unnecessary procedures such as contraceptive implants or forced sterilization.[332]

State and local policies are more likely to be discriminatory than Federal policies. However, there are few standards for ensuring equal access and equal treatment at these levels of government. With jurisdiction over this area increasingly devolving to the state and local level, there is a critical need for a clear regulatory infrastructure that removes these barriers, offers remedies and penalizes policies and practices that promote discrimination.

## CONCLUSION

Black Americans emerged from slavery with a slave health deficit that has never been rectified. In the twenty-first century, that deficit has been aggravated by a racialized health care system. Racism affects access to care and to medical treatment independently of socioeconomic class. Although the inequities in treatment decisions reflect clinical characteristics, income, and medical or biological differences, they also reflect racial bias.[333] To improve the health of Black Americans, it is not sufficient merely to remove socioeconomic barriers to access. Health care institutions must rid themselves of institutional racism.

Medicine has found cures and controls for many afflictions, improving the health of all Black Americans, Asian Americans, Hispanic Americans, Native Americans and White Americans.[334] However, health care institutions have failed to make Black Americans as healthy as they have made White Americans.[335] Health care institutions have failed to end the racial distribution of health care.[336] They also continue to perpetuate discrimination. Such a situation is intolerable. Of all the influences on Black Americans' health, the influence of health care institutions, though small, should be free of racial prejudice.

# Chapter Four

---

# TARGETING
# THE BLACK COMMUNITY

The tobacco industry specifically targets the African American community with its products. While some argue it is astute marketing, the truth is the industry disproportionately floods the African American community with advertisements and cigarettes. The industry promotes a highly addictive drug in the African American community. As a result, more African American adults smoke, become increasingly addicted, and have greater illness due to smoking than other sectors of the population. The settlement with the tobacco companies does not adequately address the needs of the African American community.

The National Tobacco Settlement and the enacting legislation are inadequate. They have left the African American community at the mercy of the tobacco companies, with little redress for specific harmful effects, such as addiction and dependency, that have already occurred and will continue to occur.[1] In order to reach an equitable result, the following courses of action are priorities:

> 1) the funding of culturally specific cessation programs targeted toward African Americans,
> 2) the funding of biomedical research specifically addressing the issues of African Americans' addiction and dependence, with particular attention to menthol and flavors,
> 3) the funding of African American events historically supported by tobacco industries,
> 4) the limiting of immunity to information disclosed prior to the enactment of any legislation, and requirement of full disclosure of all past, present and future research and other documents related to marketing, biochemical research and menthol, and most importantly, 5) the establishment of a Tobacco Injury Compensation Fund for addicted smokers.

## THE NATIONAL TOBACCO SETTLEMENT

On June 20, 1997, a group of State Attorney Generals, plaintiffs' attorneys, public health advocates, and representatives of major tobacco companies announced a historic national tobacco industry settlement.[2] The settlement was designed to restructure the tobacco industry and reimburse participating states for their expenditures on smoking-related illnesses.[3] Several bills were introduced into Congress to convert the settlement into law.[4] Special legal protection for the tobacco industry was the linchpin of the settlement. In the legislation, the tobacco industry agreed to 1) drastically limit marketing andadvertising[5], 2) accept regulation by the Food and Drug Administration,[6] 3) finance programs aimed at deterring young people from smoking,[7] 4) finance smoking cessation programs[8], and 5) partially reimburse the states for their tobacco-related health costs.[9]

The quid pro quo for the tobacco industry's magnanimous concession included 1) terminating existing class actions and barring future class actions or multi-case lawsuits against the companies[10], 2) terminating existing civil action claims and barring future civil action claims based on addiction or dependency[11], 3) capping the annual payments by the industry in judgments and settlements of lawsuits brought by individuals, starting at $2 billion and rising to $5 billion[12], 4) prohibiting future lawsuits by states against the companies, and 5) eliminating punitive damage awards against the companies for past conduct.[13]

Clearly, the most significant benefit of the tobacco settlement to the African American community was the limitation of advertising.[14] The leading advertised products in African American communities are cigarettes and alcohol.[15] The ban on outdoor advertising has had a profound, positive effect on the African American community. However, given the difficulty Black smokers have in quitting, and the substantial brand loyalty among smokers, the ban really addresses new smokers and does little to help chronic smokers.[16]

While the authorizing legislation required the funding of biomedical research, there was no requirement that biomedical research be conducted to address why African Americans smoke less and have greater dependence.[17] Similarly, while the settlement required the development of smoking cessation programs, there was no requirement to develop culturally specific smoking cessation programs.[18] Furthermore, by banning class action suits, the authorizing legislation effectively limits the ability of poor and middle class individuals to bring suits against richer tobacco companies and win. Finally, given the potential effect of mentholated cigarettes and the targeting of the African American community, the banning of dependence and addiction suits bars a primary claim by African Americans without providing any substantial relief for those individuals who are already addicted and who are unable to "kick" the habit. The tobacco companies have effectively walked away from the billions of dollars of harm they have caused (and will cause) by selling a deadly, highly addictive product.

That the authorizing legislation did not directly address the needs of African Americans was not surprising since it merely reflects the settlement. It would be surprising indeed if the settlement had adequately represented the interests of African American communities since the negotiation table did not include any health representatives of the African American community.[19] "It was pretty much a white male group that put the settlement together and the document reflects that." [20]

The obvious retort is, why should any tobacco settlement or litigation specifically address the needs of African Americans? The simple reason is that for years tobacco companies have specifically targeted the community as much as they have targeted underage smokers. As a result of pushing mentholated nicotine on the community, African Americans are more addicted and have poorer health status than White Americans. The quid pro quo for African Americans needs to be very specific. That has not happened.

## TOBACCO INDUSTRY TARGETING OF THE BLACK COMMUNITY

For well over six decades, cigarette manufacturers have specifically targeted the African American community.[21] Targeting involves disproportionately promoting dangerous or harmful products to one segment of the population. Targeting is the intentional pursuit of exchange with a specific group through advertising or other marketing activities, designed and executed to be more appealing to the target market than to people in other segments.

Recognizing a declining consumer base, tobacco companies have attempted to protect their profits by increasing smoking among African Americans.[22] The tobacco companies have disproportionately splashed inducements to smoke on billboards and buses, on subways, and in African American publications.[23] They have disproportionately sponsored athletic events, outdoor media campaigns, sports/cultural events, and academic scholarships.[24] The tobacco industry has developed specially named brands targeted specifically toward African Americans.[25] Tobacco companies have spent a disproportionate amount of their promotional budget in an effort to hook Black smokers. Unfortunately, such conduct has not been specifically addressed. Consequently, the African American community has been dealt two blows, one by the tobacco industry and one by the tobacco settlement.

### Billboard and Magazine Advertising

To say that the black community was overrun by tobacco advertising is an understatement. The size and number of billboards in minority communities created an intrusive and persistent form of advertising. There was absolutely no way to avoid it. For instance, a 1987 survey conducted by the city of St. Louis found twice as many billboards in black neighborhoods as in white neighborhoods.[26] Almost 60% of the billboards in the black neighborhoods advertised cigarettes and alcoholic beverages.[27] In another study of seventy-three billboards along nineteen blocks in a black Philadelphia neighborhood, sixty advertised cigarettes or alcohol.[28] In a 1989 survey by the Abel Foundation, 70% of the 2,015 billboards documented in the city of Baltimore advertised alcohol or tobacco products.[29] Three-quarters of the billboards were in predominately poor African American neighborhoods.[30] In fact, the Centers for Disease Control estimates that billboards advertising tobacco products were placed in African American communities four to five times more often than in white communities.[31] Furthermore, the advertisements were usually for menthol cigarettes, which are more popular with African Americans, and which may have additional significant medical effects.[32]

In addition to billboard advertisements, tobacco companies have advertised extensively in African American magazines; in an eight-year period there were 1,477 tobacco advertisements in Jet, Ebony, and Essence.[34] In fact, cigarettes advertised in African American magazines such as Ebony, Jet, and Essence, account for a higher percentage of the minority magazines' total advertising revenues.[33] The tobacco industry has poured millions of dollars into advertising in newspapers and magazines that serve the African American community.[35] The advertisements tend to be in small newspapers serving blacks. However, the industry also advertises extensively in prominent African American magazines. For instance, the April 1997 cover of Ebony had a headline, "Prostate Cancer: Why the Black Death Rate Is So High." The back cover featured an ad for Capri cigarettes. The February 1997 issue of Ebony, for Black History Month, advertised Camel, Misty, Newport, Virginia Slims, and Capri.

> "They win the "lungs of Blacks . . . [by] playing on the image of success, upward mobility, stoke[ing] fantasies of wealth and power. . . . They design socially conscious ads in Black publications that tout Black leaders and celebrities, praise Black historical figures, scientists, artists and events and promote their sponsorship of scholarship[s], business and equal-opportunity promotional programs for Blacks. . . ."[36]

## Sponsorship and Donations

Historically, the African American community has had an ambivalent relationship with the tobacco industry, and just as with slavery, Blacks are a bought people. In exchange for goodwill, the tobacco industry has been a significant sponsor of athletic, civil, cultural and entertainment events,[37] and this practice dates back to 1938, when William Reynolds. R.J. Reynolds' brother, donated money to start the Kate Bitting Reynolds Memorial Hospital for Blacks in segregated Winston-Salem, North Carolina.[38] The tobacco industry has been a significant sponsor of athletic, civil, cultural, and entertainment events.[37] For example, Philip Morris supported Operation PUSH, the Rev. Jesse Jackson's civil rights organization.[41] Further, the tobacco giant brought together presidents of black colleges for a Martin Luther King Jr., birthday remembrance, produced half-hour radio programs to celebrate Black History Month, and commemorated a Bill of Rights anniversary with ads featuring prominent African American leaders.[42] It supported the Dance Theater of Harlem, sponsored rhythm-and-blues concerts, and heavily advertised in black-oriented media in cities with large black populations.[43] Further, the tobacco industry sponsored the fortieth-anniversary gala of the United Negro College Fund, the Kool Achiever Awards, the Ebony Fashion Show, and a forum for publishers of Black newspapers regarding preserving freedoms in American life.[39]

And not surprisingly, the tobacco industry has tried to buy influence with leaders in the Black community. Key civil rights leaders have sat on the boards of tobacco companies. For example, former Urban League President, Vernon E. Jordan, Jr., who headed President Clinton's transition team, sat on the RJR Nabisco Holdings Corporation Board.[44] Raymond Pritchard, who retired as chairman and CEO of Brown and Williamson Company, sat on the board of the National Urban League from 1986 to 1992.[45] Hugh Cullman, a one-time vice chairman of Philip Morris, served as chairman of the United Negro College Fund from 1987 to 1989.[46] Whitney Young, the late Urban League chief, sat on the board of Philip Morris. His widow, Margaret B. Young, inherited the chair.[47]

African American organizations have received hundreds of thousands of dollars of tobacco money a year. For instance, organizations known to have received tobacco funding include the Congressional Black Caucus, the NAACP, the NAACP Legal Defense Fund, the Urban League, the Southern Christian Leadership Conference (SCLC), the National Black Caucus of State Legislators, the United Negro College Fund, the Thurgood Marshall Scholarship Fund, the National Council of Negro Women, the Alvin Ailey American Dance Theater, the Dance Theater of Harlem, the Ebony Magazine Fashion Fair, and the National Minority AIDS Council.[48]

Finally, Black Congress members have received significant support from the tobacco industry. For example, in 1986, 21 of the 39 members of the Congressional Black Caucus received at least $5,000 in campaign contributions from tobacco companies.[49] In fact, several highly visible African Americans in Congress received at least $5,000 of tobacco money: Senator Carol Moseley-Braun of Illinois, and Representatives Mel Watt of North Carolina, Cynthia McKinney of Georgia, Floyd Flake of New York, Carrie Meek of Florida, Louis Stokes of Ohio, J. C. Watts of Oklahoma, William Clay of Missouri, and Maxine Waters, and Julian Dixon of California.[50] They were not the worst offenders; of the 435 members of the House of Representatives, Representative Charles Rangel, who received $47,950, was 19th on the list, and Representative Ed Towns, who received $51,075, was 15th on the list.[51]

Most of the organizations maintained that the tobacco companies attached no strings and made no attempt to influence their organizational policies. However, it is clear this relationship resulted in African American leaders, newspapers, and other organizations abstaining from criticism of the tobacco industry.[52] For instance, in 1991, not one Black magazine publisher attended a meeting set up by Secretary of Health and Human Services Louis Sullivan to discuss the adverse affects of tobacco advertising in African American communities.[53]

Just as with organizations, Congressmen and women were beholding to their benefactors. While nine African American Congressmen wrote the Food and Drug Administration in support of regulating tobacco as a drug, thirteen African American Congressmen wrote in opposition.[54] Similarly, while eighteen African American Congressmen voted to kill a program that provided crop insurance and a government-run acreage allotment program for tobacco farmers at a cost to taxpayers of $25 million a year, nineteen African American Congressmen voted to keep the program going.[55] Furthermore, at a Congressional Black Caucus Foundation meeting, at which sixty-five issues were identified for discussion, not one dealt specifically with smoking.[56]

## Special Brands

Cigarette companies have developed special brands to market directly to the African American communities. In 1990, R. J. Reynolds planned to market a menthol cigarette called Uptown.[57] R. J. Reynolds denied that the name was chosen because of its connotation to New York City's Harlem community, but rather because it was a classy name. [58] However, the marketing plan called for ads suggesting glamour, high fashion, and nightlife.[59] Furthermore, the cigarettes were to be packaged with the filter facing down because black smokers tend to open their cigarettes from the bottom. Thus, with 69% of black smokers preferring menthol cigarettes, it was clear that blacks were the target audience for the product.[60] Because of the pressure from public outrage, R. J. Reynolds Company canceled the test-marketing of Uptown.[61]

In 1995, a cigarette distributor in Massachusetts packaged cigarettes in red, black and green, placed an X on them, and called them Menthol X.[62] Red, black, and green are the symbolic colors of black liberation, and "X" is associated with Malcolm X.[63] The Massachusetts black community forced the distributor to pull "Menthol X" off the shelves.[64]

In 1997, R. J. Reynolds introduced a mentholated version of Camel.[65] Many believed this was an aggressive step toward targeting the African American community that disproportionately smoked menthol cigarettes.[66] The California African American community protested R. J. Reynolds' plan and the cigarette was withdrawn.[67]

## Promotional Budget and Effort

Even though African Americans comprise only 13% of the population, a disproportionate amount of the tobacco industry's budget has been targeted toward increasing the percentage of black smokers. In 1973, Brown & Williamson spent 17% of its promotional budget for KOOL cigarettes, popular brand in the African American community,[68] even though the company was already using "virtually all known vehicles to reach Blacks effectively and efficiently",[69] Brown & Williamson recommended spending more in a response to trends among young people between the ages sixteen and twenty-four.[70] "With this additional transit effort, KOOL would cover the top twenty-five markets in terms of absolute Negroes."[71] The document also stated that "[a]t the present rate, [black] smokers in the sixteen-to-twenty-five-year age group will soon be three times as important to KOOL as a prospect in any other broad age category." [72] In 1963, the Ligget Tobacco group considered the following marketing approach:

"While in the case of the Spanish and Negro markets, there must be a racial slant. They can be reached only by a promotion that they understand, i.e. Negro salesmen and media, but not exclusively."[73]

A 1969 R. J. Reynolds memorandum suggested ways to better reach African Americans:

"It generally is not as effective to aim at the Negro consumer, as such, as it is to aim at his decisive motivations... Quality rates as a cherished attribute. Negroes buy the best Scotch as long as the money lasts, most marketers agree."[74] The memorandum also suggested that advertisements should avoid physical contact between models of different races.[75] Further, in 1981, a Reynolds marketing plan stated that "[t]he majority of Blacks do not respond well to sophisticated or subtle humor in advertising. They related to overt, clear-cut story lines."[76]

A 1973 R. J. Reynolds Tobacco Company marketing profile included a study of black smokers aged fourteen to twenty.[77] In a 1978 research study, the Lorillard Tobacco Company, noting the success of its Newport brand with African Americans of all ages, emphasized that "the base of our business is the [black] high school student."[78]

As can be expected, the tobacco industry denied targeting the African American community:

"There is absolutely no truth to the contention that the [Camel menthol] brand is being targeted to African Americans or any other specific ethnic group."[79] In fact, R. J. Reynolds asserted that the African American community was being unreasonable in believing that market strategy would target a specific population.[80] However, as a result of documents released as part of tobacco litigation settlements, it seems that "just because you're paranoid doesn't mean they're not out to get you."[81]

The above documents (and others) prove that African American perceptions were accurate.

## Being a Black Smoker

The marketing, advertising and promotional blitz had its effect.[82] A greater percentage of African American adults are smokers than White American adults.. This is particularly true for men. In 1987, 30.7% of White men twenty years and older were smokers while 40.3% of African American men were smokers.[83] The smoking rate of Black women and White women was essentially the same, with 27.3% of White American women twenty years and older being smokers, and 27.9% of African American women twenty or over being smokers. However, African American smokers smoke approximately 35% fewer cigarettes per day than White smokers.[84] Nevertheless, African Americans have higher rates of most smoking-related diseases.[85] This may be a result of the fact that African Americans smoke disproportionately more mentholated cigarettes.[86]

Eighty percent of African American smokers smoke mentholated cigarettes, while only 25% of White smokers smoke mentholated cigarettes.[87] In fact, up to 91% of young African American women smokers and 87% of young African American male smokers report smoking menthol cigarettes, compared to 34% and 24% of White smokers, respectively.[88] This use of menthol may be associated with increased health risks and may have resulted in significantly poorer health status for African Americans.[89]

## The Black Smoker

The profile of the African American smoker is distinct. African Americans start smoking later in life than White Americans.[90] Since 1970 the prevalence of smoking among African American adolescents (especially early teen girls) has declined.[91] However, even though African Americans are strongly motivated to quit smoking, fewer African Americans than White Americans are able to do so.[92] Furthermore, African Americans are less likely to abstain for over a year.[93] In addition, African Americans are not heavy smokers. The 1985 National Health Interview Survey showed that 64% of African American smokers and 35% of White American smokers consumed less than one pack a day.[94] The American Health Foundation found that on average, 35% of Black men and 50% of Black women smoked ten or fewer cigarettes a day compared with 14% and 26% for White men and White women, respectively.[95] In fact, the average African American adult smoker smokes significantly fewer cigarettes than the average White adult smoker.[96]

However, despite the fact that African Americans start later in life and smoke fewer cigarettes, they show higher levels of nicotine dependence.[97] They show higher levels of addiction. For instance, African Americans are 1.6 times more likely than Whites to be categorized as "wake-up" smokers, those who need to smoke within 10 minutes of awakening.[98]

It is puzzling that African Americans have more illnesses, particularly in view of the fact that they start smoking later in life and smoke fewer cigarettes. Part of the reason for this may lie in the African American preference for mentholated brands, which have a high tar and nicotine content.[99] It is tar that contains the carcinogens which cause cancer.[100] Although menthol is a naturally occurring alcohol, most of the menthol currently used is synthetic.[101] Menthol is used in a number of commercial products such as toothpaste, mouthwash, and foods. It is not considered directly carcinogenic, and is rated "generally regarded as safe" by the Food and Drug Administration.[102] About 75% to 90% of African Americans report a preference for menthol compared to only 23% to 25% of White Americans.[103] This menthol brand preference is not related to educational level, occupational class, or age.[104] For instance, 82% of African American teens choose menthol brands.[105] Not only do menthol cigarettes tend to be higher in tar and nicotine than non-menthol cigarettes, but they may also have their own independent effect on addiction and dependency, which has not been adequately studied.[106]

Only two studies to date have directly addressed the relationship between smoking mentholated cigarettes and increased cancer risk in African Americans.[107] The studies made opposite conclusions, leaving unanswered the question of whether menthol explains the difference in the incidence of lung cancer among Blacks and Whites. Furthermore, no study has been made into the addictive and dependency power of menthol combined with nicotine. Simple logic suggests that African Americans who smoke mostly mentholated cigarettes may be trying to kick two habits, nicotine and menthol. While simple logic may be wrong, the tobacco settlement was made without answering this question through biomedical research.

My great-grandfather, Manlis Randle, lived to be ninety-four years old; my grandfather, Tom Randall, the youngest child of slaves, lived to be ninety-seven years old. My father, an educated black man of the twentieth century, lived only to seventy-nine. He died of cancer after smoking cigarettes for over sixty years. He tried to quit smoking many times. He tried to quit smoking after developing throat cancer at the age of sixty-two years, he tried to quit after his brother, Arthur Randall, died, He tried the patches, he tried cold turkey, he tried hypnosis; he tried every smoking cessation known to man (or woman). He wanted to quit, he wanted a longer life, but no matter how hard he tried, he always returned to his mentholated cigarettes. The first thing in the morning, a

**My Dad, Ernest Randall**

smoke; the last thing at night, a smoke. My father smoked himself into an early grave. Cigarettes deprived me of a father and deprived my children of a grandfather. Who knows, with the longevity in my family, they probably deprived my grandchildren of a great-grandparent.

This lethal preference for menthol brands by African American smokers is shaped by the tobacco industry's targeted advertising campaigns, which touted these brands in culturally- specific magazines and on billboards in predominantly African American neighborhoods.[108] In fact, the success of menthol brands is almost entirely tied to the African American market.[109] Menthol cigarettes were introduced in the 1930s, but did not exceed 3% the total market until 1949. In the 1960s, advertising for menthol cigarettes began appearing in the African American-oriented magazine Ebony. By 1963, the market share was 16%, and by 1976, it was 28%.[110] Sales to African Americans accounted for the vast majority of this increase. The tobacco industry targeted the African American community and pushed on them a drugged, enhanced version (menthol), which appears to be more addictive and more deadly.

## Black Health Status

The fact that African Americans are sicker and are dying at a higher rate than White Americans is not news.[111] African Americans have more illnesses, lower survival rates, and die at greater rates than White Americans. The excess death rates for African Americans have exceeded those for White Americans for every major chronic condition except chronic obstructive pulmonary disease.[112] That is, for every 100,000 persons, 511 White persons die from major chronic illnesses while 779 Black persons die.[113] Thus, there were 268 Black persons who would not have died from major chronic illness if they had been White.[114] In fact, before the age of sixty-five, African American smokers lose twice as many years of potential life as White smokers.[115] Being a Black smoker is more dangerous to your health than being a White smoker.[116]

One of three cancer deaths in America is related to tobacco use, and African American communities are disproportionately tobacco's victims.[117] Tobacco-related cancers account for approximately 45% of the incidence of cancer in African American men and 25% of the incidence in African American women.[118] The incidence of oral cavity and pharynx cancer in Black men exceeds that in White men by 49.1%.[119] The incidence of lung and bronchus cancer in Black men exceeds that in White men by 40.7%.[120] And to a somewhat lesser degree, the same pattern is true for women.[121] For instance, the incidence of lung and bronchus cancer in Black women exceeds that in White women by 16.2%.[122] Furthermore, African American smokers (women in particular) have significantly higher lung cancer rates for any given level of smoking.[123]

After having developed cancer, White Americans are more likely to survive than African Americans. For instance, the five-year survival rate for White American men for oral cavity and pharynx cancer exceeds that of African American men by 12.9%.[124] Similarly, the five-year survival rate for White American men for lung and bronchus cancer exceeds that for Black men by 1.3%. And to a lesser degree, a similar pattern is true for women.[125]

In addition to mortality, African Americans suffer greater morbidity than White Americans do. For instance, even though African American women smoke fewer cigarettes than White American women, African Americans have lost greater permanent lung capacity.[126] For instance, "The study found that Black female smokers had 10 percent less capacity than Black females who have never smoked. White females had eight percent less capacity than their nonsmoker contemporaries. White males had seven percent less and Black males had six percent less."[127] Furthermore, tobacco smoking does not affect only the health of the smoker, but also that of the infant if a woman smokes during pregnancy.[128] In 1987, for every 100,000 infant deaths, 8.6 White infants died compared to 17.9 Black infants.[129]

# CONCLUSION

As of 2005 it is still unclear what the tobacco industry knows about the potential addictive power of mentholated nicotine. Given the significant difference in dependence and the health status of smokers of mentholated cigarettes, it would be another injury to the African American community not to have the specific harm caused by these cigarettes addressed in any tobacco litigation. African Americans find smoking socially unacceptable, they tend to start smoking later in life, smoke fewer cigarettes per day, and they are strongly motivated to quit but have a high nicotine dependence, making abstinence difficult even for lighter smokers.[130] It may be the higher nicotine dependence that makes it harder for Black smokers to quit.[131] The preference of African Americans for mentholated brands may explain why they smoke fewer cigarettes but have higher cancer rates.[132]

The tobacco industry has used targeted advertising to effectively drive up sales and profits. In doing so, the industry has driven up the death rate of African Americans. Consequently, Congress should not have passed any legislation that did not specifically address the needs of African Americans. As future governmental litigation is instituted against the tobacco industry, remedies targeted toward the African American community must be part of the package.

# Chapter Five

---

# IMPACT OF
# MANAGED CARE ON BLACKS

Consider the following:

K is facing knee surgery. She has health insurance with a Preferred Provider managed care organization (PPO) through her employer. One doctor, a member of the PPO, recommends a certain operation. Another doctor recommends a different operation that is more expensive but allows faster recuperation. K's insurer will not pay for surgery from the second doctor, who is not a member of the PPO, and she cannot afford to pay for the operation herself. When she has the PPO-recommended operation, her recovery takes three months longer.[1]

B, a teenage boy, is suicidal. B's parents have insurance for him through their employers. His doctor wants to admit B to a psychiatric hospital. However, the insurance company, which requires pre-approval of any non-emergency hospital admission, denies approval. Since B's parents cannot afford the proposed 21-day hospital stay, they must have him treated as an outpatient. Five days after being refused hospitalization, B takes his own life.[2]

R, a single woman, is pregnant with her first child. She earns minimum wage but qualifies for Medicaid (government health insurance). Because the government pays doctors significantly less for treating Medicaid patients than what they would receive from treating other patients, no doctor in her community will accept her. The nearest doctor who will treat her is one hour and two bus transfers away. Because of the three or four hours she would have to miss from work for each appointment, R does not receive adequate prenatal care. Her baby is born prematurely and with a low birth-weight.[3]

A person can have health insurance (or the financial means to afford treatment) without having adequate health care. Insurers, both private and public, ration health care by restricting the choice of provider, by modifying or denying services, or simply by withholding services. Such rationing occurs through health-insurance products that "manage" the patient's care. Insurers use Health

Maintenance managed care organizations (HMOs), PPOs, and Individual Practice Associations (IPO) managed care organizations.

The assumption behind managed care organizations is that expenditures for health care can be lowered by reducing the significant over-utilization within the current system that occurs because patients lack incentives to forego health services. Managed care organizations propose to form a partnership with physicians and other providers to reduce utilization. Under this partnership, third-party payers can use managed care organizations to reduce costs and increase profits (or, in the case of government, to lower taxes). The third-party payers do so by prospectively deciding what the managed care organization will pay for and by using financial incentives to encourage physicians and other providers to discourage patients from taking advantage of so-called unnecessary services.

Managed care organizations may do Blacks more harm than good.[4] These managed care organizations have not developed in response to the poor health status of Blacks, but rather to third-party payers' and employers' desire to control expenditures. Mechanisms such as utilization review and financial risk-shifting might be detrimental to the health status of Blacks. In fact, studies demonstrate inequities in treatment authorization based on race,[5] and Blacks demonstrate under-utilization rather than over-utilization of medical services. When that under-utilization is combined with poorer health status, it is easy to discern that these populations will need (and use) more services. Thus, health care will cost more, defeating the purpose of cost control. How will third-party payers respond? Will they accept increased costs among this population group, or will they seek stronger mechanisms to reduce costs? Will access to services remain the same or be reduced? Will the standards, criteria, and methods that determine when a service is "unnecessary" be culturally appropriate for Blacks or culturally appropriate for middle-class White American males?

Unfortunately, a multi-cultural perspective is often missing from discussions of health care reform. Yet without this perspective, managed care organizations can never effectively improve the health status of Blacks.

## HISTORY OF INSURANCE AND MANAGED CARE ORGANIZATIONS

The current discussion of health care reform focuses on cost containment for good reason. In 2003, over $11,004 billion, or 15% percent of the nation's income went to purchase health care.[6] While federal and state governments, businesses, and insurance companies are major funding sources of health care, families and individuals feel the greatest financial impact. For the poor, that impact is disproportionately large. For example, low-income families pay over twice their percentage of income for health care as do middle-income families and nearly nine times that of high-income families.[7] Finally, premiums by low-income families, as a share of income, are nearly four times that of high-income families.[8]

One reason that health care costs are out of control is that no one has had an incentive to ration health care to people who have the ability to pay. Traditionally, health care has always been rationed based on economics. One hundred years ago the primary gatekeeper to health care services was the patient.[9](Figure 05-01). Since patients had to pay for all health care services out of pocket, they factored the cost of care into their decisions to seek care.[10] The doctor was also very conscious of a patient's ability to pay because the provision of service to someone who could not pay constituted "uncompensated care."[11] Nevertheless, the primary gatekeeper was the patient

## Figure 05-01
## Traditional Contractual Relationship
## Between Patient and Provider

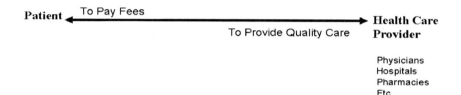

However, gate-keeping had little to do with the cost of, or access to, health care.[12] Health care was low-technology, nursing-oriented, and primarily palliative.[13] Before the mid-1800s, people who became sick or injured and could pay for treatment, received medical care at home.[14] Only the poorest people went to the "hospital", which was often only a separate wing of an almshouse, jail, or pest-house.[15]

Many United State cities had almshouses, or poorhouses.[16] These institutions provided food and shelter for the indigent, and medical care, when available, was only a secondary function. Pest-houses were quarantine stations for people known or thought to have a contagious illness.

Usually, mentally ill persons received care at home, at the almshouse, or at the jail. With advances in biotechnology, drugs, sanitation, and the scientific method the growth of hospitals and of more expensive health care procedures exploded. In only 36 years, from 1873-1909, the number of hospital beds in the United States grew from 50,000 to 907,133.[17]

However, the Depression ushered in a significant decline in bed use as patients, unable to pay for health care, rationed their own care and simply did without.[18] Hard hit by the Depression, in the 1930s, the American Hospital Association (AHA) developed health insurance (Blue Shield) to assure stable revenues.[19] After World War II, as medical technology advanced, reliable access to medical services became increasingly important.[20] Unions began to demand health care benefits, and employers began to use these benefits as a part of employee compensation.

By the early 1960s, the cost of health care far outstripped many people's ability to pay.[21] As the cost of care rose, an access gap appeared between those who had either health insurance or wealth and those who did not. Because health insurance was available almost exclusively through employment, the number of people who could not afford health care increased. In 1965, Congress, in response to the medical-insurance crisis, created Medicare[22] and Medicaid,[23] which together provided health insurance to the elderly, the disabled, and poor women and children.

By 1985, three-fourths of payments to physicians were made through public or private insurance.[24] This widespread availability of insurance has contributed to the escalating use of technology, and consequently, to higher health care costs. With the introduction of insurance, the incentive for the patient or provider to refuse services or to be selective was minimized (Figure 05-02). Imagine the houses that prospective homeowners would purchase if they only had to pay 20% of the market price. Imagine the houses that construction companies would build if they were guaranteed 80% of their charges or fees. Is it any wonder that over the last 60 years, neither of the two primary actors in health care delivery, patients and providers, had an incentive to ration care?

### Figure 05-02
### Traditional Contractual Relationships
### Among Patients, Providers and Third-party Payers

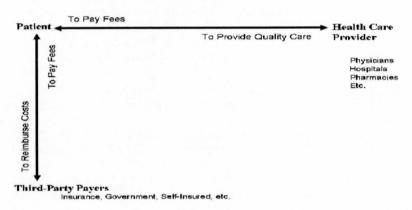

In fact, insurance has had a "perverse influence" on health service delivery.[25] Since providers make more money when they treat more patients,[26] providers de-emphasize preventive care that is not as lucrative as treatment services. They tend to rely too much on medical technology because third-party payers pay for procedures, not for time spent with patients.[27] However, as the cost of health care has spiraled upward, employers,[28] government,[29] and third-party payers [30] have gained strong incentives to restrain costs by rationing health care.[31] In 1990, private insurance and other private payers covered 37 percent of health care bills, government programs paid 42 percent, and individuals paid 21 percent (including premiums).[32]

Current cost-containment efforts by managed care organizations involve two aspects. The first is denying or modifying services before they are delivered, known as "prospective utilization review." The second is shifting the risk of financial loss for "unnecessary services" to either the patient or the providers of those services; this is known as "financial risk-shifting".[33] Managed care organizations ask providers to be health care gatekeepers in order to improve efficiency and cut costs (Figure 3).

## Figure 05-03
## Managed Care Organization Contractual Responsibilities Among Patients, Providers and Third-party Payers

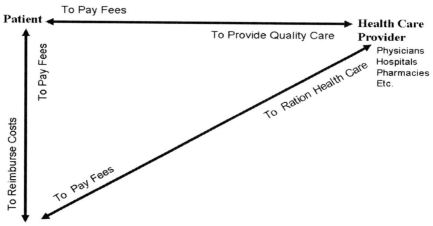

Despite providers' historical opposition to risk-shifting, the position of physicians and hospitals has been weakened by the current problems with the economy. One-third of the nation's available hospital beds is permanently idle. The number of days that patients spend in hospitals dropped from 280 million in 1980, to 240 million in 1984.[34] By the mid-1990s, the number dropped to 120 million.[35] There are now 2.2 physicians per 1,000 persons.[36]

In 1980, managed care organizations were begging for providers to enter into partnerships with them. Today, managed care organizations have become the darlings of the health care reform movement. Over 60 percent of individuals with employer-sponsored health care plans are enrolled in managed care organizations. "The growth of managed care organizations for Medicaid patients, who are disproportionately minority, has been dramatic. In 1981, there were 750,000 Medicaid beneficiaries enrolled in managed care organization plans. By 1996, that figure had surpassed 13 million persons, 40% of all beneficiaries."[37] As of 2003, 25.5 million, or 59.1% of Medicaid beneficiaries, were enrolled in an MCO.[38]

All sorts of individuals and entities, including acute-care hospitals, physicians, private and government insurers, employers, and entrepreneurs, are developing managed care organizations due to the potential for profit. Perhaps the only group that is not developing managed care organizations is the one most affected by the delivery of health services—Blacks and other communities of color.

# Rationing Health Care

Managed care system, a payer-driven system, can be mistaken for a provider-driven system.[39] In a provider-driven system, the physician has an obligation to act in the patient's best interest, and the third-party payer is contractually obligated to pay for services rendered by the physician. However, managed care organizations impose another obligation. The physician is contractually obligated to provide services under the guidelines and standards set by third-party payers if the physician wishes to be fully compensated for those services. The physician manages the patient's care for the payer not the patient, thus, the term "managed care organizational care." Thus, the physician's new responsibility requires balancing the health needs of the patient with the cost-containment needs of the third-party payer. Ultimately, the purpose of managed care organizations is to ration health care through two mechanisms, prospective utilization review and financial risk-shifting.

## Prospective Utilization Review

Utilization review is the process by which third-party payers determine whether medical services ordered (or received) are appropriate and necessary.[40] If the third-party payer decides that a service is unnecessary, it either refuses to pay the provider's charges (retrospective review)[41] or refuses to authorize the provision of the service (concurrent or prospective review)[42].

Retrospective utilization-management programs analyze data on hospital admissions, patterns of treatment, and utilization of certain procedures.[43] Under a prospective review system, the program gives prior approval to most non-emergency hospital admissions and assigns an initial approved length of stay.

There are several forms of utilization review. All rely on statistical norms, practice parameters, and other population data to decide whether a service is necessary.[44] The problem with utilization review is that standards and decisions are made from data drawn from a largely White American, middle-class, male subgroup. For several reasons, this data is inadequate and unreliable when applied to Blacks and others.

First, because of the lack of prior health care, many Blacks typically approach managed care organizations with a litany of medical conditions that have been inadequately treated, if at all. Because these conditions often have gone untreated, they are more severe and they require more intense treatment over a longer period of time. As a result, the needed treatment falls outside of the standard protocols.

Second, even for illnesses developed after enrollment in a managed care organization, the duration of the condition is likely to be longer and more severe.[45] Without adequate housing, food, and clothing, the poor are sicker than the affluent. But even middle-class Blacks have a different health status from middle-class White Americans.

Health status is related not only to the availability of necessities (i.e. food, shelter) but also to health care received during childhood and the health status of the parents. For many middle-class Blacks, a lack of health care in childhood or a family history of poor health affects current health status and the need for health care. Furthermore, the stress of living in a racist society has an ongoing and continuing impact on the health of all Blacks. If managed care organizations do not take the effects of family history and racism into account when developing protocols or practice parameters, Blacks will continue to receive inadequate health care.[46]

Third, the protocol for utilization review comes largely from research on middle-class White American males. Only in the last several years has there been a concerted effort to include women and Blacks in trial studies of drugs and other treatment protocols. Even so, health providers have failed to recognize that race can influence the desired treatment of a disease and the way in which that disease responds to treatment. For instance, although hypertension is a leading health problem for African-Americans, a study concluded that hypertension medications prescribed for African-Americans were not as effective in controlling hypertension as those medications were for White Americans.[47] The utilization review protocols of managed care organizations are not likely to recognize these differences. This may be due in part to fear of an emergence of race-based types of medicine.[48] However, what people fail to realize is that we already practice race-based medicine, and the race is white.

Finally, "utilization reviewers must, in many cases, make coverage decisions under conditions of ambiguity and uncertainty. They thus exercise considerable discretion in their own right."[49] This is problematic because when individuals have significant discretion, their unconscious and unthinking bias and stereotypes are likely to be demonstrated.[50] Furthermore, providers hired by third-party payers to conduct utilization review often lack the cultural knowledge to factor a patient's poverty, race, class, and prior health care into the providers' recommendations.[51] Thus, utilization reviewers do not take into account individual variations and unique situations. As a result, physicians often spend hours making a case for patients who don't fit into the typical profile.

While some scholars focus on the supposed inability of Blacks to "assert their needs",[52] it is the responsibility of institutions to accommodate the needs and skills of all patients. Unfortunately, many of the providers that traditionally serve Blacks are not signing contracts with managed care organizations. Indeed, Black providers are finding the doors to managed care organizations closed, both as owners and provider-employees.[53] The failure to contract with black providers may have serious consequences. Without providers who consider race, class and poverty, even culturally relevant protocols may be misapplied.

Patients may have to drop their neighborhood Black physicians when they join a managed care organization plan and may have to travel to find another Black physician in their plan, assuming one can be found. Patients on Medicaid and those enrolled in a Medicare HMOs face this problem most frequently. Those patients often have no transportation to reach a distant Black doctor. Further, they are randomly assigned to physicians if they fail to choose one on their own.[54]

Prospective decisions of utilization review have a fundamentally different impact on the patient than do retrospective decisions. Theoretically, patients know what treatments are covered by each plan. However, the two systems have quite different effects on patient behavior. In the retrospective system, a patient who makes a decision about medical care receives the care and has a strong likelihood of having the charge for that care approved. But even if the charge were denied, the services would have been received. Consequently, the potential for injury because of a mistake during utilization review is low.

In a prospective system, however, a patient knows before he or she has received the services that the insurer will not pay for the treatment. The patient's only chance of recovering the cost of that treatment is to challenge the insurer's decision. Thus, Blacks who need services that have been denied through prospective utilization review usually fail to receive the services.[55] Because of bias in the standards and the potential bias of the utilization review process, the potential to be injured due to an incorrect utilization review decision is higher for Blacks than for White Americans. [56]

Nevertheless, utilization review is not the major culprit. Under utilization review, the potential to control costs is mitigated, at least theoretically, by a patient's ability to protest denial of services. The combination of utilization review with financial risk-shifting provides the greatest potential for harm to Blacks. [57]

## Financial Risk-shifting

Financial risk-shifting causes the provider to change a pattern of practice from over-utilization to "appropriate utilization", at best, or "under-utilization", at worst.[58] Forty years ago, the risk of financial loss because of unnecessary care was borne by the paying patient and the uncompensated doctor. But insurance companies have shifted the risk of loss from these parties to third-part payers and today, the degree of risk assumed by the provider varies according to the payment arrangement. Traditional fee-for-service practices are at one end (no risk-sharing) and traditional HMOs are at the other end (full risk-shifting).[63] Preferred provider managed care organizations (and other managed care organizations) are somewhere in the middle.    Financial risk-shifting arises in ownership interests, joint ventures, or "bonus" arrangements. In these arrangements, the third-party payer and the provider share the savings from "cost-effective" care.[59] The risk-shifting occurs in various forms of rewards,[60] penalties,[61] or both.[62]

Rewards take the form of a predetermined dollar amount, a fixed percentage of the surplus distributed among the risk pool, a bonus based on a physician's productivity, or a combination. Other methods include increasing fee schedules or allowing practitioners to become investors. Penalties used to place the provider at risk beyond the withholding of payment include the following: 1) increasing the percentage of payment for physicians' fees withheld during the following year, 2) placing liens on future earnings, 3) decreasing the amount of capitation payment for the following year 4) excluding the physician from the program, 5) reducing the distributions from surplus, or 6) requiring physicians to pay either the entire amount of any deficit or a percentage of the deficit.

For example, many managed care organizations require primary care physicians to pay for outpatient laboratory tests directly from the physician's capitation payments. Other means used by third-part payers to spread the financial risk to physicians include capitation,[64] withholding,[65] discounted fee for service,[66] per diem payments,[67] and surplus (profit) sharing. The most frequently used means of shifting the risk to hospitals are case mechanisms[68] and capitated payments per patient.[69]urther, HMOs use peer pressure as an incentive. HMOs use a reporting system to compare the performance of many providers. This report identifies areas of excessive costs and service intensity.

But while the form may vary, these penalties and rewards have similar effects. Cost-containment efforts shift the risk of financial loss for health care in whole or in part to the providers of that care. Providers (especially physicians) are offered economic incentives to act as the third-party payer's gatekeeper to health care services. The gate-keeping role is not new to physicians. Physicians have used their authority to resist hospitals' and insurers' efforts to influence medical treatment. As gatekeepers, physicians have generally worked to obtain more services for the patient. Now, however, some physicians use their position to save money for third-party payers by ordering fewer services. This fundamental change in the basic ethical concern of the system, from "the best interest of the patient" to "cost containment", is revolutionary.[70]

As gatekeepers, physicians are concerned with limiting access to health care services so that third-party payers do not find excessive utilization. If a payer determines that a physician practiced within the payer's guidelines, the payer rewards the physician financially. If a payer determines that a physician has ordered too many services, the payer penalizes the physician financially. Consequently, physicians are motivated to order services for patients within a third-party payer's guidelines. Thus, gatekeeping shifts the focus of the health care system from the doctor-patient relationship to the doctor-payer relationship. Ultimately, the doctor and payer determine not only the quantity of services received by the patient, but also the quality of care.

This shift of focus has serious implications for Blacks.[71] First, given that utilization review standards are culturally insensitive, the physician is under the greatest pressure to deny or modify services to populations, such as Blacks, that are not represented in the standards.[72] These are the patients who require the most services. Physicians may also believe, either consciously or subconsciously, that Blacks are less deserving of the services or are less likely to complain. "As [managed care organizations] continue to grow, and as more physicians continue to sign contracts with them, these concerns will intensify."[73]

Second, studies have shown that some physicians already order fewer and inferior services for Blacks. This difference is based on factors other than ability to pay. It is based, at least in part, on racism. A system focused on cost containment and financial risk-shifting allows physicians to continue, if not increase, this practice of providing differential levels of treatment. Thus, some physicians will respond to risk-shifting incentives by cutting not only unnecessary and marginally necessary services, but also medically necessary care. Inequities based on race and class will inevitably be exacerbated by utilization review and financial risk-shifting.

# CONCLUSION

Managed care organizations will ultimately change the perceptions and expectations of society, physicians, patients, and third-party payers regarding what is owed to whom, what treatments are appropriate under what circumstances, and even what qualifies as a medical condition. These altered perceptions may be in conflict with the needs of Blacks, and, without safeguards, these perceptions could aggravate the inequities in health status between White Americans and Blacks. Quality assurance, utilization review, and practice parameters are designed around data based on middle-class populations who have had adequate access to health care. Blacks have less access to health care. That lack of access, combined with racism, homelessness, violence, drug abuse, and other issues means that Blacks enter managed care organizations with poorer health status and needing more (rather than fewer) health care services. In a system focused on decreasing utilization, it is easy to imagine that Blacks and the poor will not receive this additional amount of needed care, particularly since the system may create navigational challenges for patients, contributing to racial and ethnic healthcare disparities."[74] If managed care organizations do not provide culturally relevant care, then Blacks may have technical access to health care but not quality health care.

Moreover, managed care organizations' narrow focus on cost containment is inherently antithetical to the needs of Blacks. Since third-party payers will make more money when providers treat less, they will, over time, tend to place increasingly stringent requirements on providers, resisting developing culturally appropriate treatment modalities, particularly if that treatment is more expensive.[75] If health care providers and health managed care organizations that serve Blacks do not insist on the provision of culturally competent care, Blacks will not benefit from so-called health care reform.

Some commentators argue that greater political attention should be focused on socio-economic inequalities that lead to racial gaps in health status.[76] Certainly, removing socio-economic inequality is a necessary component of assuring access. However, that does nothing to remove the inequities of health care delivery from managed care systems, inequities that are based on race.

The health care financing system has been steadily moving toward managed care organizational care. Without proper oversight, something that does not currently exist, managed care organizations will limit the services available by providers. Providers may fail to develop more expensive but culturally appropriate treatment modalities, and they may refuse or minimize the expenditures necessary to develop adequate infrastructure for Black communities.[77]

It is significant that despite many studies showing racial inequities in medical treatments, neither employers, nor health care purchasers, nor managed care organizations have publicly disclosed any plans or strategies to prevent racial discrimination within their health plans.[78] The potential for racial and ethnic discrimination to occur within the context of managed care organizations has been recognized by the United States Office of Civil Rights (OCR) and by advocates for civil rights in health care services, financing, and treatment.

I am not a very chic person, and some times I can look downright poor and powerless. Such was a time when I took my son (Tshaka) to the hospital for his third knee surgery. Although the surgery was suppose to be an out-patient, they didn't get to Tshaka to almost mid-night. Around 1 am the nurse came out to tell me that Tshaka would be released to go home.

I said no I don't think so- Tshaka was a 6 foot 5 inch, 300 pound person and I was concern about being able to help him safely into the house in a drowsy state. I was insistent that I would not be taking him home.

The nurse left and a physician return. She talked slow and deliberate. She talked as if she was certain that I didn't understand and was irrational. She may have been right but what I wasn't was powerless.

I finally had enough. I remember a mental switch going on in my brain. I closed my eyes, set up straight and when I reopened my eyes I looked straight into the Doctor eyes, I said in my best lawyer voice " You understand I am a nurse and an attorney. If you think my son is ready to navigate from the car to his bedroom which includes going up some stairs without hurting himself, I will be happy to take him home after you write that you are releasing him over the specific objections of his mother. And if he falls and hurts himself I will sue both you and the hospital."

The Doctor looked startled; she and I stared at each other for a few second. Without another word she got up and left.. Two hours later a nurse returned to say that they were admitting my son for the night. What did the doctor do during the two hours? Probably check with risk management and the hospital attorneys.

Did Tshaka need to stay the night?

I don't know. I do know that I used my personal power to get the care I thought my son needed.

The problem with managed care is that as a rationing tool, those with power will always be able to get the care they _want_ and since managed care is designed to control cost the bill for that care will be borne by those without power – poor and minorities -- that includes most Blacks.

However, little has been done to protect Blacks from this type of discrimination.

The OCR has not sufficiently prepared its investigative staff to identify and confront instances of discrimination by managed care organizations. Despite indications of discrimination prohibited under Title VI, OCR has not yet developed policy guidance specifically addressing Title VI compliance in the managed care organization context. OCR indicates that it has known about the potentially discriminatory activities of managed care organizations since 1995. Yet, the Office has been loath to encourage or support its regional investigators in identifying cases.


# Appendix 05-01
# Definitions and Explanations


**Capitation -** A provider (or provider group) is paid a set fee per enrollee. The provider then provides all necessary physician services. Primary care physicians are the gatekeepers to specialists and hospital services and are financially responsible for utilization. Because the amount of payment to the provider is independent of the actual services rendered, the provider assumes the risks of an insurer.

**Withholding** - When managed care organizations use withholding, they shift part of the financial risk to the provider by withholding part of the provider's periodic fee-for-service payments, usually five to 20%, for a claim period. At the end of a claim period, managed care organizations determine a medical-claim trend and compare it to a target trend. If the actual trend is lower than the target, the withheld funds are paid to the providers. If the actual medical-claim trend exceeds the target, the withheld funds are paid to the third-party payer.

**Discounted Fee-for-Service** - If the managed care organizations use a discounted fee-for- service, they obtain an up-front agreement that providers will discount amounts due from the third-party payer. The MCO assumes the risk that the payer's premium will be sufficient to cover hospital charges. However, hospitals do not share the profits of the managed care organizations, and while payers that contract with hospitals without a discount may pressure the hospital for a discount, discounted charges may be insufficient to cover the hospital's actual costs.

**Per Diem Payments** With per diem payments, the hospitals are paid a flat rate per patient day that must cover all services. The advantage of per diem payments is that the hospital is not penalized for lengthy patient stays. However, if the MCO emphasizes early discharge, then the hospital's total income may be reduced if the predetermined per diem payments are too low for the hospital to cover its costs, or the MCO discharges the patient before the hospital can break even by averaging cheaper end-of-stay days with the more expensive beginning-of-stay days.

**Case Mechanisms** -With case mechanisms, a predetermined amount, based on the diagnosis, is paid to the hospital for each admission. The hospital is then at risk for the treatment and the length of stay.

**Capitated Payments per Patient** - Hospitals are paid capitated payments per patient in an arrangement similar to capitation. That is, a hospital is paid a lump sum, per enrolled patient in the hospital's service area, to provide all covered hospital services required by those enrollees.

# Chapter Six

---

# SLAVERY, SEGREGATION AND RACISM: TRUSTING THE HEALTH CARE SYSTEM AIN'T ALWAYS EASY!

I am a registered nurse and a family nurse practitioner. I have a Master's degree in nursing. I practiced nursing for 15 years in Alaska, Oregon and Washington. I write and work in the area of health care law. I understand the health care system and the legal system. I am Black, and I trust the health care system to work in ways that ultimately will harm Black people.[1]

Many people are surprised at the level of distrust of the health care system within the Black community. However, this distrust is a logical response to a history of experimentation and abuse. The fear and distrust shape Black lives and, consequently, Black perspectives.[2]

That perspective keeps Blacks from seeking health care treatment, participating in medical research, signing living wills, and donating organs. These sentiments have rarely been mentioned in the traditional bio-ethical and legal discourse.

Some bio-ethicists and legal scholars question the existence of a "uniquely" Black bioethical perspective.[3] They maintain that since the values and beliefs held by Blacks are shared by other oppressed groups, such as Native Americans, there is no Black perspective. However, perspective is merely a subjective evaluation of the relative significance of something—in other words, a point of view.[4] Thus, in order to acknowledge a Black perspective, it is not necessary for Black values and belief systems to be entirely different from the values and beliefs of other groups.

No group shares exactly the same value system with other groups. For example, there is no "American" ethical perspective. Rather, race, class, gender, religion, and region (among other characteristics) modify the American experience. Different groups have had unique experiences that, at a minimum, modify if not replace the "dominant" American perspective. For Blacks, the combination of slavery, segregation, and racism has conferred a distinctive set of "intervening background assumptions about such essential bioethical [and legal]

117

concepts [of] personhood, bodily integrity, the moral community, fulfilling lives and utility."[5]

Furthermore, even where there is little difference in value systems and perspectives, there is a difference in the normative application of bioethical principles. For instance, there is no question that the principles of autonomy, beneficence, non-malfeasance, and justice have not been applied to Blacks in the same manner as they have been to Whites. For example, in the "Poplar Tree Narrative", an allegory, Dr. Dick, a conscientious physician, applies the *prima facie* principles of beneficence, autonomy, and justice in such a way that castration of his Black male patient is construed as a morally justifiable act, in substance "and as a procedure . . . . [It kept the male] from getting into "trouble" . . . . [It made the male] . . . a better slave. . . . [He protected the male patient's autonomy] by getting what he construes to be [the patient's] informed consent."[6]

The principles of Eurocentric bioethics and law are "embedded in a cultural matrix that encodes them with meaning"."[7] The reality of bioethics and law is that ideas such as autonomy, choice, beneficence, justice, and informed consent, are grounded in a cultural context.[8] Perspectives are, among other things, based on class, race, and gender. The experiences of poor people are different from those of rich people, and those of Blacks are different from Whites, Native Americans, Hispanic Americans or Asian Americans. Women and men have different experiences. Furthermore, rich people, White people, and men have more power than poor people, Blacks, or women, respectively. Power also affects experiences. A group's perspective reflects both cultural context and power differentials. [9]

But what then forms the basis of the Black perspective?[10] Certainly, Black culture is rooted in African culture. That means a belief system that includes a humanistic orientation,[11] a focus on both personal and social responsibilities,[12] and a high value placed on community.[13] To the extent that bioethical discourse and practice do not incorporate these values, they do not reflect the values of the Black community.[14]

However, Blacks' distrust of the health care system is based on more than a lack of certain African-based values in the dominant culture. Our distrust is the result of our unique cultural birth in America. The Black culture is uniquely American. In some ways Blacks, like Indians, are native Americans; as a culture, Blacks exist only in America. Blacks are a blend of all the races of the world. Most Blacks have parents, grandparents, or other ancestors who are not only of African descent, but also of White, Asian American, Hispanic American, and Native American descent. My family history is typical. On my maternal side, my grandmother's parents were Cherokee and African. My grandfather's parents were Italian and African. On my paternal side, my ancestors were all African. Thus, the dominant racial basis for Blacks is a blend of features from many African tribes.

The most prominent influence on Black culture has been its past (and present) experiences of slavery, segregation, and racism. These Black experiences are clear evidence of cultural context, power, and status differentials that have resulted in a distrust of the health care system. This historical distrust is reinforced through current, continued, and ever-present institutional racism.[15] These experiences fuel the basis for Black distrust.[16]

# THE HISTORICAL BASIS OF BLACK DISTRUST

Blacks' distrust of the health care system arose from a history of experimentation, the Sickle Cell Screening Initiative, involuntary sterilization, and the complicity of the medical system in racism and discrimination.[17]

## Experimentation and Teaching Materials

The American health care system was built on the bodies of Blacks. The nineteenth century marked the beginning of modern medicine in the United States. The advances in medicine were legion:

> "Advances in basic sciences such as pathology, histology, physiology and pharmacology; the introduction of the statistics and the numerical methods which forever changed the nature and scope of clinical medicine and public health, the clinical acceptance of vaccination for smallpox; introduction of the stethoscope, . . . controlling puerperal fever, rapid advances in clinical schools . . . laboratory medicine . . . and publication of Percival's Code of Medical Ethics."[18]

However, during the same period, the American health care system did not support esoteric research and pure science. As a result, physicians performed "bold, occasionally brilliant, clinical medical feats which were not being performed anywhere else on earth." [19] It seems to be of little importance that those "bold, occasionally brilliant . . . medical feats" were practiced on Blacks and the poor.

Understanding the extent of the experimentation is crucial to understanding why Blacks have little faith in the medical community. Slaves served both as instructional material for medical students and as a source of entertainment at medical conventions.[20] Access to medical facilities was often expanded to include Blacks in order to have a constant flow of clinical subjects.[21] For example, in Virginia in 1853 and 1854, there was a proposal to establish the "Virginia Free Hospital" solely for Blacks.[22] Even though the proposal was never put into effect, "the state legislature deemed the [Medical College of Virginia's] need for clinical material sufficiently important enough to appropriate $30,000 toward the construction of a new hospital in 1860."[23]

## Experimentation During Slavery

Perhaps the most insidious medical practice was the use of Black bodies in the interest of improving White health. "Slaves and the free poor of both races had little choice in the matter; the former had to abide by the master's decision, and the latter, by the physician's (since treatment was without charge)." Examples of the use of Black bodies are numerous.

- In the 1800s, Dr. McDowell successfully performed the removal of an ovarian tumor, a dangerous and radical surgery that he perfected on slaves.[24]

- In 1800, hundreds of slaves, including slaves of Thomas Jefferson, were used as test subjects for a new vaccine for smallpox.[25] Although a previous test with the vaccine had been unsuccessful, Jefferson still vaccinated over 200 of his slaves.[26]

- Dr. Crawford Long's early experiments used as a general anesthetic, were conducted largely on slaves. [27]

- Placing slaves in pits with only their heads above ground, Dr. Thomas Hamilton tested which medication would allow a person to withstand high temperatures.[28]

- Dr. Walter F. Jones poured five gallons of boiling water down the spines of slaves to test a remedy for typhoid pneumonia.[29]

- While never documented, slaves suspected physicians of killing other slaves or letting them die for purposes of dissection.[30] In fact, slaves' bodies were dug up and sold to medical schools.[31]

- Dr. Alexander Somervail used slaves to test his theory of how to relieve the retention of urine.[32]

- Dr. Robert Jennings experimented on thirty slaves and free Blacks in order to perfect his vaccination against typhoid infection.[33]

- Dr. P.C. Spencer, who gained notoriety with his discovery of an efficient and relatively safe technique for treating painful bladder stones, perfected his technique by performing the painful experimental surgery on slaves.[34]

- Dr. Marion Sims, considered the father of gynecological surgery, perfected his techniques on slaves.[35] To sedate and immobilize them post-operatively, Dr. Sims addicted the women.[36] He performed the surgery on the same women repeatedly.[37] For instance, one slave, Anarcha, underwent twenty-nine major experimental surgeries.[38] Though the social norms have changed dramatically, Sims is still revered by physicians and others as a hero and an icon. His role in abusing slaves has been dismissed.[39]

## Post-Slavery Experimentation

The most well known experiment on Blacks is the Tuskegee Syphilis Experiment which the United States engineered from 1932 through 1972.[40] The Tuskegee Experiment involved four hundred Black men in a study to research the effects of untreated syphilis.[41] While the men were not deliberately exposed to syphilis, as some rumors maintained, they were never told that they were not being treated or that effective treatment was available.[42] Nor were their female contacts ever considered even after the experiment was exposed.

Furthermore, even though the experiment was regularly reported in medical journals over the course of the forty years, there was no outcry from the medical establishment.[43] The effects of the Tuskegee Syphilis Experiment in reinforcing suspicions about the health care system cannot be underestimated. The Tuskegee study confirmed the belief within the Black community that the medical system did not have the community's welfare at heart.[44]

On July 23, 1973, attorney Fred Gray filed a $1.8 billion class action civil suit in the United States District Court of Alabama on behalf of all the Tuskegee Experiment participants and their survivors.[45] The plaintiffs demanded $3 million in damages for each surviving participant and a similar amount for the estate of each deceased participant.[46] Among the defendants named in the complaint were the United States government, the United States Public Health Services, the Centers for Disease Control, and the State of Alabama.[47] In December, 1974, the government agreed to pay $10 million in an out-of-court settlement.[48] The plaintiffs agreed to cease further action for a cash payment of $37,000 to each participant in the experiment who was still alive on July 23, 1973, $16,000 to every member of the control group still alive as of July 23, 1973, and $15,000 to the heirs of the deceased.[49] All participants and heirs had three years in which to file claims.[50] Unfortunately, many of the men with syphilis who had not been treated were never located.[51] Also affected were the known 50 wives who were infected by their husbands, 20 children who were given the disease congenitally, and unknown others that were infected. But we know there were many more women and children who were affected.

The Tuskegee Syphilis Experiment is not the only case of post-slavery abuse. In 1945 at the U.S. Army Manhattan Engineer District Hospital in Oakridge, Tennessee, injected 18 patients, most of whom were Black, with plutonium at a dose 41.2 times that an average person receives in a lifetime.[52] Dr. Karl Morgan, a physicist from the University of Chicago who came to Oakridge in 1943, wrote about Dr. Robert Stone, the doctor who injected the plutonium, in a letter to "The Oakridger",[53]

> "Dr. Stone was particularly concerned because, as he said, this man was part of an experiment to determine the risk to man from exposure to plutonium. This poor 'expected casualty' had suddenly gotten up out of his bed at the hospital and disappeared. I was upset and concerned when I heard about this human experiment because, as described to me, this Black man was unconscious and not expected to live when he was injected with plutonium. I was disturbed for two reasons: One, the poor man could not possibly have given his consent to be a guinea

pig, and two, I was afraid he was selected for this experiment in part because he was Black and it was unlikely any of his family would learn of the plutonium injection."[54]

During 1953 and 1954, seven newborn babies, six of whom were Black, were injected with radioactive iodide at the John Gaston Hospital in Memphis, Tennessee.[55] In an interview, the lead researcher, Lester Van Middlesworth, said, "Naturally, Blacks hoped there was no damage."[56] However, he lost track of the babies and did not do any follow-up.[57] Five similar experiments were carried out in Detroit, Michigan, Omaha, Nebraska, Little Rock, Arkansas, and Iowa City, Iowa, with a total of 235 newborns and older infants experimented on, most of whom were Black.[58]

For over 10 years, at least 300 Blacks, mostly female patients, were involved in 15 studies designed by researchers from Tulane University and Charity Hospital in New Orleans, Louisiana.[59] The experiments involved swallowing radioactive capsules and injections of radioactive mercury that resulted in blisters. The blisters were then intentionally cut open and subjected to up to 118 degree heat, causing diarrhea in the patients.[60] While the stated purpose of the studies was to determine the effect of mercury on people with congestive heart failure, the 300 Black patients did not have that disease.[61]

Eighty-two patients were exposed to full-body radiation at the University of Cincinnati Medical Center.[62] The level of radiation was 10 times the level believed, at the time, to be safe. Twenty-five patients died of radiation poisoning.[63] Three-quarters of the patients in the study were Black men and women.[64] The consent signatures were forged by the researchers.[65]

In 1997, the University of Maryland Shock Trauma Center treated 25 gunshot and stabbing victims by giving them a blood substitute without their consent or the consent of their families.[66] The experiment followed the United States Food and Drug Administration's decision in 1996 to partly lift a 50-year ban on involuntary medical testing on human subjects.[67] The experiment was halted after two years because 24 of the 52 critically ill patients who were given the substitute had died, representing a 46.2 percent mortality rate. The Deerfield, Illinois-based maker of the blood substitute had projected only a 42.6% mortality for critically ill patients seeking emergency treatment.[68]

In 1963, the United States Public Health Service, the American Cancer Society, and the Jewish Chronic Disease Hospital of Brooklyn, New York conducted experiments on 22 chronically ill and debilitated Black patients. Without the Blacks' consent or awareness, the patients were injected with live cancer cells.[69]

In 1970s, in Washington, D.C., the government collected blood samples from 7000 Black children.[70] Parents were told that their children were being tested for anemia, but instead the government was looking for signs that the children were genetically predisposed to criminal activity.[71] In Maryland, a similar experiment was performed on 6000, approximately 85 percent of whom were Black.[72] The children's confidentiality was not protected and the blood-test results were disclosed to the courts.[73]

In 1972, 20 poor, Black, young women were bused from Chicago to Philadelphia to receive abortions in an outpatient clinic. At the clinic, a new experimental contraceptive device called the Super Coil was inserted into their uteruses as birth control.[74] Uncontrolled bleeding was a complication of using theSuper Coil.[75] The bleeding eventually lead to shock and all of the women required a complete hysterectomy. [76]

Finally, many women of color have been sterilized without their informed consent so that medical residents could practice performing tubal ligation and hysterectomies.[77]

## Prison and Military Abuse

One area of significant abuse of Blacks has been in experimentation in prisons. Because Blacks make up forty-four % of all prisoners, almost four times their proportion in the general population, Blacks are over-represented in any prison abuse.[78] Racism does not require that only Blacks be affected but only that Blacks are disproportionately represented. It is this kind of over-representation that contributes to Blacks' distrust.

In 1962, at least 396 Ohio State Prison inmates were injected with live cancer cells so that researchers could study the progression of the disease.[79] Between 1963 and 1971, radioactive thymidine, a genetic compound, was injected into the testicles of more than 100 prisoners at the Oregon State Penitentiary to determine whether the rate of sperm production was affected by exposure to steroidal hormones.[80]

Between 1967 and 1969, Alabama inmates were used in flawed blood plasma trials.[81] The study was conducted by Dr. Austin R. Stough at the Kilby, Draper, and McAlester prisons. There was no informed consent, and no accurate records were kept.[82] Dr. Stough was barred from several hospitals and prisons after inmates became sick and died from diseases stemming from his experiments.[83]

At a California medical facility, between 1967 and 1968, prisoners were treated with succinylcholine, a paralyzing neuromuscular compound, used by anesthetists.[84] Because their breathing capacities was significantly diminished, many of the survivors likened the experience to drowning. When five of the 64 prisoners refused to participate in the experiment, the institution's special treatment board gave "permission" for prisoners to be injected against their will.[85] In 1990, Federal law forced 1.7 million soldiers, twenty-two% percent whom were Black, to take an experimental vaccine.[86] The law stipulates that soldiers cannot refuse to participate in the government's medical experiments.[87]

Holmesburg Prison in Philadelphia housed prisoners who participated as human research subjects for various skin experiments.[88] Prisoners were made to apply creams and ointments to their skin, and some suffered severe burns. Many of the test subjects continued to suffer mental and physical effects years after volunteering.[89] The majority of prisoners that participated in the experiments were Black.[90] Some Black prisoners believed they were signed up for more hazardous experiments than the White prisoners.[91]

The above instances are cited not because they are the only instances of experimentation and abuse of Blacks, but because they are the most notorious.[92] While many Blacks may not know all of the details of the experimentation and abuse, these episodes are a part of the collective Black consciousness that influence Blacks' attitudes toward the health care system

## Sickle-Cell Screening

The debacle of sickle-cell screening in the 1970s also increased Blacks' distrust of the medical system.[93] Although sickle-cell disease was first diagnosed in 1910, it did not become a priority for federal or private funding until the 1970s.[94] In 1971, Congress passed a law authorizing the funding of a large scale screening program the goal was to change Black reproductive behavior.[95] Unfortunately, the initiative promoted confusion regarding the difference between people who carried the sickle-cell gene and those who had sickle-cell disease.[96]

This confusion resulted in a new kind of discrimination against Blacks .[97] Some states passed legislation requiring all school-age Black children to be screened for the sickle-cell trait even though there was no treatment or cure for the disease.[98] Some states required prisoners to be tested even though, without conjugal visits, there would be no opportunity to pass on the trait.[99] The military considered banning all Blacks. Black airline stewardesses with the sickle cell trait were fired. Insurance rates went up for people who had the sickle-cell gene; some companies denied coverage.[100] During that period, many Blacks came to believe that the sickle-cell screening initiative was merely a disguised genocide attempt as Blacks with the trait were often advised, "Don't have kids."[101]

## Family Planning and Involuntary Sterilization

Family planning initiatives have been described as another attempt to reduce the Black population.[102] Many Blacks believe that the roots of family planning and birth control are to control the population growth of Blacks. Some argue that Margaret Sanger, considered the "mother of family planning and reproductive freedom", supported and promoted the use of reproductive technology to diminish the reproductive liberty of Blacks.[103]

While Margaret Sanger's specific role in racial eugenics is in dispute, there is no doubt that throughout United States history, family planning and birth control have been used to limit the population growth of Blacks. In the 1930s, the government funded the first birth control clinics as a way of lowering the Black birthrate. In 1939, the Birth Control Federation of America planned a "Negro Project" designed to limit reproduction by Blacks who "still breed carelessly and disastrously, with the result that the increase among Negroes, even more than among Whites, is from that portion of the population least intelligent and fit, and least able to rear children properly."[104] In fact, the early birth control movement included strong factions advocating eugenics or compulsory sterilization.[105] Sanger promoted the use of sterilization, abortion, and contraception in order to eliminate "human weeds."[106]

By 1935, approximately 20,000 forced eugenical sterilizations had been performed in the United States.[107] Many of these sterilizations were carried out pursuant to 32 state statutes mandating eugenical sterilizations.[108] In 1927, the Supreme Court explicitly held that these statutes *were* constitutional.[109] In *Bell v. Buck*, the Court stated that

> "[I]t is better for all the world, if . . . society can prevent those who are manifestly unfit from continuing their kind. . . . Three generations of imbeciles are enough."[110]

In the 1960s, the government expanded the subsidization of family planning clinics as a way to reduce the number of welfare recipients.[111] In so doing, the number of clinics were proportional to the number of Blacks and Hispanics in a community.[112] In the 1970s, some doctors would only deliver babies or perform abortions on Black women if the women consented to sterilization.[113] Other Black women were threatened with the withdrawal of their welfare benefits if they did not agree to sterilization.[114] In a case brought by poor, teenage Black women in Alabama, a Federal District Court found that an estimated 100,000 to 150,000 poor women were sterilized annually under federally funded programs.[115] In the 1970s and 1980s, public assistance officials deceived Black welfare recipients into having their teenage daughters sterilized.[116]

A 1982 study determined that only 25% of White women were sterilized as compared to 34% of Black women.[117] Both single and married Black women were more likely than White women to use sterilization as a contraceptive method.[118] Further, Blacks in the South have the highest rates of hysterectomy and tubal ligation in the United States.[119]

Today, some doctors encourage Black women to be sterilized because the doctor thinks that the women have had too many children or because the women are incapable of using contraceptives responsibly.[120] Furthermore, the Federal government still subsidizes sterilizations for women eligible for Medicaid coverage, though in some states it will not pay for abortions.[121] Therefore, Blacks' distrust of family planning is justified.

## Medicine Participation in Justifying Racism

In the 1800's Louis Agassiz, Samuel George Morton, Samuel Cartwright, and Josiah Clark were the leading U.S. academic physicians to advocate the theory on Black inferiority.[122] The doctors advocated for the establishment of a uniquely Southern-oriented medical education to address the unique diseases of Black slaves, such as drapetomania, the disease causing Negroes to run away.[124] The doctors' ideas were widely accepted. Oliver Wendell Holmes, Dean of Harvard's Medical School from 1847 to 1853, believed in and promoted the scientific value of the work of these "scientists."[125] Holmes held such regard for Samuel Morton's work that he considered Morton's research "permanent data for all future students of ethnology"[126] In fact, many physicians used science to create elaborate theoretical systems to justify the difference in the medical treatment of Blacks and Whites.[123]

# BLACKS AND BIOETHICAL ISSUES

Like all Americans, Blacks are wrestling with many bioethical issues including abortion, the Human Genome Project and genetic testing, organ transplantation, AIDS, physician-assisted suicide and the right to die, reproductive technology, and violence. Unlike the dominant group, Blacks view these issues through a lens colored by slavery, segregation, and racism that causes Blacks to believe that the principles of bioethics (autonomy, beneficence, nonmalfeasance, and justice) will not protect their community.

## Abortion

Abortion is an issue that deeply divides American society. For Blacks, the abortion debate is very important.. Since 1984, the rate and ratio of abortion among Black women has increased significantly. For instance, in 1984, approximately two-thirds of women obtaining legal abortions were White, compared to 54% in 2001.[127] Furthermore, the abortion ratio (abortions to live births) for Black women has increased since 1984 from 475 to 491 per 1000 live births[128], while the abortion ratio for White women has decreased during the same period from 288 to 165.[129] In 2001, the abortion rate for Black women (49.1 per 1,000 live births) was almost 3.0 times the rate for White women (16.5 per 1,000 live births).[130]

Table 06-01
Abortion Rate and Excess Abortion
In Black Community by Selected Years

| Year | Black | White | Excess Abortion Rates |
|---|---|---|---|
| 1973 | 42.0 | 32.6 | 9.4 |
| 1980 | 54.3 | 33.2 | 21.1 |
| 1990 | 53.7 | 25.8 | 27.9 |
| 2000 | 50.3 | 16.7 | 33.6 |
| 2001 | 49.1 | 16.5 | 32.6 |

Source: Table 16. Legal abortions and legal ratios, according to selected patient characteristics: United States, selected years 1973-2001, Health United States, 2004.

But focusing on statistics ignores the fact that for Blacks, the abortion issue is more complex than being "pro-life" or "pro-choice." The abortion debate generally ignores issue such as prenatal care, infant mortality rates, or teen pregnancy rates.[131] Furthermore, while many Blacks believe that every woman has the right to make her own decision about abortion, those same Blacks believe that abortion is genocide.[132] Some Blacks believe that this increase in abortion represents a form of eugenics:

"Black women do not realize that the people forcing abortion on our people as a panacea to our social problems have a long history of beliefs in eugenics. They have a long history of racism."[133] In short, some Blacks view abortion as "elitist, racist and genocidal."[134]

Thus, a bioethical discussion centered on either right-to-life or pro-choice principles fails to take into consideration the social problems driving Blacks to abortions or the fear that abortion is merely another form of genocide.

## Human Genome Project and Genetic Testing

The Human Genome Project is a group of research projects, organized under the supervision of the Federal government, devoted to the long-term goal of identifying every gene in the human body.[135] There are both positive and negative ramifications of the Human Genome Project.[136] The advantage of the Project is its promotion of scientific knowledge, especially the diagnosis and treatment of diseases.[137] The disadvantages include the potential for providing a basis for a eugenics program,[138] concerns about privacy and confidentiality,[139] and the specter of compulsory genetic testing.[140] It is generally agreed that the project's potential for discrimination is significant and serious. The discriminatory use of genetic information is particularly relevant in the context of schools,[141] employers and employees,[142] and insurers.[143] But few authorities acknowledge that Blacks will be disproportionately affected by the discrimination that is based upon genetics.[144]

White scientists have used genetic information to reinforce negative stereotypes about Blacks.[145] Moreover, given the racial barriers to access and the racial inequity in medical treatment, the potential benefits of gene mapping will be also be racially distributed.[146] Finally, given the disparate health status of Blacks, the money being used to support gene mapping should be used to remedy the social conditions that contribute to the current health status problems.[147] Developing a technology such as the Human Genome Project in a racist society is akin to developing a bomb and giving it to a child. The United States has had a long history of using genetics to subjugate Blacks.[148]

For instance, Dr. Frank R. Ervin and Dr. Lawrence Razavi conducted a research project suggesting that law-abiding citizens and criminals could be distinguished genetically.[149] It was hoped that the tests for criminality would "serve as a screening device for men upon entry into the military or perhaps at the time they first entered the criminal justice system."[150] Although "the XYY theory for the association of abnormal fingerprints with an additional Y chromosome" was later discredited by the medical and psychological establishment, a popular belief in the theory continues to persist.[151]

Furthermore, many people still assume that there is a relationship between race and intelligence. This belief was fueled by Dr. Arthur R. Jensen's so-called "discovery" of the genetic relationship between race and I.Q.[152] According to Jensen, "Blacks averaged about fifteen points below the average of Whites on IQ tests, [suggesting] that this phenomenon was responsible for a difference in scholastic aptitude between the groups."[153] The United States Office of Technology Assessment has acknowledged the potential problems raised by eugenics programs, stating:

> "The ethical debate about eugenic applications more properly focuses on how to use new information rather than on whether to discover it. Eugenic programs are offensive because they single out particular people and therefore can be socially coercive and threatening to the ideas that human beings have dignity and are free agents."[154]

Yet, as usual, the fears of Blacks are, at best, ignored, and, at worst, discounted as unreasonable.

## Organ Transplantation

Blacks have unequal access to organ transplantation, they wait almost twice as long as Whites for their first transplant:, 13.9 and 7.6 months, respectively.[155] Although Whites represent only 61% of the dialysis population, they receive seventy-four percent of all kidney transplants.[156] In 1988, Blacks represented 33.5% of dialysis patients but only 22.3% of kidney transplants.[157] In fact, in any given year, White dialysis patients have approximately a 78% higher chance of receiving a transplant than Black dialysis patients.[158]

Most bioethicists attribute this inequity to Blacks' reluctance to donate organs. For instance, in 1988, Blacks donated only 12% of living-related transplants and only 8% of cadaveric kidneys.[159] However, this inequity also exists because of the level of mandated tissue matching required, a level that may not be necessary for successful transplantation.[160] Studies from New York, Los Angeles, Miami, and Washington D.C. document that Blacks were markedly under-represented in donor statistics.[161]

Organ transplantation presents two dilemmas for Blacks. First, Blacks remain on waiting lists almost twice as long as Whites, even when such factors as blood type, age, immunological status, location, and the decreased organ donations by Blacks are taken into account.[162] This is due in part to allocation rules such as "antigen matching rules which favor Whites."[163] However, there are alternative allocation rules that could reduce, if not eliminate, the racial inequity in access to donated kidneys and other organs.[164]

Second, there are many personal and social issues involved in organ transplantation that are unique to Blacks. The most common reasons for donor reluctance are lack of information, religious convictions, distrust of medical professionals, fear of premature death, a preference to donate only to members of the same race, and the failure of health care professionals to ask Black families for consent in an effective way.[165] The fear of premature death is fueled by popular shows and community rumors. In an episode of Law and Order, a White philanthropist bought his daughter a perfect kidney from an unscrupulous surgeon. The surgeon obtained the organ by mugging a pre-selected victim, a Black man.[166] Moreover, a popular urban legend in the Black community is of a Hispanic man who was found mugged. When the ambulance took him to the hospital, he was declared brain dead, and his organs were removed before his family was notified.

Thus, popular culture encourages Blacks to be suspicious of the medical establishment, and for good reason. The world's most enduring line of human cell cultures, used to test the polio vaccine, new drugs, and potential cancer cures, was taken without informed consent from Henrietta Lacks, a Black woman in Baltimore who was treated for cervical cancer at Johns Hopkins Hospital in 1951.[167] The cancer killed Henrietta Lacks, but the HeLa cells harvested from Ms. Lacks live on in labs around the world.[168] Laws in Pennsylvania, California, Florida, Michigan, Ohio, and Texas allow coroner's offices to remove eyes and brains for transplant without prior consent or permission from next of kin.[169] Blacks, other minorities, and the poor are most affected by these laws.[170] Given the current level of mistreatment based on race, there is reason for Blacks to believe that their bodies will become a source of organs for Whites.[171]

The variation between legal systems has allowed abuse of the simplest method of organ procurement, organ sales from live donors. This system is generally poorly regulated and fraught with health risks to both the donor and recipient. Often, it is the poorer citizens of developing countries who are supplying organs for the members of the upper class, who purchase the organs either directly or through organ brokers. However, when the organ, like any other valuable commodity, cannot be bought, it is stolen, resulting in flagrant violations of human rights.[172]

## Reproductive Technology

Black women, like most women, want "reproductive choice."[173] Black women want the power to make genuine choices about their own reproductive health.[174] However, Black women tend not to have that choice. Reproductive choice involves more than a "right to an abortion." It involves the ability to choose to have healthy children or not to have children at all. In order to have real reproductive choice, Black women need access to reproductive health care including prenatal care, access to infertility services including fertility counseling, freedom from coerced or ill-informed consent to sterilization, economic security that could prevent possible exploitation of the poor with surrogacy contracts, freedom from toxins in the workplace, healthy nutrition and living space, and the right to safe, legal, and affordable abortion services.[175]

## Reproductive Health--Workplace Toxins

Black women are less healthy than White women, due in part to their disproportionate presence in jobs that have high levels of workplace toxins.[176] Blacks are over-represented in industries such as laundry and dry cleaning, tobacco manufacture, fabric mills, smelters, hospitals, and farm work", all of which utilize carcinogenic chemicals.[177] Protecting the reproductive health of women is an important legal issue that has a disproportionate effect upon Black women.

The ruling in the *United Automobile Workers v. Johnson Controls, Inc.* case has not helped.[178] In 1991, the Supreme Court decided that Title VII of the Civil Rights Act of 1964 prohibits an employer from excluding women of child-bearing capacity from certain jobs, even if the employer wishes to prevent possible damage to potential or developing fetuses.[179] Certainly, the decision protects women from forced sterilization in order to maintain higher paying jobs. However, because the decision does not address the workplace conditions that threaten the health and safety of pregnant women, Black women could be rendered infertile simply by doing their jobs.[180] Reproductive health of Black women will continue to lag behind White women as long employers are allowed to evade their responsibility for maintaining toxic-free environments.

## Reproductive Health Care

The lack of adequate prenatal care has resulted in both high maternal and infant mortality rates. In 1986, Black women were 3.8 times more likely than White women to die from pregnancy-related complications.[181] Nearly one Black baby out of ten is born to a mother who received late or no prenatal care. Among Black teenage mothers under age fifteen, the proportion increases to 2 in 10.[182]

## Contraception—Norplant

On December 10, 1990, the United States Food and Drug Administration (FDA) gave approval to a long-acting contraceptive drug, Norplant.[183] The abuse of Norplant is enormous and already apparent. On December 12, 1990, the Philadelphia Inquirer published an editorial, "Poverty and Norplant: Can Contraception Reduce the Underclass?"[184] All fifty states have already incorporated Norplant into their welfare systems, providing either reimbursement for the cost of Norplant to women on Aid to Families with Dependent Children or a cash bonus for women who agree to be implanted with the device.[185] Several high schools considered offering Norplant to girls in order to prevent them from becoming pregnant.[186]

The courts and legislatures have considered conditioning probation on the acceptance of Norplant.[187] These proposals, aimed at poor Black women, are based upon the assumption that Black women are less deserving of motherhood than White women.[188] "Real" women are expected to be pious, pure, submissive, and domestic, middle-class, and White. Black women, on the other hand, are precluded from living up to this ideal. Four stereotypes of Black women have emerged, all of which deviate from the middle- and upper-class White standard: 1) the "mammy", who is faithful, obedient, nurturing, and caring domestic servant, 2) the "matriarch", who is domineering, unfeminine, and emasculating, 3) the "welfare queen", who is irresponsible, lazy, and immoral, and 4) the "Jezebel", who is hypersexual. As a result, Black women are seen as "somehow less female, perhaps even less human as well." Thus, the prevailing attitude appears to be that Black women are not deserving of motherhood.[189]

## Sterilization

Black women have not had access to voluntary sterilization but have been victims of involuntary surgical procedures that strip them of their reproductive choices. After the abuses of the 1970s, the Department of Health and Human Services adopted regulations to ensure that informed consent was obtained for all federally funded sterilizations.[190] However, there is inadequate monitoring of the consent regulations, and the data that is collected is not released to the public.[191]

## Infertility Treatment

The ability to have children is as important as the ability to prevent having children. Yet, discussions of reproductive issues concerning Black women seldom include the need for infertility services.[192] This is a crucial issue because the risk of infertility is one and a half times greater for Blacks than for Whites.[193] Yet, 75% of low-income women in need of infertility services have not received them.[194] "Given that the average fee for each infertility treatment is between $2,055 and $10,000, it is no wonder that poorer couples, a disproportionate number of whom are Blacks, do not pursue infertility treatment."[195] While infertility services are covered under Medicaid and Title X,[196] little information is available on the amount of public funds spent on infertility services.[197]

## Surrogacy

There are two types of surrogacy arrangements.[198] In the first type, a couple with the female partner unable to bear children uses the male partner's sperm to inseminate a fertile woman, who becomes the "surrogate mother."[199] The surrogate mother carries the fetus to term. Most of these arrangements are governed by a contract whereby the surrogate mother is paid a sum of money and agrees to relinquish all parental rights to the child.[200] "The rate is usually between $10,000 and $15,000, and the surrogate is paired with the infertile couple either through a fertility agency or privately."[201] Because this is a costly arrangement, it is limited to affluent couples who are disproportionately White. While there is significant potential for abuse of poor women, it is not likely that those women will be Black, because an egg obtained from a Black woman would produce a Black child.[202] Very few White couples are wanting to give birth to African-American children. However, other women of color, particularly women from Third World countries, may be exploited.[203] For instance, a chain of clinics in India, Jordan, Pakistan, Egypt, Malaysia, Singapore, and Taiwan has been set up by U.S. and Australian entrepreneurs. In vitro fertilization clinics in Brazil, India, Malaysia, and Indonesia have been established particularly for sex predetermination.[204]

The second type of surrogacy arrangement involves the use of an egg from a female donor who is not the surrogate. The egg is fertilized and then transferred into the uterus of another woman. This woman, the "gestational mother", has no genetic connection to the child.[205]

This type of arrangement is significantly more dangerous to poor, Black women. It literally turns women into uterus prostitutes, wombs for rent. It raises the issue, what constitutes motherhood: biology, genetics or environment? The case of Anna Johnson, a Black woman who gave birth to the child of a White husband and an Asian wife, highlights the conflicts. The California Court of Appeals ruled that genetics was the determining factor in parenthood.[206] This decision is reminiscent of slavery.

Since slave women were classified as "breeders" as opposed to "mothers", their infant children could be sold away from them like calves from cows. One year after the importation of Africans was halted, a South Carolina court ruled that female slaves had no legal claims to their children. Consequently, children could be sold away from their mothers at any age because "the young of slaves [. . .] stand on the same footing as other animals."[207]

If Blacks and other women become breeders for the affluent, it will be "painfully reminiscent of slavery and the days of the breeder woman whose feelings for her child, whether born out of love or out of rape, were disregarded when men with power over her made decisions about the child."[208]

## Violence as a Public Health Issue

A young Black male's risk of becoming a homicide victim in the United States is one in 27, compared with one in 205 for young White males. The risk of becoming a homicide victim for young Black females is four times higher than for young White females in the White community. Violence in the Black community is a public health issue. Unfortunately, rather than look at violence with a public health approach that is amenable to reduction through public health strategies, there is more focus on violence as a biological issue as evidenced by the failed Federal Initiative to Combat Violence.[209] The Violence Initiative was a proposed Federal initiative to combat violence in the inner-city, supposedly by focusing a more efficient effort toward collective policy making.[210]

Violence has been a long-standing problem in the Black community as it is in most communities especially oppressed ones. Grandmother Maude had one son killed in an argument over a woman. My Uncle Red vow to avenge his brother by killing the man and instead the man killed him. Thus, my Grandmother lost 2 young sons (they were both in their 20s) in a week. My father had a scar that started at his forehead and went all the way down the left side of his fact to chin – black on black violence. I remember a Black family where the father took the life of both himself, his wife and all his children. Black-on-Black violence is a part of our history – just as White-on-White violence a part of their history.

However, the Violence Initiative was based on two disturbing premises. The first was that much of violent behavior in the inner city may have biological or genetic origins.[211] The second premise was that "factors of individual vulnerability and predisposition to violent behavior exists, factors that may be detected at an early age." [212] Dr. Frederick Goodwin, in one of the first introductions of the Violence Initiative, stated:

> "If you look, for example, at male monkeys, especially in the wild, roughly half of them survive to adulthood. The other half die by violence. That is the natural way it is for males, to knock each other off and in fact, there are some interesting evolutionary implications of that because the same hyper-aggressive monkeys who kill each other are also hypersexual, so they copulate more to offset the fact that more of them are dying. Now, one could say that if some of the loss of social structure in this society, and particularly within the high impact inner-city areas, has removed some of the civilizing evolutionary things that Blacks have built up and that maybe it isn't just the careless use of the word when people call certain areas of certain cities jungles, that Blacks may have gone back to what might be more natural, without all the social controls that Blacks have imposed upon ourselves as a civilization over thousands of years in our evolution." [213]

As a result of Dr. Goodwin's announcement concerning the intent and the rationale of the Violence Initiative, he was dismissed as Director of the Alcohol, Drug Abuse, and Mental Health Administration and demoted to the position of Director of the National Institute of Mental Health.[214] Under the new Clinton Administration, part of the Violence Initiative was canceled amidst doubts about its integrity and legitimacy.[215]

For the Black community, the Initiative's intervention and problem-solving policy mandate was to focus on the children of the inner city.[216] The advent of the Federal Violence Initiative threatened the personhood and the voice of Blacks, and more particularly of Black children, by fostering biological and reductionist theories of genetic linkage between criminally-violent behavior and inner-city youth. Furthermore, it removed the contextual and historical concepts of violence, and devalued the worth of the Black child by reinforcing gender and stereotypical concepts of Black women and men.[217]

The Federal Violence Initiative failed because it blamed people for their own problems in their own environment. Yet, a public health approach that tries to counteract political and economic forces that legitimize violence in our society is warranted. If Blacks want to reduce violence, Blacks will have to deal with the system that produces violence.

Unfortunately, most public health approaches focus on human development in our community. This focus will necessarily be flawed because any actions or behaviors of the Black community will be viewed in the historical context in which slavery legitimized the image of Blacks as unworthy of respect and bodily integrity, and undeserving of psychological well-being.[218] Furthermore, the images of sex and subjugation legitimizes the attempts to link social conditions with so-called genetic deficiencies.[219]

"Thus, even though Blacks are free from slavery, Black men and women are bound now by a caste of racism and poverty. They are "welfare queens", and members of the "underclass." They have become parents of sons who have been labeled an "endangered species", and of daughters who are caught in a cycle of "teenage pregnancy" The social value of Black children has never been recognized and their economic value is seen as marginal or as having ceased to exist. Black people bear children who, by their very existence, become the tools for their own destruction, the murderers of their own spirits. These children become individuals who are seen as obsolete. Black men and women in the inner city give birth to disposable children." [220]

Subsuming and denying the individuality of Blacks, these images represent "inherent and permanent inequality . . . apart from any environmental influence." [220]

# IMPLICATIONS OF A
# BLACK BIOETHICAL PERSPECTIVE

Bioethics "addresses the ethical problems posed by modern medicine and biotechnology." [221] Bioethics is not a single, distinct academic discipline, but is comprised of practitioners from philosophy, theology, law, nursing, medical history, medical anthropology, medical sociology, and related fields. [222] While bioethics lacks a single, accepted methodology [223], it has traditionally focused on "mid-level ethical principles", such as autonomy, beneficence, justice, and nonmalfeasence. [224] These principles are intended to be a regulative guideline, stating conditions of the "permissibility, obligatoriness, rightness, or aspirational quality of actions falling within the scope of the principle[s]." [225] However, there have been a number of challenges to the content of the principles. [226]

First, Eurocentric bioethics focuses on the individual to the exclusion of the family and the community. [227] This focus on the individual is based on a philosophy that regards the self, and only the self, as the end. [228] However, the Black perspective views this ethical egoism as misplaced. [229] Blacks believe that "it takes a whole village" to raise a child, and thus view ethical egoism to be incompatible with the raising of healthy children. [230] Furthermore, even as adults, none of us function as islands; we all must rely on others at least for reaffirmation of our self-assessment. [231]

Second, Eurocentric bioethics embraces Kantian ethics, which are antithetical to Afrocentric bioethics. Kantian ethics require universal norms and an impartial perspective, which is inattentive to relationships and community. [232] Kantian privileges place reasoning over virtue, character, and moral emotions. [233] Kantian ethics maintain that the only way people can morally constitute themselves is by free and rational choice. [234] The exclusivity of that claim is troubling. Blacks believe that Blacks morally constitute values not only through free and rational individual choice but also through parents and community.[235]

Third, Eurocentric bioethics views the patient or research subject generically, paying attention primarily to one race (White) and one gender (male).[236] As a result, the development of laws and bioethical principles, discourse, and practices are informed by the values and beliefs of one group, which is White, middle-class, males.[237]

Eurocentric bioethical principles such as autonomy, beneficence, and informed consent do not have the same force when viewed through the Black bioethical perspective. These principles leave considerable room for individual judgment by health care practitioners.[238] The flaw of a principle-based paradigm is this individual judgment. The application of the principles will be subject to other values held by the society. In our racist society, the judgment is often racist.

Thus, Eurocentric bioethics has adopted rules and has applied them with little, if any, concern for how race or other characteristics affect the working of the rules.[239] In fact, numerous studies have documented a inequity between traditional bioethical practice and the needs of minority populations. For instance, Blacks differ from Whites, both in their unwillingness to complete advance directives and in their desires regarding life-sustaining treatment.[240] Substantially more Blacks and Hispanics "wanted their doctors to keep them alive regardless of how ill they were, while more . . . Whites agreed to stop life-prolonging treatment under some circumstances. . . ."[241]

Eurocentric bioethics fail Blacks because bioethicists "believe, first, that people behave in ways that can so far be predicted *a priori* that empirical evidence about their behavior is superfluous and, second, that people think and act rationalistically, seeking always to maximize and exercise autonomy."[242] However, the reality is very different.[243] People act in ways that are more consistent with the values they hold, rather than following any particular bioethical principles.[244] Also, racism is a strongly held value in our society. Furthermore, when dealing with bioethical concepts, courts have shown little interest in dealing with empirical evidence or the effects of judicial doctrines.[245]

Blacks have been experimented on without their consent, in violation of their autonomy.[246] Blacks have been treated in ways which have caused harm, thus violating the principles of nonmalfeasence[247] and beneficence.[248] Blacks are given different treatment and provided different access to health care, thus violating the principle of justice.[249] At best, the judgment in applying the articulated principles has been exercised in a manner that consistently harms Blacks.

The implication for the Black community is the failure of bioethics to take into consideration those factors that can rectify the problems in the Black community. Most of the problem solving has been at odds with the affirmation of the Black individual and community. In fact, most mainstream bioethicists and jurists have neglected to comment on the social ills or injustices such as "the [Blacks'] enslavement, the injustices and discrimination they have suffered, the stereotyping of their language and culture, and their disadvantaged economic, political, educational, and health status."[250] As a result, Blacks are in danger of losing their own perspectives, their own gifts.[251]

The continued destruction of the Black community results from the exclusion of Black perspectives in policy development. The Black community has a history and context that are characterized by medical mistreatment and exploitation. Whites have a history that is racist and "conspicuously indifferent to community, religion, virtue, and personal experience."[252] Blacks face the health care system with anxiety, fear, and suspicion.[253] Such attitudes will not change until bioethics constructs a practical, ethical remedy that will lead to lead to community empowerment.[254] Such a practical approach would require reinstatement of community hospitals,[255] assuring urban perinatal health care,[256] encouraging traditional lay-midwifery,[257] and reestablishing the extended family.[258] However, such an approach must be based not only on the traditional Eurocentric principles but also on:

- recognizing the needs of the community
- Formulating bioethical and legal solutions involving both the family and the community
- Training health care providers and institutions about the Black perspective
- Eliminating inequities in health status
- Ending inequities and inequities in health care.

One problem that some bioethicists and jurists may have with acknowledging a Black perspective is the failure of all Blacks to have a single definition of an ethical belief system. However, such a requirement is not necessary. There are differences among the members of all groups. No one expects all Whites to accept the dominant view in their culture. Nevertheless, a particular view may be an accurate description of some significant aspect of that culture. However, attempts to assert, define, and explain the impact of bioethical or legal behavior on Black culture are met with resistance. Whites often base their resistance on an assertion that such perceptions about Black culture are not representative. One wonders if this resistance is based on some conscious or unconscious attempt to avoid having to structure a multi-cultural society. [259] Until bioethicists and legal jurists address these concerns, Blacks are not likely to trust the American health system. Ultimately, bioethicists, lawyers, and policymakers must recognize the existence of a "spirit, a set of social structures and norms in Black life that are worthy of acquisition by Blacks and Whites."[260]

# Chapter Seven

---

# BLACK HEALTH STATUS AND HEALTH CARE AS A VIOLATION OF INTERNATIONAL HUMAN RIGHTS

**"Of all the forms of inequality, injustice in health is the most shocking and the most inhuman."**[**]

"Equal access to quality health care is a crucial issue facing the United States.[1] For too long, too many Americans have been denied equal access to quality health care on the basis of race, ethnicity, and gender.[2] Cultural incompetence of health care providers, socioeconomic inequities, disparate impact of facially neutral practices and policies, misunderstanding of civil rights laws, and intentional discrimination contribute to inequities in health status, access to health care services, participation in health research, and receipt of health care financing.[3]

This inequity in health care is doubly significant given the devastating racial inequity in health status that exists. The combination of racial inequity in health status,[4] institutional racism in health care,[5] and inadequate legal protection[6] points to serious human rights violations[7] under the International Convention on the Elimination of All Forms of Racial Discrimination (ICERD)."[8]

The International Convention on the Elimination of All Forms of Racial Discrimination (ICERD) was adopted in 1965 by a unanimous vote of the United Nations General Assembly.[9] Until ratification of the Convention on the Rights of the Child in 1993[10], ICERD was the most widely ratified of the core human rights treaties.[11] Some commentators argue that the Racial Discrimination Convention had widespread support because it was viewed primarily as a statement against apartheid and colonialism.[12] Nevertheless, the ICERD was the first of the core human rights treaties that followed the adoption of the Universal Declaration of Human Rights.[13] The Convention was followed in 1966 by adoption of two Covenants: The Covenant of Economic, Social and Cultural Rights[14] and The International Covenant on Civil and Political Rights.[15]

---

[**] The Rev. Martin Luther King, at *The Second National Convention of the Medical Committee for Human Rights*, Chicago, Illinois, March 25, 1966.

The ICERD was signed on behalf of the United States on September 28, 1966.[16] It was not transmitted to the United States Senate for advice and consent to ratification until February 23, 1978.[17] The United States Senate resisted its adoption and ratification for seventeen years.[18] Sociologist James Jennings identified several reasons for this resistance.

> "First, the United States was in the midst of the Cold War with the Soviet Union, and the human rights issue was seen as a political football between the two superpowers. Second, the federalist structure of the United States government required approval by the United States Senate. The third factor was the relative political weakness of the Black community. Fourth, the United States has traditionally claimed that its domestic arena is off limits to international bodies.[19] Thus, it was almost thirty years (1994) between the ICERD's adoption by the United Nations and the United States Senate vote giving its advice and consent[20] to ratify the ICERD."[21]

The ICERD prohibits racial discrimination, a term broadly defined as any distinction based on "race, color, descent. or national or ethnic origin [22] that has the purpose or effect of impairing human rights and fundamental freedoms."[23] In this treaty, the term "racial discrimination" means any "distinction, exclusion, restriction or preference based on race, color, descent, or national or ethnic origin, which has the purpose or effect of nullifying or impairing the recognition, enjoyment or exercise, on an equal footing, of human rights and fundamental freedoms in the political, economic, social, cultural or any other field of public life."[24]

Nations that have ratified the ICERD are required to take effective measures to review governmental, national, and local policies and to amend or nullify any laws and regulations that have the effect of creating or perpetrating racial discrimination wherever it exists. [25] However, the United States ratified the ICERD with an unprecedented number of limitations, three reservations, an understanding, and a declaration that qualified the extent to which the United States would adhere to the Treaty.[26]

Reservations are limitations, qualifications, or contradictions of the obligations in a treaty, especially as they relate to the reserving party.[27] The three reservations addressed the following: 1) First Amendment concerns regarding freedom of speech, 2) limiting the reach of the ICERD's provisions to nations, and 3) withholding the jurisdiction of the International Court of Justice from considering Nation Party complaints alleging U.S. failure to implement the ICERD. The effect of the reservations is that the United States refuses to outlaw hate speech, refuses to apply the ICERD to private individuals and organizations, and refuses to allow its citizens to have access to the International Court of Justice for issues of racial discrimination.

Declarations are statements of policy, purpose, or positions relating to the subject matter of the treaty, but not necessarily affecting its provisions.[28] The declaration rendered the ICERD non-self-executing, meaning no legal private causes of action can be based on any provision of the treaty. The United States claims that because its laws provide extensive protections and remedies against racial discrimination, it does not need to enact additional legislation to comply with the ICERD. Furthermore, United States citizens are restricted from invoking rights under the Treaty, thereby limiting the Treaty's effect in the United States.

Understandings are interpretations, clarifications, or elaborations assumed to be consistent with the obligations of the treaty as submitted.[29] The ICERD understanding addressed the United States' intent to implement the ICERD within its jurisdiction and to ensure state and local government compliance with the ICERD.

Provisos relate to issues of United States law or procedure and are not intended to be included in the formal instruments of ratification because they do not involve the other parties to the treaties. The proviso to the ICERD stated that any legislation enacted under ICERD "must be constitutionally permissible."[30]

Despite these limitations, the ICERD still has value to the United States anti-racism community. For instance, under the reporting procedure of the ICERD's Article 9, the United States agreed to submit reports every two years, with the first report due in 1995.[31] The United States did not submit a report until 2000.[32] This report purported to bring together in a single document the initial, second, and third periodic reports of the United States of America, which were due on November 20, 1995, 1997, and 1999 respectively.[33] No reports were submitted for 2001, 2003, or 2005.

Under the ICERD, a committee (the ICERD Committee) reviews the reports and determines whether adequate legal protections for groups that have experienced racial discrimination have been implemented. The Committee also examines evidence of de facto discrimination.[34] In fact, the ICERD provides that, because governments are accountable to an international forum on racial discrimination, those governments must make changes in national law to bring the law into compliance with ICERD..[35] Although not legally binding,[36] the ICERD Committee makes concluding observations about the reports and may make suggestions on how the reporting states could improve their application of the ICERD.[37] The nation report is to consist of legislative, judicial, administrative, or other measures adopted by the nation Party that implement the ICERD.[38]

The ICERD procedure permits interested non-governmental organizations to submit shadow reports on a government's compliance with the treaty.[39] The ICERD has extensive authority over reports, government complaints, and individual communications, something that places it in a powerful position to expose government violations.[40] Numerous organizations submitted shadow reports. The Allied Research Center, through its Transnational Racial Justice Initiative, issued a report entitled "The Persistence of White Privilege and Institutional Racism in United States Policy: A Report on United States Government Compliance with the International Convention on the Elimination of All Forms of Racial Discrimination" (hereinafter White Privilege Shadow Report).[41] The White Privilege Shadow Report included an introduction by Makani Themba-Nixon, Editor for the "Transnational Racial Justice Initiative." Ms. Themba-Nixon noted a number of problems with the initial United States report[42] and provided a summary of issues relating to United States noncompliance with the Treaty.[43] The White Privilege Shadow Report also included discussions of welfare policy,[44] health policy, education policy,[45] and land use policy.[46]

This chapter discusses inequity in health status, institutional discrimination in health care, and inadequate legal enforcement, all of which point to serious human rights violations by the United States under the ICERD.[47] This chapter then makes specific recommendations to the ICERD Committee[48] and includes several appendices, including one entitled, "Concluding Observations of the ICERD Committee." This chapter's premise is that persistent discrimination in United States health care perpetuates health inequities, in violation of the United States obligations under the ICERD.

## VIOLATIONS OF THE INTERNATIONAL CONVENTION ON THE ELIMINATION OF ALL FORMS OF RACIAL DISCRIMINATION

As indicated in the United States Report on the ICERD, the Federal government has laws making it illegal to discriminate based on race (for example, Title VI of the Civil Rights Act of 1964).[49] This report fails to admit that the effort of the United States in ensuring equal access to quality health care has not only been ineffective and inefficient, but has also perpetuated racial discrimination. Astonishingly, the United States fails to even mention its own assessment of civil rights enforcement in health care that was conducted by the United States Commission on Civil Rights.[50] In a two-volume critical analysis, this Commission accused the government of perpetuating inequities in health status and access:

> "[The government] has failed to enforce civil rights laws vigorously and appropriately. The failure [of the government] to be proactively involved in [civil rights] health care issues or initiatives has resulted in continuance of policies and practices that, in many instances are either discriminatory or have a disparate impact on minorities. Thus, there remain disparities in access to health care and in health care research and unequal distribution of health care financing."[51]

Although Congress has enacted civil rights laws designed to address specific rights, such as equal opportunities in employment, education, and housing, Congress has not given health care the same attention .[52] As a consequence, discrimination in health care is uncorrected, perpetuating differences in health status.[53] The United States Commission on Civil Rights found that the failure to recognize that differences in health care delivery, financing, and research are discriminatory barriers to health care translates into, and perpetuates, differences in health status.[54] Thus, in the area of health care, the United States has failed to meet its obligation under Article 2(l)(a), Article 2(1)(c), Article 2(l)(d), and Article 5(e)(iv) of the ICERD.

## Article 2(1)(a)

Under Article 2(1)(a), "Each State Party [Nation] undertakes to engage in no act or practice of racial discrimination against persons, groups of persons, or institutions, and to ensure that all public authorities and public institutions, national and local, shall act in conformity with this obligation."[55]

The United States has failed to "ensure that all public authorities and public institutions, national and local, shall act in conformity" with its obligation under Article 2(1)(a).[56] In its 1999 report to the President and Congress, the United States Commission on Civil Rights found significant weaknesses in governmental enforcement efforts in health care. Specifically, the Commission noted:

> "The deficiencies in the [governmental] enforcement efforts ...largely are the consequences of [a] fundamental failure to recognize the tremendous importance of its mission and to embrace fully the opportunity it has to eliminate disparities and discrimination in the health care system. Although the government [through the Office of Civil Rights (OCR)] has attempted to identify noncompliance with the Nation's civil rights laws over the years, it has failed to understand that all of its efforts have been merely reactive and in no way have they remedied the pervasive problems within the [health care] system. [The government's] failure to address these deeper, systemic problems is part of a larger deficiency... a seeming inability to assert its authority within the health care system. As a result of the myopic perspective ... the [government] appears unable to systematically plan and implement the kind of ... "redevelopment" policy that it so clearly needs."[57]

Further, the Commission found significant weaknesses in the enforcement efforts of the OCR. . In particular, the Commission noted the governmental failure to implement many of the recommendations suggested by the Commission in its 1996 report on Title VI enforcement.[58] That report was a comprehensive evaluation and analysis of the United States Department of Justice performance in its leadership and coordination responsibilities for Title VI, and included the United States Commission on Civil Rights analysis of the Title VI enforcement efforts of 10 Federal agencies and 10 sub-agencies.[59]

Despite some focus on the health of minorities, the government has failed to enforce civil rights laws vigorously and appropriately. The failure of the government to take the initiative in health care issues has resulted in the continuation of policies and practices that, in many instances, are either discriminatory or have a disparate impact on minorities and women.[60] Thus, there remain inequities in access to care, treatment, research, and financing in the United States as a result of the United States' failure to meet its obligation under Article 2(I)(a).[61]

## Article 2(1)(c)

Under Article 2(1)(c), "Each State Party shall take effective measures to review governmental, national and local policies, and to amend, rescind or nullify any laws and regulations which have the effect of creating or perpetuating racial discrimination wherever it exists."[62]

The United States has failed to meet this obligation. While the United States has undertaken extensive measures to review national laws and regulations "which have the effect of creating or perpetuating racial discrimination", it has failed to make the necessary revisions and modifications in the laws that were recommended by the United States Commission on Civil Rights. As noted by the Commission:

> "In the United States today, there remain tremendous racial and gender disparities in access to quality health care services and health care financing, as well as in the benefits of medical research. Many of these disparities continue to plague the Nation's health care system because the [government] has failed to enforce the crucial nondiscrimination provisions of the Federal civil rights laws with which it is entrusted. The ... enforcement operation is lacking in virtually every key area. Most significantly, ... [the government] generally has failed to undertake proactive efforts such as issuing appropriate regulations and policy guidance, allocating adequate resources for onsite systemic compliance reviews, and initiating enforcement proceedings when necessary."[63]

The United States, while undertaking extensive measures to review the national effects of "creating or perpetuating racial discrimination", has failed to "amend, rescind or nullify any laws and regulations" that have such effects.[64] There has been little judicial activity in reviewing and shaping anti-discrimination law in health care.[65] Despite taking five years to submit a report, the government's report failed to identify this lack of oversight. Furthermore, the United States failed to review state and local laws and regulations.

## Article 2(1)(d)

Under Article 2(1)(d), "Each State Party shall prohibit and bring to an end, by all appropriate means, including legislation as required by circumstances, racial discrimination by any persons, group or organization."[66]

The United States failed to meet its obligation to "bring to an end, by all appropriate means, including legislation", racial discrimination in health care.[67] For instance, the United States Congress has not enacted civil rights laws relating to health care, even though it has enacted specific anti-discrimination laws in the areas of employment, education, and housing.[68]

Unequal access to health care is a nationwide problem that primarily affects women and people of color.[69] The United States Commission on Civil Rights states the following:

"For 35 years, [the government through the Department of Health and Human Services (HHS)] and its predecessor agency, the Department of Health, Education, and Welfare (HEW), have condoned policies and practices resulting in discrimination against minorities and women in health care. In many ways, segregation, disparate treatment, and racism continue to infect the Nation's health care system. [The government] ... has pursued a policy of excellence in health care for White Americans by investing in programs and scientific research that discriminate against women and minorities. [The government] ... essentially has condoned the exclusion of women and minorities from health care services, financing, and research by implementing an inadequate civil rights program and ignoring critical recommendations concerning its civil rights enforcement program. The Commission, the HHS Office of Inspector General, and the HHS Civil Rights Review Team have offered many recommendations for improving civil rights enforcement ... However, failure to implement these recommendations has resulted in failure of the Federal Government to meet its goals of ensuring nondiscrimination and equal access to health care for minorities and women."[70]

## Article 5(e)(iv)

Under Article 5(e)(iv),

"In compliance with the fundamental obligations laid down in Article 2 of this Convention, States Parties undertake to prohibit and to eliminate racial discrimination in all its forms and to guarantee the right of everyone, without distinction as to race, color, or national or ethnic origin, to equality before the law, notably in the enjoyment of the following rights: ... e) Economic, social and cultural rights, in particular: ... (iv) The right to public health, medical care, social security and social services."[71]

The United States failed to "prohibit and to eliminate racial discrimination in all its forms and to guarantee the right of everyone, without distinction as to race, color, or national or ethnic origin, ... [including] [t]he right to public health, medical care, social security and social services."[72] Such failure has been noted by the United States Commission on Civil Rights:

"Over the past 35 years, the United States Commission on Civil Rights has been monitoring health care access for minorities and women, focusing on the important role civil rights enforcement efforts can play in providing equal access to quality health care. Although there have been some improvements in accessing health care over the last three decades, the timid and ineffectual enforcement efforts of the [government through the] Office for

144 • Dying While Black

Civil Rights (OCR) at the United States Department of Health and Human Services (DHHS) have fostered, rather than combated, the discrimination that continues to infect the Nation's health care system. This is evident in the segregation, disparate treatment, and racism experienced by African Americans, Hispanic Americans, Native Americans, Asian Americans and Pacific Islanders, and members of other minority groups, as well as in the persistent barriers to quality health care that women continue to confront."[73]

As outlined above, discrimination in health care delivery, financing, and research does exist. This is largely due to the failure to enforce federal laws against inequality in health care. Specifically, the Commission noted that the government's failure to remove the historical access barriers to quality health care continued to perpetuate discrimination.[74]

From 1980 to 1999, the government has also abdicated its civil rights enforcement responsibilities.[75] This neglect is well documented by the Commission on Civil Rights, the Department of Health and Human Services, the General Accounting Office, the House of Representatives Committee on Government Operations, the Department of Health and Human Services Office of Inspector General, and the Department's own Civil Rights Review Team.[76] According to the United States Commission on Civil Rights,

"[The government's] steadfast refusal to address concerns about the quality of its efforts indicates a fundamentally limited view of the role civil rights enforcement can and should play in the health care industry, a view that is deeply ingrained within the culture of the Department of Health and Human Services (HHS). What makes this disregard of recommendations for vigorous civil rights enforcement efforts particularly shameful is that HHS provides Federal assistance to medical programs and facilities that save lives every day. While the activities of agencies charged with protecting the rights to equality of opportunity in education and employment are matters of tremendous importance, the failure to conduct strong civil rights enforcement in health care literally can mean the difference between life and death [for Black people]."[77]

It is important to remember that all the major actors in the government have failed to fulfill their responsibilities to eliminate discrimination. Presidents have "failed to offer the oversight, support, and assistance to civil rights enforcement."[78] Congress not only failed to provide oversight, it drastically reduced appropriations.[79] While several minority health initiatives have been implemented by the government, "None of these efforts contains a strong civil rights enforcement component or attempts to develop the key role that OCR should be playing in these efforts".[80] The United States Commission on Civil Rights notes that this lack of civil rights enforcement is "particularly ineffective when compared with some of the more sophisticated civil rights enforcement programs the Commission has evaluated."[81] Finally, the Commission notes that this lack of enforcement is of particular concern:

> "[B]ecause many new forms of discrimination against minorities have emerged as the Nation has moved from "fee-for-service" medicine to managed care. Without appropriate [civil rights enforcement] ... neither recipients or beneficiaries of Federal funding, nor OCR investigative staff can develop a clear understanding of what constitutes discrimination by managed care and other health care organizations."[82]

One such form of discrimination is embedded in the business necessity rationale where, under the guise of cost cutting and fiduciary risk reduction, policies and practices that are biased against racial minorities are considered justifiable discrimination. The ICERD term "unjustifiable disparate impact" indicates that the treaty also covers those practices that appear racially neutral but create statistically significant racial inequities and are unnecessary, i.e., unjustifiable.[83] In considering the criteria that may have been employed, the Committee has acknowledged that particular actions may have varied purposes. In seeking to determine whether an action has an effect contrary to the treaty, the Committee will look to see whether that action has an unjustifiable disparate impact upon a group distinguished by race, color, descent, or national or ethnic origin.[84]

# CONCLUSION

United States health policy is in violation of several provisions of the ICERD, including all of Articles 2 and 5. Federal agencies have repeatedly found discrimination and bias in health care but have consistently failed to address those practices. Inequities and bias range from treatment and diagnosis, to access, funding, training, and representation of racial minorities in the health care system. Millions suffer and thousands lose their lives each year as a result of this kind of discrimination. Current trends toward managed care only exacerbate inequities.

Medicine has found cures and controls for many afflictions, and improved health for all Americans - African Americans, Asian Americans, Hispanic Americans, Native Americans, and White Americans. However, health institutions have failed to extend the same magnitude of improvement in health among White Americans to minority populations. Health institutions have failed to eliminate the inequitable racial distribution of health care. They also perpetuate distinctions among racial groups. The laws in the United States have been proven ineffective in eliminating racial discrimination in health care. This intolerable situation is a violation of basic human rights. Furthermore, the United Nation Committee on the Elimination of Racial Elimination agrees:

> The Committee emphasizes that the adoption of special measures [such as, Affirmative Action to ensure the adequate development and protection of certain racial, ethnic or national groups] by States Parties when the circumstances so warrant, such as in the case of persistent disparities, is an obligation stemming from Article 2, Paragraph 2, of the Convention.

# APPENDIX 07-01

## SELECTED PARAGRAPHS
## FROM THE 2000 UNITED STATES REPORT PURSUANT TO
## ARTICLE 9 OF THE CONVENTION[85]

Although there has been significant progress in the improvement of race relations in the United States over the past half-century, serious obstacles remain to be overcome. Overt discrimination is far less pervasive than it was 30 years ago, yet more subtle forms of discrimination against minority individuals and groups persist in American society. In its contemporary dimensions discrimination takes a variety of forms, some more subtle and elusive than others. Among the principal causative factors are the following:
* * *

(k) Disadvantages for women and children of racial minorities. Often, the consequences of racism and racial discrimination are heightened for women and children. Whether in the criminal justice system, education, employment or health care, women and children suffer discrimination disproportionately. Startlingly high incarceration rates for minority women and children have placed them at a substantial social, economic and political disadvantage;
***

(1) Health care. Persons belonging to minority groups tend to have less adequate access to health insurance and health care. Historically, ethnic and racial minorities were excluded from obtaining private insurance, and, although such discriminatory practices are now prohibited by law, statistics continue to reflect that persons belonging to minority groups, particularly the poor, are less likely to have adequate health insurance than White persons. Racial and ethnic minorities also appear to have suffered disproportionately the effects of major epidemics like AIDS. For example, in 1999, 54 per cent of new cases of HIV infection occurred among [African- Americans], even though they make up less than 15 percent of the population;
***

(n) Discrimination against immigrants. Whether legal or illegal, recent immigrants often encounter discrimination in employment, education and housing as a result of persistent racism and xenophobia. Some also contend that United States immigration law and policy is either implicitly or explicitly based on improper racial, ethnic, and national criteria. Language barriers have also created difficulties of access, *inter alia*, to health care, education and voting rights for some.
* * *

136. The President has executive authority to direct the activities of Federal agencies in furtherance of the Constitution and laws of the United States. In exercise of this authority, the President has issued executive orders that prohibit discrimination in Federal programs and that encourage diversity in the Federal workplace to the extent that such actions are consistent with Federal law. For example,
* * *

(d) On 11 February 1994, in Executive Order 12898, President Clinton directed every Federal agency to identify and consider adverse human health or environmental effects of its programs, policies, and activities on minority and low-income populations. The Order also established a working group on environmental justice comprising the heads of the major executive agencies. The working group's task was to coordinate, provide guidance and serve as a clearinghouse for the Federal agencies on their environmental justice strategies;
* * *

182. The President convened an Advisory Board of seven distinguished Americans to assist him with the Initiative. The Advisory Board worked with the President to engage the many diverse groups, communities, regions, and various industries in this country. The President asked the Advisory Board to join him in reaching out to local communities and to listen to Americans from all different races and backgrounds, to achieve a better understanding of the state of race relations in the United States. The Advisory Board also studied critical substantive areas in which racial disparities are significant, including education, economic opportunity, housing, health care and the administration of justice. Once the year-long effort was completed, the Advisory Board submitted a report to President Clinton concerning its findings and recommendations for creative ways to resolve racial disparities.
* * *

376. Health and health care. Although the United States health care system provides the finest overall care in the world, the data show significant disparities with regard to certain health measures. For example,

-- Infant mortality rates are 2.5 times higher for African Americans than for Whites, and 1.5 times higher for Native Americans. In 1997, the infant mortality rates for Whites was 6.0 deaths per 1,000 live births, compared to 13.7 deaths per 1,000 live births for [African- Americans];

-- [Black] men under age 65 have prostate cancer at nearly twice the rate of White men;

-- The death rate from heart disease for [Blacks] is 41 per cent higher than for Whites (147 deaths per 100,000, compared with 105 deaths);

-- Diabetes is twice as likely to affect Hispanics and Native Americans as the general population. Diabetes rates are 70 per cent higher for [Blacks] than for Whites;

-- [Black] children are three times more likely than White children to be hospitalized with asthma;

-- The maternal mortality rate for Hispanic women is 23 per cent higher than the rate for non-Hispanic women. [Black] women have a 5 percent higher death rate in childbirth than non-Hispanic White women;

-- [Blacks] experience disproportionately high mortality rates from certain causes, including heart disease and stroke, homicide and accidents, cancer, infant mortality, cirrhosis and diabetes;

-- Native Americans are 579 per cent more likely to die from alcoholism, 475 percent more likely to die from tuberculosis, and 231 per cent more likely to die from diabetes than Americans as a whole;

-- Individuals from minority racial and ethnic groups account for more than 50 percent of all AIDS cases, although they represent only 25 per cent of the United States population;

-- The rate of AIDS cases was 30.2 per 100,000 for Whites in 1993. It fell to 9.9 in 1998. The rate for [Blacks] in 1993 was 162.2; 84.7 in 1998. The rate for Hispanics fell from 89.5 in 1993 to 37.8 in 1998.
* * *

377. Health care professionals. In 1996, about 740,000 medical doctors practiced in the United States (280 per 100,000 population). Minorities are likely to live in areas under-served by these and other medical professionals. Poor urban communities with high proportions of [Blacks] and Hispanics averaged only 24 physicians per 100,000 population. Poor communities with low proportions of [Blacks] and Hispanics averaged 69 doctors. This shortage is exacerbated by data that show [Black] physicians are five times more likely than other doctors to treat [Black] patients, and Hispanic doctors are 2.5 times more likely than other doctors to treat Hispanic patients. Minority doctors are also more likely to treat Medicaid or uninsured patients than White doctors from the same area;
***

378. Health care facilities. There are about 6,200 hospitals in the United States providing more than one million beds. Before the 1960's, hospitals were voluntary

organizations and did not face the same legal requirements as public institutions. In addition, hospital medical staffs were self-governing, giving hospitals the freedom to select members, choose patients, and adopt their own payment policies. In many parts of the country, health care services and providers were segregated by race. Since passage of civil rights laws in the 1960's, these practices are no longer legal;

\*\*\*

379. Health care financing. It is primarily through health insurance that Americans pay for their health care. Employer-provided health plans cover some of the costs of health care, while other individuals rely on private health insurers or managed care organizations, such as health maintenance organizations. Those without insurance must rely on financial assistance to obtain health coverage, and may qualify for public assistance, such as supplementary security insurance.

\*\*\*

380. Public assistance for health care includes Medicare (for the elderly) and Medicaid (for the non-elderly poor). Medicare provides health insurance coverage for persons aged 65 years and older, and for individuals with disabilities. Medicare provides health care coverage for more than 38 million people at a cost of about $200 billion per year. Medicaid provides coverage for low- income persons. It is administered by the states with additional matching funds from the Federal Government. Medicaid covers 37 million people at a cost of about $164 billion per year. While Medicaid rules and policies are set and monitored by Federal and state agencies, the administration of the programs is run by insurance companies.

\*\*\*

381. Although Medicare and Medicaid provide more than 70 million people with health coverage, a large number of Americans remain uninsured and unable to access quality health care. Most of the uninsured are minorities and women with children, resulting in unequal access to health care. Almost 30 percent of Hispanic children and 18 per cent of [Black] children are estimated to be without health insurance. Moreover, immigrants, those who are unemployed, work part-time, or are retired often have inadequate insurance.

\*\*\*

382. Eliminating disparities in health care access. The United States Government has long sought to address the need for equal access to quality health care. During the past 35 years in particular, Federal civil rights laws and policies have addressed the need to ensure equal access to health care and non-discrimination in health care programs for racial and ethnic minorities. Congress has created several Federal statutes designed to achieve equal protection of the laws through an emphasis on equality of access to institutions, including the nation's health care system. These statutes have helped establish the framework for the Federal Government's efforts to eliminate discrimination in the health care delivery system.

\*\*\*

383. Two statutes are particularly relevant to health care: (a) the Hill-Burton Act (formally, Title VI and XVI of the Public Health Service Act of 1964, Public Law Number 79-725, 60 Statute 1040 (1946), codified as amended at 42 United States Code section 291-291-0 (1994) and Public Law Number 93-641, 88 Statute 2225 (1974)); and (b) Title VI of the Civil Rights Act of 1964, Public Law Number 88-352, Title VI, 78 Statute 252 (codified as amended at 42 United States Code section 2000d-2000d-7 (1994).

\*\*\*

384. When it was first enacted in 1946, the Hill-Burton Act was designed as a means for facilitating hospital construction, especially in rural communities. In 1964, however, Congress reformulated Hill-Burton as a key provision in the Public Health Service Act to include the modernization of existing hospital facilities. In 1974 the Act was amended yet again, this time requiring that hospitals receiving funds provide a specified amount of service to those unable to pay. Additionally, a facility receiving funds was to be

made available to all members of the community in which it was located, regardless of race, color, national origin or creed.
\*\*\*

385. The Department of Health and Human Services (HHS) is the Federal agency with primary responsibility for enforcing Title VI in the health care context, as well as other civil rights statutes and provisions addressing equal access to quality health care. HHS seeks to ensure compliance with the non-discrimination provisions of these laws by relying on implementing regulations, policy guidance, comprehensive full-scope compliance reviews, complaints investigations, mediation, settlement agreements, technical assistance, and outreach and education programs, as well as through enforcement actions.
\*\*\*

386. The impact of Medicare and Medicaid, originally passed by Congress in 1965, has been enormous. In 1964, Whites were almost 50 per cent more likely than [Blacks] to see a physician. By 1994 this ratio had been reversed: [Blacks] were about 12 per cent more likely than Whites to have seen a doctor in the preceding two years. However, [Blacks] continue to be twice as likely to use hospital outpatient services, while Whites are substantially more likely to visit a private physician.
\*\*\*

387. President Clinton has committed the nation to an ambitious goal of eliminating disparities in health status experienced by racial and ethnic groups in the United States by 2010. President Clinton targeted six health priority areas: infant mortality, breast and cervical cancer screening and management, cardiovascular disease, diabetes, child and adult immunization levels, and HIV / AIDS. As part of this effort, for example, the Centers for Disease Control recently awarded $9.4 million to 32 community coalitions in 18 states to reduce the level of disparities in one or more of the priority areas.
\*\*\*

388. Furthermore, in response to studies showing that language barriers in health care present serious problems for a large percentage of Americans with limited English proficiency (LEP), on August 11, 2000, President Clinton issued Executive Order 13166, "Improving access to services for persons with limited English proficiency." The President ordered the following:

Each Federal agency shall examine the services it provides and develop and implement a system by which LEP persons can meaningfully access those services consistent with, and without unduly burdening, the fundamental mission of the agency. Each Federal agency shall also work to ensure that recipients of Federal financial assistance (recipients) provide meaningful access to their LEP applicants and beneficiaries. To assist the agencies with this endeavor, the Department of Justice has today issued a general guidance document (LEP Guidance) which sets forth the compliance standards that recipients must follow to ensure that the programs and activities they normally provide in English are accessible to LEP persons and thus do not discriminate on the basis of national origin in violation of Title VI of the Civil Rights Act of 1964, as amended, and its implementing regulations.

As described in the LEP Guidance, recipients "must take reasonable steps to ensure meaningful access to their programs and activities by LEP persons."
\*\*\*

390. On February 1994, President Clinton issued Executive Order 12898 to all departments and agencies of the Federal Government directing them to take action to address environmental justice with respect to minority populations and low-income populations. Agencies were directed, among other things, to address disproportionate human health or environmental effects of programs on such populations, to collect additional data on these subjects, and to coordinate their efforts through a newly established inter-agency working group.
\*\*\*

391. While most environmental laws do not expressly address potential impacts on low-income and minority communities, Executive Order 12898 directs the

Environmental Protection Agency (EPA) "[to the greatest extent practicable and permitted by law... [to] make achieving environmental justice part of its mission by identifying and addressing, as appropriate, disproportionately high and adverse human health or environmental effects of its programs, policies, and activities on minority populations and low-income populations."

\* \* \*

446. "Changing America: Indicators of Social and Economic Well-Being by Race and Hispanic Origin", documents current differences in key indicators of well- being including education, labor markets, economic status, health, crime and criminal justice, and housing and neighborhoods. The information in this publication provides a factual base on which to build dialogue about race.

# Appendix 07-02

## EXCERPTS FROM
## THE WHITE PRIVILEGE SHADOW REPORT[86]

Introduction [87] (Written by Makani Themba-Nixon)

A. OVERVIEW OF PROBLEMS WITH THE INITIAL US ICERD REPORT
\*\*\*

4. The government report ignored the ICERD framework.

5. The government failed to undertake an adequate assessment of policies and practices as outlined by the Convention. Furthermore, it limited what examination it did undertake on the Federal or national level.

\*\*\*

7. The report makes several misleading claims including

a. The government claims that it has met its obligations outlined in Article 7. There has been no government public education campaign on these issues.

b. Throughout the document the government describes the role of courts to limit and proscribe policies that address racial discrimination as if courts operate independently, away from government influence and outside of the framework of law and public debate.

c. [T]here are a number of laws that are inconsistent with United States obligations under ICERD and further, that government action has played a primary role in "creating or perpetuating racial discrimination."

8. Throughout the United States report, the government has attempted to rationalize what is actually policy-based discrimination (e.g., its failure to address disparate racial impact in public education, health, and more) as a result of legal conditions beyond its control (decisions made by "independent" courts) and even the purview of ICERD.

\*\*\*

SUMMARY OF ISSUES RAISED IN THIS REPORT REGARDING UNITED STATES NONCOMPLIANCE WITH THE CONVENTION

9. The UNITED STATES Government has not undertaken any "effective measures to review governmental, national and local policies" (Article II (I)(c).

10. The United States Government has not undertaken "special and concrete measures to ensure the adequate development and protection of certain racial groups" (Article II)(2) despite a preponderance of evidence of racism from both non-governmental organizations and government agencies.

11. The United States Government has not acted in compliance with provisions in Article 5 to prohibit and eliminate discrimination in such areas as: equal treatment

before the law; right to housing, public health, medical care and other social services; and equal access to public services.

12. The United States Government does not assure "effective protection and remedies [or] adequate reparation or satisfaction for any damage suffered" (Article 6).

13. The United States Government has not undertaken "effective measures particularly in the fields of teaching, education, culture, and information, with a view to combating prejudices."

# Appendix 07-03

## SELECTED PARAGRAPHS FROM THE SUMMARY RECORD OF THE 1475TH MEETING: UNITED NATIONS COMMITTEE ON ICERD: UNITED STATES OF AMERICA. 22/08/2001[88]

Concluding Observations of the Committee on the Elimination of Racial Discrimination: United States of America 14/08/2001 A/56/18, 380-407 (Concluding Observations/comments) Committee on the Elimination of Racial Discrimination, 59th Session July 30 - August 17, 2001.
* * *

12. Mr. PILLAI stressed that education in its entirety was the most basic and critical component of a State's efforts to promote racial equality and harmony, and its impact on health, employment and poverty could not be overemphasized. The United States Government would pay due regard to the various reports circulated by a number of civil society organizations relating to racial discrimination in education.
***

13. Ms. BRITZ said she wondered in general, how, in a country with such a large amount of anti-discrimination legislation, such a high degree of inequality could still exist in matters such as health care, criminal justice, educational opportunities and housing; and whether the legislation itself had particular weaknesses or whether it was not the appropriate cure for racial inequality. A more specific question concerned discrepancy as to what was understood by discrimination, as defined in Article 1, Paragraph 1 of the Convention and further clarified in the Committee's General Recommendation XIV. According to a Supreme Court interpretation (Paragraph 235 of the Report), discriminatory intent, as well as disparate impact, had to be shown in order to demonstrate a constitutional violation of equal protection. But intent was much more difficult to prove than impact. Reading between the lines of the Report, it was clear that its authors were aware of that discrepancy.
***

21. Ms. JANUARY-BARDILL, while recognizing that the Fifth and Fourteenth Amendments to the Constitution prohibited racial discrimination on the part of any public authority (Report, Paragraph 77) and that there existed a vast legal environment for implementation of measures relating to the Convention (Report, Paragraphs 84-144), expressed concern that, despite the existence of the legal framework and implementing mechanisms, numerous factors continued to have a negative effect on implementation (Report, Paragraphs 71 and 72). High levels of institutional and systemic racial discrimination persisted, as evidenced, for example, by lack of educational opportunity, discrimination within the criminal justice system, unequal health care for minorities and disadvantaged women, and continued inequality for the African American population. She stressed that covert racial discrimination was sometimes more dangerous than overt racial

discrimination and its effects more devastating. She therefore wondered who was to blame for factors that continued to affect implementation, inadequate funding of public services, and how local, state and federal authorities were reacting to violations of legislation at the institutional level. The questions also remained regarding who would address issues relating to equal access and ensure that equal treatment continued.

\*\*\*

23. Mr. YUTZIS, referring to Article 5 and the obligation of State Parties to guarantee the rights of all, noted that among the factors affecting implementation described in the report was the "under-funding of Federal and State civil rights agencies (Report, Paragraph 71b). He requested statistics on levels of funding for human rights activities, specifically statistics expressed not only in actual figures, which were relative and could be misleading, but also as a percentage of gross domestic product, which would provide a better understanding of the priority and resources allotted to human rights questions, noting that the statistics should preferably be broken down by areas, such as housing, health, etc.

\*\*\*

31. [Mr. THORNBERRY] On the question of affirmative action, Article 2, paragraph 2, of the Convention made it very clear that special measures to remedy disadvantage were mandatory when the circumstances so warranted. Such were the special measures taken by the United States Government on behalf of Native Hawaiians (Report, Paragraph 48). Although the Supreme Court had cast doubt on Congress' authority to legislate in such a manner, and although various lower-court judgments [sic] had ordered an end to other affirmative action programs (Report, Paragraph 275), the notion of equality employed in the Convention was one of equality in fact, which implied that those at a disadvantage must be treated differently and that such affirmative treatment could legitimately be ended only when the need for it had clearly ceased. That goal had not been reached in the United States, as indicated in paragraph 276 of the Report.

# APPENDIX 07-04

## SELECTED CONCLUDING OBSERVATIONS OF THE COMMITTEE ON THE ELIMINATION OF RACIAL DISCRIMINATION: UNITED STATES OF AMERICA. 14/08/2001[89]

The Committee on the Elimination of Racial Discrimination issued a report outlining its observations regarding compliance by the United States. Several paragraphs related to health are below:

\*\*\*

380. The Committee considered the initial, second and third periodic reports of the United States of America (ICERD/C/351/Add.l), submitted as one document, which were due on 20 November 1995, 1997 and 1999 respectively, at its 1474th, 1475th and 1476th meetings (ICERD/C/SR.1474-1476) on August 3 and August 6, 2001. At its 1486th meeting (ICERD/C/SR.1486) on August 13, 2001, it adopted the following concluding observations:

\*\*\*

383. In view of the dialogue held, the Committee wishes to emphasize that irrespective of the relationship between the Federal authorities, on the one hand, and the States, which have extensive jurisdiction and legislative powers, on the other hand, with regard to The Federal Government's obligation under the Convention it has the responsibility to ensure the ICERD's implementation on its entire territory.

\*\*\*

390. The Committee, concerned by the absence of specific legislation implementing the provisions of the Convention in domestic laws, recommends that the State Party undertake the necessary measures to ensure the consistent application of the provisions of the Convention at all levels of government.

\*\*\*

392. The Committee also notes, with concern, the position of the State Party with regard to its obligation under Article 2, Paragraphs (c) and (d), to bring to an end all racial discrimination by any person, group or organization, and that the prohibition and punishment of purely private conduct lies beyond the scope of governmental regulation, even in situations where the personal freedom is exercised in a discriminatory manner. The Committee recommends that the State Party review its legislation so as to render liable to criminal sanctions the largest possible sphere of private conduct that is discriminatory on racial or ethnic grounds.

\*\*\*

393. The Committee draws the attention of the State Party to its obligations under the Convention and, in particular, to Article I, Paragraph I, and general recommendation XIV, to undertake to prohibit and to eliminate racial discrimination in all its forms, including practices and legislation that may not be discriminatory in purpose, but in effect. The Committee recommends that the State Party take all appropriate measures to review existing legislation and Federal, State and local policies to ensure effective protection against any form of racial discrimination and any unjustifiably disparate impact.

\*\*\*

398. While noting the numerous laws, institutions, and measures designed to eradicate racial discrimination affecting the equal enjoyment of economic, social and cultural rights, the Committee is concerned about persistent disparities in the enjoyment of, in particular, the right to adequate housing, equal opportunities for education and employment, and access to public and private health care. The Committee recommends that the State Party take all appropriate measures, including special measures according to Article 2, Paragraph 2, of the Convention, to ensure the right of everyone, without discrimination as to race, color, or national or ethnic origin, to the enjoyment of the rights contained in Article 5 of the Convention.

\*\*\*

399. With regard to affirmative action, the Committee notes with concern the position taken by the State Party that the provisions of the Convention permit but do not require States Parties to adopt affirmative action measures to ensure the adequate development and protection of certain racial, ethnic or national groups. The Committee emphasizes that the adoption of special measures by States Parties when the circumstances so warrant, such as in the case of persistent disparities, is an obligation stemming from Article 2, Paragraph 2, of the Convention.

# Chapter Eight

# USING REPARATIONS TO REPAIR BLACK HEALTH

Before one can engage in a discussion about repairing "Black health" and reparations, one needs to understand the definition of reparation. Too many Americans of all races view reparation as a paycheck, some undetermined amount of money for harm that was inflicted decades or centuries ago. This is the "damage" view of reparations. The problem with this view is that it is incomplete and in many ways destructive. Damage requires payment of money to the injured parties, and once the payment is made the obligation is settled. This is true even if the amount paid is inadequate to compensate for the harm.

Rather, reparation is an obligation to make the repairs necessary to correct current harms that arise from past wrongs. This is the "equity" view of reparations. This view is much more expansive than merely calculating economic harm and writing a check. *Under the equity view, the focus is not on money but on repairing the harm.* Thus, no money is given to the person injured but rather the harm is repaired. Under this view, reparation restores hope and dignity and rebuilds the community. It does so because before reparations can be undertaken there must be a clear acknowledgment and assessment of the harm. Reparations for Blacks, conceived as repair, can help mend this larger tear in the social fabric for the benefit of both Blacks and mainstream America. This view allows responsibility and action by all parties. It allows healing to begin by cleansing the souls of Blacks and Whites. Thus, when speaking about reparations, one means taking up the burden to eliminate the "Black health deficit" something that has its roots in slavery.

> "This the American Black man [and woman] knows: [the] fight here is a fight to the finish. Either he dies or wins. If he wins, it will be by no subterfuge or evasion of amalgamation. He will enter modem civilization here in America as Black man [and woman] on terms of perfect and unlimited equality with any White [person], or [we] will enter not at all. Either exterminates root and branch, or absolute equality. There can be no compromise. This is the last great battle of the West."[1]

Institutional racism in the United States is as old as the nation itself. Institutional racism comprises those policies, practices, and activities that injure or damage a person or group because of that person's or that group's race. Like those of individual racism, the effects of institutional racism can derive from intentional or unintentional conduct. For Blacks who face disproportionate rates of morbidity and mortality, intent of the conduct is irrelevant. When medical institutions erect racial barriers to access and provide racially disparate treatment of Blacks, they thereby injure the people that those institutions purport to help. The institutions are racist.

Blacks have not profited from the early advances in health care as much as Whites have. In fact, the gap between Black health and White health has widened over the last ten years.[2] Racism has compromised Black health independent of other factors that contribute to excessively high rates of Black morbidity and mortality. The nation has much to lose by its persistent neglect of Black health care.

Institutional racism within a system that professes to be dedicated to improving the life of all Americans is a powerful indictment of that system.[3] Despite having ultimate responsibility for providing health care for all Americans, and despite a belief in this country that all persons have certain rights to life, liberty and health, American health care institutions have contributed to and perpetuated racism. As Tom Wicker noted:

> "What White Americans have never fully understood, but what the Negro can never forget, is that White society is deeply [racist]. White institutions created it, White institutions maintained it, and White societies condone it."[4]

If health care institutions are to overcome the stigma of racism, they must develop specific solutions. To raise Black health to a comparable level with White health, there must be a delivery system designed and implemented to effectively address the health issues of Blacks. The "Slave Health Deficit" will be removed only if the United States makes a significant and sustained commitment. The same level of commitment the United States used to land on the moon it must now use in undertaking whatever actions that are necessary to repair Black health. Specifically, to eliminate the "Slave Health Deficit", the government will need to 1) eliminate the inequities in disease, illness and death, 2) assure access to quality health care, and 3) eliminate racial discrimination in health care and health research.

# ELIMINATE INEQUITIES IN DISEASE, ILLNESS AND DEATH

Eliminating the inequities in sickness and death will require 1) education and prevention through targeted Health Care services, 2) provision of a livable wage for all persons and families, 3) eradication of environmental hazards, and 4) eliminate targeting by the tobacco and alcohol industries on the community.

## Assure the Appropriate Education and Prevention Services

The health inequities among Blacks have been well established. Until the last 10 years, eliminating health inequities has not been a goal of the government, the health care industry, or American society. For instance, the United States health population goals in *Healthy People 2000* [5] focused on reducing, not eliminating, the inequities. It was not until *Healthy People 2010*[6] that eliminating health inequities became a goal with the same health goals for Whites being set for Blacks.

Targeting health care services to Blacks would focus resources on Black's specific health problems. States could design and promote services for Blacks. In particular, a long-term, sustained effort must be undertaken to eliminate health inequities in diabetes, cardiovascular disease, maternal and infant mortality, HIV/AIDS, cancer, oral health, mental health, drug, alcohol and tobacco addiction, asthma, and violence (including domestic violence).

Targeting health care services to Blacks would direct resources to the amelioration of their specific health problems. For example, funds could be allocated to open clinics in Black communities.[7] Targeting services to specific population groups has already been implemented in the areas of maternal-child health, family planning, and children with disabilities. Clinics have been used to serve the residents of low-income communities who are disproportionately black.

Congress passed the Disadvantaged Minority Health Improvement Act (DMHIA), to improve the health status of people from disadvantaged backgrounds, including racial and ethnic minorities, and to increase the numbers of minorities in health professions.[8] These goals were to be accomplished by establishing an Office of Minority Health (OMH) and by giving the Office funding authority. The establishment of the OMG within the Office of the Assistant Secretary for Health in the Department of Health and Human Services was codified in Title XVII of the Public Health Service Act.

The DMHIA provided for a broad range of activities relating to improving the health status of Blacks and other minorities. For instance, the OMH is required to establish objectives for, and to coordinate all activities related to, minority health, including disease prevention, health promotion, service delivery, and research with the Department of Health and Human Services. Furthermore, OMH is required to enter into agreements with public health service agencies in order to increase the participation of minorities in those services and promotional programs.

The DMHIA also established a program of primary health care services for residents of public housing.[9] DMHIA revived and extended the program entitled Centers for Excellence in Health Professions Education for Minorities.[10] The Act established loans, scholarship, and loan repayment programs for people from disadvantaged backgrounds who are pursuing a degree in a health profession.[11] It revised and extended the authority for the National Center for Health Statistics and it created a new program of grants for data studies on the health of ethnic and racial minorities.[12] The DMHIA established grants to encourage minorities to serve as health professionals in their communities.[13] It expanded Community and Migrant Health Centers[14] and created a program of grants for improving the health of Pacific Islanders.[15] Furthermore, Congress earmarked funding for the improvement of Black health. However, the Act has not been sufficiently funded to achieve the desired effects.

States could take steps to design services for Blacks. In 1991-1992, only nineteen states had minority health agencies. Seven states[16] established these minority health entities by statute[17], four states[18] established them by executive order,[19] and the appointed health officer of the eight remaining states established the entities.[20] However, the budgets for these minority health agencies indicate that the agencies are more accurately described as "advisors" on minority health rather than "service providers". In 1991-1992, only three states had budgets that exceeded $500,000[21, 22], for these agencies and eleven states budgeted less than $100,000.[23]

An essential public health approach needs to include primary, secondary and tertiary care. Primary care services prevent harm by changing individual and collective behavior through a focus on education and prevention. For instance, outlawing the sale of alcohol within 10 miles of schools would be a primary service since it would reduce the purchase and consumption of alcohol. Secondary services are designed to intervene early and minimize harm. For instance, early prenatal care can encourage women who are pregnant to stop drinking early in their pregnancy, thus reducing the harm to the unborn child. Tertiary services involve rectifying the harm that has been done and can involve policy or legislative action. For instance, tertiary services would involve alcohol treatment programs for pregnant women and those who were unwilling to use the service they could face commitment.

*Reparations should assure that the full spectrum of educational, preventive and treatment health services and actions are available to the Black community.*

## Assure a Livable Wage

As discussed above, health status is caused by many factors, including individual behavior. However, recognizing the importance of individual behavior in health status does not at all minimize the need to focus on systemic influences such as poverty and racism.

Poverty affects housing choice, job choice, nutrition, and education. Since Blacks are disproportionately poor, the elimination of poverty is essential to improving their health.[24] Inadequate income is also a problem for the "working poor" who are also disproportionately Blacks.[25] The working poor are people whose full-time, year-round earnings are so meager that despite their best efforts, they cannot afford decent housing, nutrition, health care, or child care. Poverty and the problems of the working poor could be eliminated by assuring everyone in the United States a "livable wage", not merely a minimum wage.[26] A "livable wage" provides enough income to pay for the necessities of shelter, food, clothing, health care, child care, and transportation.[27] Without income based on a livable wage, people suffer not only a lack of dignity but also a variety of social and health problems. A 2000 study conducted by the San Francisco Department of Public Health reported that livable wages diminish mortality rates, decrease unnecessary hospitalization of the poor, eliminate some costs associated with caring for the homeless, and save lives.[28]

*Livable wages are the cornerstone to eliminating the "Slave Health Deficit" and reparations should be in the form of assuring a livable wage..*

## Eradicate Environmental Hazards

A livable wage, however, must be accompanied by the eradication of environmental racism. Of particular importance to Black health is the locating of environmental hazards and toxic dumps in Black communities as well as hazards in the workplace and the home.[29]

Studies have documented that hazardous waste landfills are disproportionately located in Black communities.[30] In fact, such studies have concluded that race, more than poverty, land values, or home ownership, is a predictor as to the location of hazardous waste facilities.[31] Race is independent of social-economic class in the distribution of air pollution, consumption of contaminated fish, location of municipal landfills and incinerators, abandoned toxic waste dumps, cleanup of superfund sites, lead poisoning in children, and asthma.[32] In 1987, more than 15 million of the United States' Blacks (57%) resided in communities with one or more uncontrolled toxic-waste sites.[33] Blacks, faced with a polluter moving into their backyard, often have the least mobility because of limited financial resources,[34] exclusionary zoning practices,[35] and discrimination in employment and housing.[36]

In addition, Blacks are disproportionately represented in jobs with the greatest environmental hazards, such as fast food, pesticide-intensive farm labor,[37] rubber making,[38] coke production,[39] battery manufacturing, lead plating and smelting,[40] industrial laundering and janitorial work.[41] In the workplace, Black men have a 27% greater chance than White men of facing safety hazards and a 60% greater chance of facing health hazards.[42] In fact, even controlling for the level of job training and education, Blacks find themselves in substantially more dangerous occupations than Whites.[43]

Finally, lead poisoning in the home is a serious health issue for Black children. Blood lead levels in urban Black children under the age of five significantly exceed the levels found in White children of the same age living in the same cities.[44] This inequity persists across income levels. Thus, for families with annual incomes less than $6000, 68% of Black children and 36% of White children had unsafe levels of lead in their blood. In families earning more than $15,000, 38% of Black children and 12% of White children had excessive levels of lead in their blood.[45]

*Reparations should be used to remove toxic dumps and landfills from Black communities or to completely relocate the communities to a safe environment. Reparations should make work places safer and eliminate lead paint from all housing.*

## Eliminate the Impact of Tobacco

The primary focus of the tobacco settlement and the resulting legislation was to decrease the number of youth who smoke.[46] Certainly, decreasing underage smoking is a commendable goal, but it remains insufficient for the Black community. Underage smoking has been on the decline in Black communities for many years. Only 1% of Black girls are frequent smokers compared to 20% of White girls.[47] Black boys also smoke at lower rates than Whites, 9% compared to

18%.[48] This racial gap in smoking remains consistent across education and economic lines. [49] Thus, an agreement that focused primarily on underage smoking and advertising failed to focus on the most significant problem for Blacks--adult smoking caused by targeting the Black community.[50]

The settlement and the resulting legislation failed to mention Blacks and their "special" relationship with the tobacco industry. The goal of "decreas[ing] tobacco use by all Americans by encouraging public education and smoking cessation programs and to decrease the exposure of individuals to environmental (second-hand) smoke" is worthwhile.[51] However, just as the industry targeted the Black community for the sale of its product, the remedies from the settlement should also be targeted to the Black community.

*Reparation would result in: (1) funding culturally-specific smoking cessation programs targeted toward Blacks, (2) funding biomedical research specifically addressing the issues of Blacks' addiction and dependence, including the impact of menthol and flavors, (3) funding Black events historically supported by tobacco industries, (4) disclosure of all information (past, present and future) related to menthol, flavors or the targeting of the Black community, and (5) establishment of a Tobacco Injury Compensation Fund for addicted smokers*

# ASSURE ACCESS TO QUALITY HEALTH CARE

Eliminating the inequities between Black Americans and White Americans regarding the rates of sickness and death will require access to quality care. Assuring this access will require: 1) providing universal health care, 2) locating adequate health care facilities within the Black community, 3) training a competent health care workforce to work in Black communities, 4) ensuring cultural competence in the health care workforce, and 5) increasing knowledge about Black health and translating that knowledge into effective clinical practice.

## Provide Universal Health Care

The United States and South Africa are the only major industrialized nations without a universal health insurance system. In the United States, instead of universal health care, there exists a scheme of employer-financed insurance and government programs. In 1965, Congress responded to medical insurance problems by creating Medicare and Medicaid. Congress established Medicare to provide medical care for the elderly and established Medicaid to provide health care to the "deserving poor".[52]

Since 1965, Medicare and Medicaid have grown significantly. Medicare currently accounts for approximately 35% of national health care expenditures and 40% of hospital revenues.[53] Patient's ability to pay is irrelevant.[54] Yet Medicare and Medicaid's impact extends well beyond the program. For example, other institutional purchasers of health care, such as private insurers, follow Medicare and Medicaid's lead with regard to medical technology and payment schedules.[55] Despite these programs, the United States still has more than 45 million Americans without the means to afford health care.[56]

Lack of health insurance is a particular concern for Blacks who are less likely to have employer-financed insurance.[57] In 1985, only 47% of Blacks had employment-related insurance, compared to 62% of non-Blacks.[58] While public programs such as Medicaid and Medicare are important sources of health care coverage for many low-income Whites and Blacks, these programs do not reach all of the uninsured poor.[59] Only 28% of Blacks have public insurance.[60] In fact, 25% of Blacks have no health insurance.[61] Even more disturbing is the rise in the number of uninsured Blacks and the widening gap between the Black uninsured and the White uninsured. For instance, while the proportion of uninsured non-elderly Whites increased only 3% from 1977 to 1987 (from 12% to 15%), the proportion of uninsured non-elderly Blacks increased 7% (from 18% to 25%) during that same period.[63]

Since private health insurance coverage is linked to employment, racial barriers to employment are one explanation for the striking inequity in insurance coverage. For example, in 1990, the Black unemployment rate was 24% higher than the White unemployment rate.[64] Even when employed, Blacks are more likely to be in lower paying jobs that do not provide employer-based health insurance.[65] In 1988, the mean earnings for White males was 36% higher than that that of Black males.[66]

Another factor affecting insurance coverage is the higher percentage of Black families headed by a single adult.[67] In 1990, 61% of Black families with children under the age of 18 were single caregivers, (i.e. single parent, single foster parent, single relative, single grandparent) compared to 23% of similar White families.[68] Families with two working adults are more likely to have at least one adult with employer-based insurance.[69]

However, while the absence of health insurance is common among lower- income people, race is an independent variable in whether or not an individual will be insured. In fact, the racial difference in the proportion of uninsured is most marked at higher incomes.[70] For example, low income Blacks are uninsured at about the same rate as poor/low income White Americans; however, middle/high income Blacks are almost twice as likely to be uninsured than middle/high income Whites.[71] Of poor people, 36% of Whites are uninsured compared to 35% of Blacks. Of low income people, 31% of Whites are uninsured, compared to 30% of Blacks. Finally, among middle/high income people, 9% of Whites are uninsured, compared to 16% of Blacks.[72] Blacks are more likely to be uninsured because they are more likely to be unemployed or employed in low-paying positions that do not offer health care benefits. For instance, in 1989, 30.7% of Blacks were poor, compared to 12.8% of Whites. In 1990, the Black unemployment rate (11.3%) was 2.4 times Whites (4.7%).[73]

Expanding insurance coverage so that everyone will have either employer- or government-based insurance is one way of ending inequities in the health care system.[74] There has been no shortage of proposals for increasing insurance coverage. The two main proposals are employer-mandated coverage and the expansion of Medicaid.[75] However, even combining employer- mandated and Medicaid expansion, an estimated 2.1 million Black Americans will remained uninsured.[76] Thus, a third proposal, universal health insurance, is the most desirable alternative.[77]

Since the lack of health insurance explains some of the inequity in the use of health care services between Black Americans and White Americans, Expanding insurance coverage is certain to increase the use of health care services. For example, in 1977, uninsured Black Americans in the South saw physicians an average of 1.5 times a year, while insured Black Americans saw physicians an average of 2.8 times a year.[78] However, while Black Americans' physician visits almost doubled for those with insurance, the racial differential between Black Americans and White Americans remained unchanged.[79] In other words, uninsured White Americans had 150% more visits per year than uninsured Black Americans, and insured White Americans had 132% more visits per year than insured Black Americans.[80]

From a Black American perspective, expanding insurance coverage does little more than provide people with a piece of paper that says that they may obtain health care if they can find someone to accept the coverage. Expanding coverage does nothing to ensure that a provider in the community will furnish health care, nor does the expansion solve the problem of disparate medical treatment. Nevertheless, universal health insurance or universal health care removes the major economic barriers to health coverage.

*Reparations should be used to expand insurance coverage so that all Blacks have either employer-based or government-based comprehensive, insurance or a system of universal access.[81]*

# Locate Sufficient Health Care Facilities in the Black communities

Racial barriers to access to health care are largely based on the availability of services in a community. Hospitals that serve the Black community are closing, relocating, or privatizing. In a study conducted between 1937 and 1977, researchers showed that the likelihood of a hospital's closing was directly related to the percentage of Blacks in the population in the surrounding community.[82] Throughout the 1980s many hospitals relocated from heavily Black communities to predominantly White suburban communities.[83] A total of 210 hospitals either closed or relocated during the period studied.[84] A disproportionate number of the hospitals that closed or relocated were originally located in predominantly Black communities.[85]

This loss of services to the community results in Blacks losing some or all of their access to health care. Geographic availability and proximity are important determinants to seeking health care services early. If Blacks fail to seek health care as soon as it is needed, they are more likely to be sicker when they do enter the system. The costs to the patient and for the system to provide services are then likely to be greater. Therefore, the loss of services forces Blacks, and society as a whole, to pay more for health care.[86]

Another devastating trend for the Black community is the privatization of public hospitals. Hundreds of public and non-profit hospitals have elected to restructure as private, for-profit corporations.[87] As public hospitals, many were obligated to provide uncompensated care under the Hill-Burton Act.[88] As private hospitals, these institutions are most likely to discontinue providing health services to indigent populations[89] and essential primary health care services for Black communities.[90]

The problem of limited resources has plagued the Black community since the days of enslavement. Historically, Black communities have responded to the problem by establishing Black hospitals. In the 1930s there were more than 200 Black hospitals in the United States.[91] Blacks relied on these institutions to "heal and save their lives."[92] Now, these institutions are fighting for their survival. By the 1960s, only 90 Black hospitals remained in the country. .[93] Between 1961 and 1988, 57 Black hospitals closed and 14 others merged, converted, or consolidated.[94] By 1991, only 12 hospitals continued to "struggle daily just to keep their doors open."[95] As a result of closures, relocations, and privatization, many Blacks are left with limited access or no access to hospitals.

*Reparations should provide adequate number of hospitals, clinics, alcohol and drug detoxification centers, dental health clinics, and mental health clinics in the Black community.*

## Assure An Adequate and Competent Health Care Workforce in the Black Community

A central aspect of access to care is the availability of health care providers including physicians, nurses, pharmacists, dentists and many other professionals who serve Black communities

Proximity promotes utilization. Very few White physicians have offices in the Black community. Consequently, Black physicians have been called upon to fill the availability gap. However, the effort has been unsuccessful. Without local physicians and providers, Blacks are likely to delay seeking health care. That delay can result in greater severity of illness, increased health care cost, and greater mortality.

Given the increased morbidity and mortality among Blacks, there should be more, not fewer, health care providers in Black communities and more Blacks in health care professions. Scrutiny of the physician listings in the Yellow Pages of any major city clearly indicates that many do not serve the Black community.

Furthermore, although Blacks represent 13% of the population, only 3% of the physicians in the United States are Blacks.[96] A mere 2.5% of the dentists in the United States are Blacks,[97] and only 3.6% of pharmacists are Blacks.[98] This lack of representation is a serious problem for Black communities who rely on Black physicians.[99] In fact, 75% of Black physicians practice in or near Black communities, and 90% of Black physicians have patient loads that are at least 50% Black.[100] This shortage of Black health care providers results in sicker people and higher health care costs. If Blacks are sicker, they need more physicians, not fewer. Yet, the same limited availability of providers and hospitals to service Black communities exists.[101] Black health professionals have historically practiced in low-income areas in service to minorities. Black health professionals are more likely to be general practitioners and practice primary care.[102]

In addition, even programs like Medicaid do not necessarily expand access since many primary care providers either do not accept Medicaid or limit the number of Medicaid patients that they will accept. It is only natural to look to the Black physicians to "fill" this gap.

The shortage of Black professionals also limits Black input into the health care system.[103] Empowerment through input diminishes the need for others to act on the behalf of the black community. The number of health professionals from disadvantaged backgrounds should be increased in the interest of improving the access of similarly disadvantaged people to health services.[104]

The control of health care distribution is in the hands of the individual physician, that control is influenced and limited by law, hospital practices and policies, the American Medical Association, the medical organization of the physician's practice, and the insurance industry, particularly managed care.. Many Blacks have attempted to influence the system including the National Medical Association, but with so few Black health care professionals, their voice is virtually inaudible. This lack of sufficient number of Blacks perpetuates White ignorance about Black health. As a result, when health care issues are defined, policy makers overlook or minimize Blacks' health concerns.

Clearly, in order for health inequities to disappear more providers have to be available in Black communities. This lack of Black representation in health care is traceable to segregation in medical schools.[105] For instance, a Black did not graduate from an American medical school until 1847.[106] While nine medical schools admitted Blacks before the Civil War, most did not.[107] As late as 1971, 21 of 85 medical schools still had no Black students.[108] Even with the admission of more Blacks to predominantly White schools, Howard University, Meharry Medical School, Morehouse School of Medicine and Charles Drew Medical Schools (Black medical schools) still train a disproportionate number of Black physicians.[109]

Assuring an adequate health care workforce could be done by providing scholarships for Blacks to attend health care professional schools, by providing grants to universities and colleges in order to increase their graduation rate of persons who will work in urban areas, by increasing the capacity of historically Black colleges to train and graduate students, by increasing health care reimbursement for services provided to inner-city residents, and by providing economic incentives to doctors and other health care professionals to locate in Black communities.[110]

*Reparations should be used to assure the availability of adequate numbers of all types of health care providers in the Black community.*

## Assure Cultural Competence of the Health Care Workforce.

A person does not have meaningful access to health care if that person does not receive health care within his or her cultural context.[111] The term "culture" has been defined as an "integrated system of learned patterns of behavior, ideas, and products characteristic of a society".[112] It is a set of learned values, beliefs and behaviors that are common to a social group. "Culture provides the basic framework by which people interpret their surroundings, interpret the behavior of the people around them, and interpret the events that befall them."[113] Race, nationality, native language, education, occupation, religion, income, and area of origin contribute to a person's culture.[114] These factors affect values, beliefs, and behaviors. A subculture consists of the values, beliefs and behaviors that are particular to a subgroup within a culture.[115]

For centuries Americans indulged in the fantasy that Native Americans, White immigrants, and the descendants of African slaves blended into one great "melting pot" to become Americans. While it is true that there are American cultural similarities common to all groups, this country has always had a diverse population of races, ethnic groups, subcultures, and religions.

Because a person holds an insurance policy or has a provider is no guarantee that the person will receive the health care that he or she deserves. The medical care system is a microcosm of the middle-class, middle-aged, White subculture. The system is tailored to individual autonomy rather than family involvement.[116]

The existing health care system has not promoted family involvement. The system focuses on the individual and illness care rather than family and wellness care. This is unfortunate since the concept of family has a special influence on wellness care and health promotion.[117] Furthermore, "family" has different meanings across cultures and ethnic groups. Different cultural priorities affect the degree to which immediate and extended families participate in treatment decisions. Particularly offensive to some cultures may be the White method of personal decision-making that focuses on the individual to the exclusion of the family. For many Blacks, an illness is a family affair.[118] To provide access to quality health care, providers must appreciate cultural differences in kinship terms, in role expectations, and in the role of the family in decision-making.[119]

The current health care system assumes that the patient has a basic trust in the system instead of distrust.[120] The existing health care system supposes that a patient will accept that a medical provider knows best and will act in the patient's best interest. However, many Blacks have no faith in the health care system. Blacks' distrust is rooted in slavery, sharecropping, peonage, lynching, Jim Crow laws, disenfranchisement, residential segregation, job discrimination, insufficient health care, and unethical scientific experimentation.[121] For instance, Blacks may believe that managed care providers will deny or withhold necessary services. Consequently, after years of neglect and cultural insensitivity, there is often a deep distrust of the health care system. This is true even when health care providers are Black.[122]

Furthermore, the current health care system relies on a western, White concept of communication.[123] Communication is indispensable to seeking and obtaining quality health care. A person may have doctors in the community, money in his or her pocket, and insurance, but if health care provider cannot communicate with his or her patient, the provider cannot deliver effective quality health care. The manner in which different cultures communicate is very important. Speakers of different languages see and conceive reality differently.[124] Americans' views of health care are shaped by their language. To the extent that a person's primary language is not English, communication and language barriers will exist.[125]

The American health care system is built on a western European concept of illness and wellness.[126] For instance, health care professionals who treat elderly immigrants need to understand and respect the immigrants' cultural beliefs about etiology and appropriate treatments for illness.[127] Consequently, the more a patient departs from the cultural prototype (middle-class, middle-aged, White), the more likely the person will not have meaningful access to health care. Merely providing health care coverage does nothing to assure that Blacks will have access to culturally competent care.[128]

One barrier to culturally competent care is some physicians' negative perceptions about Blacks.[129] This barrier exists in part because the health care system is designed for the cultural needs of middle-class Whites. Blacks seem less compliant and more difficult to care for because their needs and problems in accessing care are different.[130] The problem, however, is not Blacks, but instead is the health care system's inability to meet the needs of diverse populations.[131] If increased compliance and improved health status are the goals, then the health care system must be flexible enough to accommodate a community's cultural and socioeconomic needs.[132]

Health care requires interaction between the patient and the provider. When people do not understand, speak or read English, they may avoid contact with the health care system. Although some Americans do not understand English well enough to converse with their physicians, the law does not require health care plans to overcome language barriers.[133] Language barriers can defeat the provision of health care if essential information cannot be conveyed.[134]

Communication barriers transcend the role of language in shaping reality. An emphasis on written communication does not take into consideration the preference of many people for oral or visual communication. Simply providing information (written, oral or visual) does not ensure that it will be understood. Providing written information may not be an adequate means of communicating with people who are not middle-class Whites. Furthermore, language, whether written or oral, is a major source of conflict and misunderstanding in intercultural situations. For instance, an inability to understand the cultural expressions of others can be frustrating for Blacks, discouraging them from seeking care. Even for patients who speak English as a second or third language, illness, depression, frustration, and embarrassment may cause them to revert to their native language. Culture also influences the forms of response in conversation. Similarly, a patient's emotional response to treatment will differ across cultures. Finally, culture influences which topics a person considers appropriate for conversation with a medical professional who is a stranger.

Some individuals question the existence of a "uniquely" Black bio-ethical perspective. They maintain that, since the values and beliefs held by Blacks are also held by other oppressed groups, including Native Americans, there is no such thing as a Black perspective. However, this misses or ignores an important point: perspective is merely a subjective evaluation of the relative significance of something, a point-of-view. Thus, to acknowledge a Black perspective, it is not necessary that Black values and belief systems be entirely different from those of others.

It is faulty to assume that any group shares exactly the same value system with other groups. For example, Americans do not have one ethical perspective. Rather, race, class, and gender modify the commonality of the American experience. Different groups have had different experiences that, at a minimum, modify the dominant American perspective, if not replace it with an entirely different value structure. For Blacks, the combination of slavery, segregation, and racism have resulted in a different cultural view.

Consequently, although universal health coverage makes it easier for many Blacks to seek and obtain effective health services, language barriers will continue to inhibit their use of the health care system, unless the system is required to address those concerns.[135] Communication barriers exist because of the ways in which different linguistic groups see and conceive reality. Barriers exist because of cultural differences in interpreting expressed language. Culturally different forms of response, affect, approach, and appropriateness of the topic for conversation, all maintain communication barriers. Universal coverage does not remove those barriers.

> *Reparations should be used to assure culturally competent care by requiring that 1) all health professional schools to train providers to provide culturally competent care, 2) all physicians to have a rotation during their internship and externship that focuses on providing culturally competent care, 3) all providers to take continuing educational units in cultural competency, 4) all providers to provide language interpreters and translators, 5) all health care facilities and managed care organizations complete and submit, on a regular basis, a cultural competency assessment to a regulatory agency, and 6) all health care be provided in accordance with realities of the needs of the different socioeconomic classes within the Black community.*

## Assure Health and Health Care Research on Black Issues

Despite voluminous literature describing the importance of race, ethnicity, and culture in health, health care, and treatment, there is relatively little information available on the racial, ethnic, and biological differences that affect the manifestations and treatment of certain illnesses.[136] Billions of dollars are spent each year on health research ($35.7 billion in 1995).[137] However, only a very small percentage of those funds is allocated to research on issues of particular importance to women and minorities and to research by women and Black scientists (21.5% and .37%, respectively).[138] In response to years of exclusion of minorities and women, several statutory requirements have been enacted to ensure that research protocols include a diverse population.[139] The health condition of Blacks will continue to suffer until they are included in all types of health research. The results of that research have to be translated into clinical practice without being becoming just another stereotype.

> *Reparations should be used to assure that health care research and development will be focused on the health issues of Blacks.*

# ELIMINATE RACIAL DISCRIMINATION
# IN HEALTH CARE AND HEALTH RESEARCH

Activist speak of health care inequities. But the use of the term inequities makes it sound as if the problem is something different that discrimination and it is not. Inequities in health care that is due to the conduct of a provider or an institution is discrimination and it is a civil rights issue and it needs to be treated as such.

> "It might be that civil rights laws often go un-enforced; it might be that current disparities spring from past prejudice and long standing economic differences that are not entirely reachable by law; or it might be that the law sometimes fails to reflect, and consequently fails to correct, the barriers faced by people of color." Derrick Bell[140]

Numerous federal laws address access to health care: Title XVIII (Medicare)[141] and Title XIX (Medicaid)[142] of the Social Security Act, Title IX,[143] and the Hill-Burton Act.[144] However, the only Federal law designed to eliminate racial discrimination in health care delivery is Title VI of the Civil Rights Act.[145]

Due to the inadequacy of Title VI, racial inequality in health care persists in the United States despite laws against racial discrimination.[146] On its face, Title VI should be an effective tool for eliminating racial discrimination. The Civil Rights Act of 1964 provides the legal force for desegregation efforts in health care.[147] According to Section 601 of Title VI:

> "No person in the United States, shall, on the grounds of race, color, or national origin, be excluded from participation in, be denied the benefits of, or be subject to discrimination under any program or activity receiving federal financial assistance."[148]

In short, Title VI appears to prohibit discrimination of all kinds. Still, nothing in anti-discrimination law is as simple as it appears. The Supreme Court ruled, in *Alexander v. Choate*[149], that Title VI only pertained to instances of intentional discrimination. Excluded from this definition is subtle discrimination. Subtle discrimination[150] is generally considered to be intentional based, in large part, on micro-aggressions[151], with the primary difference being the reliance on circumstantial evidence to prove intent.[152] Title VI has been analogized to Title VII and in *Lynn v. Regents*, the Court said,

> "We are saying only what Title VII commands: when plaintiffs establish that decisions regarding academic employment are motivated by discriminatory attitudes relating to race or sex, or are rooted in concepts which reflect such discriminatory attitudes, however *subtly*, courts are obligated to afford the relief provided by Title VII."[153]
> (Emphasis added)

However, the reliance on intent, subtle or direct, is particularly problematic for health care, where most discrimination is either disparate impact discrimination or "unthinking or unconscious."[154]

> "[T]he course of treatment physicians . . . recommendations to their patients may be influenced by stereotypical beliefs about the behavior of their patients. Physicians . . . may believe that poor and minority patients are more likely to break appointments and to misunderstand complex information, and less likely to adhere to their orders. These perceptions may affect, perhaps subconsciously, the decision-making process and lead physicians to refrain from orders that require patient compliance and to hesitate before recommending certain procedures if they assume the patient does not live in an environment that is conducive to the aftercare needed for the best outcomes of the procedure."[155]

While legal standards for discrimination have not always centered on intent, they do so now.[156] To prove a disparate treatment claim, an individual must show that the defendant deliberately engaged in discrimination.[157] Such a standard means that few of the discriminatory acts that occur in the health care system can be successfully litigated, since most result from "unthinking" or "unconscious" biases. Psychiatric, psychological, and legal literature generally supports the idea that in our society most contemporary discrimination is based more on unconscious bias and stereotyping rather than on conscious bigotry.[158] As suggested by Professor Charles Lawrence:

> "Traditional notions of intent do not reflect the fact that decisions about racial matters are influenced in large part by factors that can be characterized as neither intentional, in the sense that certain outcomes are self-consciously sought, nor unintentional, in the sense that the outcomes are random, fortuitous, and uninfluenced by the decision maker's beliefs, desires, and wishes."[159]

The problem confronting the legal system is that an individual who stereotypes a group is more likely to discriminate against people who fit that stereotype.[160] This stereotype-linked bias is both an automatic process and an unconscious one.[161] Furthermore, it occurs even among persons who do not have any conscious prejudices.[162] According to Professor David Williams, several factors contribute to the unbiased discrimination in health care:

> "First, healthcare providers are a part of the larger society that views racial and ethnic minorities negatively on multiple social dimensions . . . Second, research on stereotypes indicates that encounters in the healthcare setting contain ingredients that enhance the likelihood of the use of stereotypes. Stereotypes are more likely to be activated under conditions of time pressure, the need to make quick judgments, cognitive overload, task

complexity, and when the emotions of anger or anxiety are present . . . Third, . . . [physicians view their Black patients] . . . more negatively than their White counterparts. . . . Physicians viewed Black patients (compared to their White counterparts) as less likely to adhere to medical advice, less likely to be kind, intelligent, and educated, more likely to lack social support, and more likely to abuse alcohol and drugs."[163]

However, even though the discrimination is based on some unconscious or unthinking processes, an individual can change.[164] Social psychological research, reviewed here in four sections, has found that stereotyping, prejudice, and discrimination are sustained by both automatic and socially pragmatic aspects. Stereotyping, prejudice, and discrimination are individually controllable and are socially conditioned. For these reasons, these beliefs and behaviors can be changed, especially where there is appropriate incentive. Regulations and laws provide such an incentive.

Recognizing the need to broaden the interpretation of the law to encompass more than just intentional discrimination, the OCR was delegated the responsibility of enforcing Title VI. The DHHS issued interpretive regulations against disparate impact discrimination:[165]

"A recipient . . . may not . . . utilize criteria or methods of administration which have the effect of subjecting individuals to discrimination of their race, color or national origin, or have the effect of defeating or substantially impairing accomplishment of the objectives of the program as it respects individuals of a particular race, color, or national origin."[166]

The regulations defined a recipient as any public or private entity or individual that receives Federal financial assistance.[167] Federal financial assistance includes Federal money awarded through grant, loan, or contract.[168] Because of these two definitions, Title VI had the potential of having a broad effect. Once a program or individual has been found in violation of Title VI, the program or individual "must take affirmative action to overcome the effects of prior discrimination."[169] Furthermore, the regulations prohibit the following:

➤ Criteria or methods of administration which have the effect of subjecting individuals to discrimination[170]
➤ Criteria or methods of administration which have the effect of defeating or substantially impairing accomplishment of the objectives of the program[171]
➤ Difference in quality of services[172]
➤ Differences in quantity or the manner in which the benefit is provided[173]
➤ Locating services with the purpose or effect of excluding individuals from the benefits of the program[174]

In theory, then, the Title VI regulation should improve access to and quality of health care services. Title VI regulations clearly prohibit policies and practices that result in segregation within and between institutions. Title VI regulations had the potential to force health care practitioners and institutions to evaluate their policies and practices that have a disparate impact on racial minorities.

Unfortunately, because of *Alexander v. Sandoval,* and because of unique problems of health care discrimination, Title VI and its regulations are virtually useless.

In *Sandoval,* the Court held, in a five-to-four decision, that despite a line of Title VI precedents, disparate impact regulation issued under § 602 could not be enforced through a private right of action that is by an individual.[175] Only the government can bring an action for disparate impact discrimination. Since the law requires a conscious discriminatory purpose or intent, individual discrimination claims cannot assert unconscious discrimination. Without disparate impact claims, health care providers will not be "appropriately motivated" to identify and eliminate discrimination.[176]

Even without the problem with *Sandoval,* Title VI enforcement has been problematic.[177] First, although required by regulation to produce data,[178] the OCR's Title VI enforcement effort has produced little consistent data for evaluating compliance with Title VI.[179] Second, there has been "little uniformity in how different states handle Title VI requirements, little guidance, little analysis of the information collected by this process, no research and development."[180] Third, Title VI lacks specific definitions of prohibited discrimination and acceptable remedial action.[181] Fourth, the OCR has relied on individual complaints to enforce Title VI.[182] Finally, Title VI has limited application to health care treatment discrimination, since the DHHS has released private physicians who received money for treating patients covered under Medicare Part B from the provisions of Title VI.[183] Thus, under Title VI physicians who are not recipients of Federal financial assistance are not covered by Title VI.[184]

Even if the problems with Title VI enforcement did not exist and Title VI functioned perfectly, the health care industry presents unique problems that would still make Title VI ineffective. First, when racial minorities use housing and lending institutions and are denied a lease, loan, or mortgage, they are, for the most part, unaware that the provider or institution has discriminated against them. Similarly, because of the very specialized knowledge required in medical care, people can be unaware that they have been injured. Finally, the health care system, through managed care, has actually built in incentives that encourage "unconscious" discrimination. For all of these reasons, only a reformed legal structure can eliminate discrimination in health care.

> "There is substantial evidence that discrimination in health care delivery, financing, and research continues to exist. Such evidence suggests that Federal laws designed to address inequality in health care have not been adequately enforced by Federal agencies . . . [Such failure has] . . . resulted in a failure to remove the historical barriers to access to quality health care for women and minorities, which, in turn, has perpetuated these barriers."[185]

For a public health policy to be effective, state and Federal laws must be passed in order to eliminate discriminatory practices in health care. Thus, the crux of the problem, given managed care, the historical inequity in health care, and unthinking discrimination, is that the laws do not address the current barriers faced by minorities. The Executive Branch, the legislatures, and the courts are singularly reluctant to hold health care institutions and providers responsible for institutional racism.[186]

A Health Care Anti-Discrimination Act would 1) recognize multiple forms of discrimination, 2) authorize and fund testers, 3) recognize disparate impact, 4) assure fines and regulatory enforcement, 5) require a health scorecard for health agency, provider or facility, and 6) require data collection and reporting.

## Recognize Multiple Forms of Discrimination

Racial inequities in medical treatment rarely occur as a result of overt, intentional discrimination. Most racial discrimination in health care is the result of unconscious bias or the disproportionate impact of policies and practices and health care anti-discrimination law should, at a minimum, include intentional discrimination, subtle discrimination, unthinking discrimination, and disparate impact discrimination. The law should define intentional discrimination to include knowledge of disparate impact and failure to take the necessary steps to reduce that impact. Furthermore, any affirmative defenses, such as business necessity, should be limited and narrowly defined.

## Authorize and Fund The Use Of Medical Testers

To discourage health care discrimination, an "aggrieved person" should include not only the injured party, but also anyone who believes that he or she will be injured, as well as any individuals engaged as testers and organizations engaged in testing. In testing, persons pretending to be patients, who share traits or symptoms except for their race, are sent to health care facilities or providers to prove that patients of a particular race receive differential treatment.[187] For instance, in *Desnick v. American Broadcasting*, the use of test patients with concealed cameras did not support claims for trespass under Illinois law, infringement of right of privacy, or illegal wiretapping.[188] A law will allow the use of testers to prove discrimination. This is important because much health care discrimination goes unreported and undetected.

Even when discrimination is suspected, the victim will have an almost impossible time gathering adequate proof because there will be almost no opportunity to witness better treatment to a similarly situated White patient. Testing could provide both evidence for the individual's case and accurate empirical data on the overall rate at which discrimination occurs in health care.[189] Testing has been widely used to enforce Title VIII[190] which prohibits discrimination in the sale, advertising, and rental of housing.[191] However, while the use of tests under Title VIII is well-established, testing is controversial in areas such as employment discrimination under Title VII and Section 1981 of the Civil Rights Act of 1866.. [192] A statute that authorizes the use of testers will bypass debate in the courts because the Supreme Court has already ruled that "Congress may enact statutes creating legal rights, the invasion of which creates standing [the right to bring suit], although no injury would exist without the statute."[193]

## Provide Individual and Organizational Right Of Action

An anti-discrimination health care statute should provide for private and organizational rights of action. In *Alexander v. Sandoval*,[194] the Supreme Court held that Section 602 of the Civil Rights Act of 1964 implies no private right of action. Prior to *Sandoval*, private citizens enforced Federal regulations by bringing private causes of action. There are many reasons why limiting enforcement of Federal regulations to agencies may be inadequate. For instance, the DHHS may not have sufficient staff to devote the resources necessary to enforce the civil rights violations that were once handled by private parties.[195] By not being able to go to court with Administrative complaints against Federal agencies, some avenues of redress may close. The DHHS may not have the power to mandate redress for aggrieved plaintiffs.[196] Furthermore, termination of funds, the only penalty an agency can impose, is so onerous that it is highly unlikely to happen.[197] Without a private right of action, diminished enforcement may increase the number of violations of Title VI.[198] Thus, without a private right of action for disparate impact, racial discrimination in health care will be impossible to eliminate.

The private right of action would assure that individuals (including testers) would have standing to sue not only under the statute but also under any implementing regulations, thus avoiding the problem that has occurred in Federal civil rights enforcement.

An organizational right of action is essential to the occurrence of more general testing on the part of civil rights organizations. These organizations and testers would have standing to sue and could thereby recover testing costs. This would provide the incentive for civil rights organizations to create and publicize testing programs.

## Require Data Collection and Reporting

Current data collection efforts have failed to capture the diversity of racial and ethnic communities in the United States. Racial and ethnic classifications are often limited on surveys and other data collection instruments, and minorities often are misclassified on vital statistics records, surveys, and censuses.[199] It is important to collect comprehensive data on Blacks and sub-populations to fully understand the health status of all people and to recognize barriers to their quality health care.[200] The lack of data makes it difficult to conduct research studies and comparative analyses.[201] Furthermore, the lack of a uniform data collection method complicates the task of collecting an accurate and specific description of racial discrimination in health care. The existing body of data does not allow for the regular gathering of racial inequity data on provider and institutional behavior.[202]

Collecting health status and health care data, disaggregated based on race, may make racism and racial discrimination in health care more visible, but the process is not without its difficulties.

First, while proper classification of illness and assessment of health status requires accurate data on members of certain populations, Native Americans, Asian Americans, and Hispanics are often misclassified.[203] One example of a classification problems may be undercounting as a result of observer bias.[204] In other words, when race is reported by an observer rather than the person or a relative, there can be significant misclassification. For instance, in Oklahoma, 28% of death certificates issued for Native American infants misclassified their race.[205]

Second, changes in racial identity pose reliability problems.[206] For instance, between 1960 and 1990 there was a six-fold increase in the American Indian population that cannot be explained by natural increase or by migration.[207]

Third, there are definitional problems, i.e., classification of multiracial people, identification of groups and subgroups, and absence of a uniform taxonomy.[208] The great diversity in health needs and actions within each study population emerges as the greatest limitation on the extent to which we are able to examine health issues.

> "Gender, age group, country of origin, documentation status, generational status or length of residence in the United States, geographic location within [the State], level of family or community support, unmeasured psychological characteristics, health status, cultural factors, and the varied availability of health insurance and health services within each population and sub-group make it impossible to examine all issues in all permutations of ethnicity and other characteristics."[209]

Fourth, some populations are difficult to count, for example, homeless. This results in a census undercount and an inflated denominator in rates.[210] "Particularly lacking are data which recognize that concepts and measurements of health may differ within racial/ethnic groups and that traditional medical practices are often at odds with Western medical practice, making standard definitions of care inappropriate."[211] Finally, other issues include the small size of some of the population groups and geographic dispersement.[212]

Given the array of potential issues, some researchers have argued against disaggregating health data by race.[213] In particular, it is argued that the use of race in health data promotes and maintains the view of race as a biological concept, or that racial categorizations perpetuate and encourage racial fragmentation or that such views can lead to a new type of scientific racism.

However, there are several compelling reasons for disaggregating health status and health care data by race. First, the use of race is not the cause but the result of racism. That is, individuals have been discriminated against based on color, and race is the terminology that has been used to capture this situation. Consequently, racism and racial discrimination will continue to exist even if terminology changes or disappears. Even though race data is not collected in the European Union, as it is in the United States, racism and racial discrimination continue to exist worldwide. Even when controlled for socioeconomic status, health status and health care differentials based on race continue to exist.

Second, racism and racial discrimination has implications for every institution and social practice. Health status is affected by racial discrimination in housing, employment, environment, education and other institutions. An equitable society cannot be established without identifying unacceptable discrimination.

Third, calls not to disaggregate data ignore the power and status differentials that exist within all racial groups.[214] This point is illustrated in light of the disproportionate percentage of people who are both poor and racially disadvantaged. Without data to support claims of discrimination Blacks will be powerless to force institutions to change.

Fourth, as long as some groups continue to suffer discrimination, it is important to monitor their well-being.[215]

Fifth, to fully understand the health status of all people and to recognize the barriers they face in obtaining quality health care, it is important to collect the most complete data on "racially disadvantaged" groups, and "sub-groups."[216] The lack of a uniform method of data collection makes obtaining an accurate and specific description of racial discrimination in health care difficult, if not impossible. Such data collection has to include data on provider and institutional behavior.

"Although not useful as a biological category, race has been and is likely to continue to be an important social category. It is what sociologists call a master status-a central determinant of social identity and obligations, as well as of access to societal rewards and resources. From our earliest health records, race has been an empirically robust predictor of variations in morbidity and mortality. Collecting the appropriate data on race can facilitate ongoing monitoring of the magnitude of differentials, enhanced understanding of their causes and the development of effective interventions to address them." [217]

Race matters. Race matters because racism and racial discrimination matters.[218] Disaggregating data based on race reveals the impact of racism and racial discrimination and, thus allows us to attack the root of the problem.

## Require A Health Report Card For Health Agency, Provider Or Facility [219]

If we are serious about eliminating racial discrimination, the systematic collection and reporting of data from each health care provider on racial inequities in the use of services and the choices of diagnostic and therapeutic alternatives would provide an additional tool in civil rights monitoring.[220] The "report card" approach would "assure accountability, consumer choice, and goal-directed action."[221] Existing and proposed health care "report cards" could be used and only need to be stratified by race.[222] As Professor Sidney Watson discussed,

"Reporting race-based data on health care is relatively easy once we get over our squeamishness about talking about race and recognize the need for this information. Physicians already gather information on patient race as part of a standard medical history. All that is needed is to compile and report racial and ethnic information in a format that protects patient confidentiality and privacy.[223]

Report cards that reflect racial inequities will provide a strong evidence that racism, "intentional or unintentional, institutional or individual, is affecting patient care."[224b] This data would then be used to issue a health report card, direct regulatory enforcement and provide the base for litigation

## Establish An Equality Health Care Council

The act should establish a "Health Care Council", patterned after Fair Housing Councils. This Council could educate the public, train health care providers, institutions, and managers, provide counseling and health care-finding services to individuals, investigate discrimination complaints through testing, and pursue legal remedies.[225] The Health Care Council would provide a focal point for anti-discrimination work in health care.[226] It could easily be an extension of existing state minority health efforts. Thus, anyone who suspects that he or she has encountered discrimination in health care would have a place to turn for help.

## Assure Adequate Fines And Regulatory Enforcement

The importance of rigorous enforcement of regulation as a primary vehicle for policing the health services cannot be over-emphasized The collection of data and development of a report card requires the teeth of regulatory enforcement. Thus, a statute that imposes a hefty civil penalty for violation of regulations designed to eliminate racial inequities will increase the likelihood of compliance Current administrative penalty involves termination of funds. Such a step is the effective equivalent of having no penalty at all. If substantial fines were mandated and collected for violating anti-discrimination law, then such fines could be collected and deposited directly into a restricted account that could be used only to eradicate racial inequities.

## Pay Prevailing Plaintiff's Attorney Fees

The health care anti-discrimination statute, like many Federal statutes, would pay the legal fees for the plaintiff who wins his or her case.[227] The statute should grant prevailing party status when, because of the lawsuit, a plaintiff's ends are accomplished. Under the catalyst theory, the focus is on whether the party obtained its desired result, not whether or not the party obtained a favorable ruling. Prevailing party attorneys' fees would help to provide the financial incentives needed to pursue litigation.[228]

## Allow Punitive Damage, In Part Or In Whole, To Fund Monitoring And Assessment Programs

Compensatory damages make victims of discrimination whole.[229] Punitive damages, on the other hand, punish past conduct, teaching defendants not to commit these acts again and to deter similar behavior in others.[230] As of

2003, 12 states have statutes allowing the punitive damages to be split (split-recovery statutes). The twelve states are: Alaska, Colorado, Florida, Georgia, Illinois, Indiana, Iowa, Kansas, Missouri, New York, Oregon, and Utah.[231] Similar to split-recovery statutes, all or part of punitive damages should be placed into a fund earmarked to promote equality health care, including discrimination testing.[232]

> *Reparations requires the passage and enforcement of a Health Care Anti-Discrimination Act .*

## Summary

Why not modify either existing Federal law (Title VI) or adopt a Federal Health Care. Anti-Discrimination Law? The first question has been answered. Title VI is hopelessly flawed and tinkering with it will not make it stronger. As to the question why not a Federal law, the answer lies in political feasibility. From a political perspective, the antagonism to civil rights within the present George W. Bush administration makes it highly unlikely that such an approach will work. Furthermore, the states are influential in the civil rights arena, and have the infrastructures on which a new civil rights law could be based.

The discussion of discrimination in health care has been limited to Title VI of the Civil Rights Act[233] and on assuring access to facilities and providers.[234] In an effective public health policy, state *and* Federal laws must prohibit discriminatory practices in health care. The crux of the problem for the legal system, given managed care, the historical inequity in health care, and unthinking discrimination, is what is the best way to remedy racial inequity (discrimination) in the health care system?

## CONCLUSION

Health care institutions have a social responsibility to identify all causes of disease and disability in a population and then to mobilize the resources necessary to attack those causes. It has been shown that the health of Blacks is markedly lower than White. It necessarily follows that "this situation would have to be called, in part, a . . .consequence of the actions and structure of [racism within] those health institutions."[235]

All institutions must accept responsibility for getting rid of institutional racism as well as accept the burden of identifying and effecting solutions. Doing nothing is an unacceptable option. Doing nothing allows the continuation of economic and social apartheid based on race. Reform efforts that call for only expanded insurance coverage are inadequate, not only because it is possible that only a small minority of Blacks will continue to be uncovered, but more importantly, reform based only on expanded coverage does nothing to relieve racial barriers in access to quality health care. Furthermore, a focus on access fails to eliminate the non-health care barriers to quality health care. While special health services could be targeted to Blacks, fiscally and politically this alternative is very unlikely. No single approach will adequately address the multi-faceted problem of improving the health care status of Blacks.

It is clear that the health care system is undergoing enormous changes designed to make it more just. The following quote is taken from an article about South Africa, with "South Africa" changed to "United States and "Apartheid" to "Racism". This quote is equally true about the United States of America:

> "[Racism remains a] prime cause of the unequal and racially discriminatory provision of funds for health services; of the over-crowding of the ill-equipped Black hospitals and the underutilization of White hospitals; of miserable housing, gross pollution, poor sanitation, and lack of health care."

> "[Racism] in consequence, is the underlying structure causing the dreadful burden of excess morbidity and mortality, much of it preventable, that is borne by the Black population. These health-specific effects are superimposed on the more general consequences of [racism] which bars the majority of [Black] citizens from participating in decisions on the allocation of resources for health or other needs."

> "We believe that the [American] health care system is, in consequence, fundamentally flawed. Fragmentation and duplication of services. . . . is costly and inefficient.

> For the majority of the Black population, the whole spectrum of health services (but most urgently, primary care) is inadequate. Entire generations suffer through much of their life-times."

> "Even if. . . [racism] ended tomorrow, their effects on health would persist for years, in part because of the health consequences of the profound poverty that [racism] itself has engendered and in part because widespread attitudes that encourage racism, elitism, sexism, a colonialist mentality, and prejudice against the poor take time and commitment to change."

> "Clearly, [America] has the ability to reduce markedly, if not eliminate, the serious health problems that exist among the Black population. It can, if it chooses, eliminate the institutionalized system of racism and discrimination that have made the country, for decades, a symbol of human rights violations. The task facing[us] is to continue to extend the process that [civil rights reforms] have begun, until profound and lasting improvements in health care . . . are a reality."[236]

The current status of Black health is based on a long-term system of neglect built on a "Slave Health Deficit". Another way to think about the kind of commitment needed is to consider that of the total time that persons of African descent have had a presence in the new world, 63.7% of that time was as chattel slavery and another 25.9 % of that time was spent in *de jure* or Jim Crow segregation. That is, only 9.7% of the total time in the United States have persons of African descent had full legal status as citizens. But even during that time, less than 6.0% (the Affirmative Action era and 1997 to 2006) has been focused on eliminating the Black health inequities. From a health perspective, 94% of the time was spent in establishing and maintaining a health deficit and at no point has that deficit been removed.

## Black Health/Health Care Experience
## 1607 to 2006

| Time Span | Years | % US Experience | Legal and Health Care Experience |
|---|---|---|---|
| 1607 to 1864 | 258 | 64.5% | Chattel Slavery "Slave Health Deficit" Established |
| 1865 to 1964 | 100 | 25% | Legal "Jim Crow" Segregation Continuation of Health Inequalities |
| 1965 to 1979 | 15 | 3.8% | "Affirmative Action" Era Continuation of Health Inequalities |
| 1980 to 1996 | 17 | 4.3% | "Racial Re-entrenchment" Era Continuation of Health Inequalities |
| 1997 to 2006 | 10 | 2.4% | Active Work on Eliminating Health Inequalities Inequalities Continue |
| FUTURE | ??? | ??? | ???? |

*Based on Drs. W. Michael Byrd and Linda A Clayton's Formulation

Thus, the burden of a slave health deficit has been a continuous burden and will only be relieved with an aggressive reparations program. In its most expansive sense, reparations provide the descendants of slaves an escape from hopelessness of the "slave health deficit". Reparations ultimately are about social justice since they are about rectifying the harm that has been done to one social group. Reparations are not a one-way action. They require the Black community to take action and rebuild itself. Reparations will provide the resources necessary to rebuild community and cleanse the soul of the nation. Most importantly, reparations will restore the health of the people of African descent in America.

W.E. Dubois said that the problem of the 20th century was the problem of the color line.[237] That color line was overt and legally enforced. Here at the beginning of the 21st century, the problem of the color line continues. However, now it is institutionally and structurally enforced. In the absence of laws, policy, practices, and reparations that address institutional racism and discrimination, the problem of the color line in health care will continue for another 100 years and the problem of "Dying While Black" will continue.

# REFERENCES

## HEALTH

### HEALTH - ARTICLES

*Abortion Surveillance, 1984-1985*, 38 MORBIDITY AND MORTALITY WEEKLY REPORT (10/1/89).

*Abortion Surveillance --- United States, 2001*, 53 MORBIDITY AND MORTALITY WEEKLY REPORT (11/26/2004 ).

Adler, Nancy, et Al., *Socioeconomic Inequalities in Health: No Easy Solution*, 269 JOURNAL OF THE AMERICAN MEDICAL ASSOCIATION 3140 (1993).

Ahijevych, Karen & Mary Ellen Wewers, *Factors Associated with Nicotine Dependence among African American Women Cigarette Smokers*, 16 RES. NURSING & HEALTH 283, 289 (1993).

Altman, David G., *How an Unhealthy Product Is Sold: Cigarette Advertising in Magazines, 1960-1985*, 37 JOURNAL OF COMMUNITY HEALTH 95-106 (1987).

Anderson, A., *Cigarette Brand Use Among Adult Smokers-- United States, 1986*, 39 MORBIDITY & MORTALITY WEEKLY REPORT 665 (1990).

Andersen, Ronald M. et al., *Black-White Differences in Health Status: Methods or Substance?*, in HEALTH POLICIES AND BLACK AMERICANS 72, 75 (D. Willis, ed. 1989).

Andrews, Lori B., *Confidentiality of Genetic Information in the Workplace*, 17 AMERICAN JOURNAL OF LAW AND MEDICINE 75 (1991).

Annas, George J., *Life, Liberty and Death*, 12 HEALTH MANAGEMENT QUARTERLY 5 (1990).

Arras, John D., *Getting Down to Cases: The Revival of Casuistry in Bioethics*, 16 JOURNAL OF MEDICINE AND PHILOSOPHY 29 (1991).

Austoker et al., *Smoking and Cancer: Smoking Cessation*, 308 BRITISH MEDICAL JOURNAL 1478 (1993).

Aved, Barbara M., et . al., *Barriers to Prenatal Care for Low-income Women*, 158 WESTERN JOURNAL OF MEDICINE 493 (1993).

Axelson, Diana E., *Women as Victims of Medical Experimentation: J. Marion Sims'*

*Surgery on Slave Women, 1845-1850*, 2 SAGE 10 (1985).

Bagley, C., A *Plea for Ignoring Race and Including Insured Status in American Research Reports on Social Science and Medicine*, 40 SOCIAL SCIENCE MEDICINE 1017 (1995).

Bailey, Deborah Ann, *Maternal Substance Abuse: Does Ohio Have an Answer?*, 17 UNIVERSITY OF DAYTON LAW REVIEW 1019 (1992).

Baines, Loretta, *Study Claims Black Females at Greater Risk from Smoking*, TRI-STATE DEFENDER, Mar. 22, 1996, at 3A.

Balsa, Ana I., Naomi Seiler, Thomas G. McGuire, & M. Gregg Bloche, *Clinical Uncertainty and Healthcare Disparities*, 29 AMERICAN JOURNAL OF LAW AND MEDICINE 203 (2003).

Barker, Judith, *Cultural Diversity—Changing the Context of Medical Practice*, 157 WEST JOURNAL OF MEDICINE 248 (1992).

Bates, Karen Grigsby, *Tobacco Pins a Bull's-Eye on Black Kids Smoking: Industry Papers from the 1970s Help Explain the Preponderance of Cigarette Advertising in the Inner City*, LOS ANGELES TIMES, Feb. 20, 1998, at B7.

Beauchamp, Tom L., *Response to Jorge Garcia*, in BLACK PERSPECTIVES ON BIOMERICAL ETHICS 67, 72 (Harley E. Flack & Edmund D. Pellegrino eds., 1992).

*Black Clergy, Anti-Tobacco Group Campaign Against Camel Brand*, GREENSBORO NEWS & RECORDER (N.C.), Mar. 14, 1997.

*Black Smokers Object to Tobacco Settlement*, BATON ROUGE ADVOCATE, June 6, 1997.

Blaine, Aaron, *Causes of Death Among Laundry and Dry Cleaning Workers*, 69 AMERICAN JOURNAL OF PUBLIC HEALTH 508 (1979).

Boadle, Anthony, *Film Exposes Black Market in Body Parts From Humans*, SEATTLE TIMES, November 12, 1993, at A14.

Bobinski, Mary Anne & Phyllis Griffin Epps, *Women, Poverty, Access to Health Care and the Perils of Symbolic Reform*, 5 JOURNAL OF GENDER, RACE & JUSTICE 233 (Spring 2002).

Boring, C.C. et al., *Cancer Statistics For African Americans*, 42 CANCER: CANCER JOURNAL FOR CLINICIANS 7 (1992).

Bowman, James E., *Genetic Screening Programs and Public Policy*, 38 PHYLON 117 (1977).

Breggin, Peter R., & Ginger R. Breggin, *The Federal Violence Initiative: Threats to African American Children (And Others)* 24 PSYCHIATRY DISCOURSE 8 (1993).

Bridges, Khiara M., *On the Commodification of the Black Female Body: The Critical Implications of the Alienability of Fetal Tissue*, 102 COLUMBIA LAW REVIEW 123 (January, 2002).

Bristow, Lonnie R., *Mine Eyes Have Seen*, 261 JOURNAL OF THE AMERICAN MEDICAL ASSOCIATION 284 (1989).

Brown, Lawrence D., *The Medically Uninsured: Problems, Policies and Politics*, 15 JOURNAL OF HEALTH POLITICS, POLICY & LAW. 315 (1990).

Buchanan, *The Right to a Decent Minimum of Health Care*, 13 PHILOSOPHY AND PUBLIC AFFAIRS 55 (1984).

Callender, Clive O. et al., *Attitudes Among African Americans Toward Donating Kidneys for Transplantation: A Pilot Project*, 74 NATIONAL MEDICAL ASSOCIATION JOURNAL 807 (1982).

Callender, Clive O., *Organ Donation in the African American Population: Where Do We Go From Here?*, 19 TRANSPLANTATION PROC. 36 (1987).

Capron, Alexander Morgan, *Health Care Costs: Ethical and Legal Implications of Changes in the Methods of Paying Physicians*, 36 CASE WESTERN RESERVE LAW REVIEW 708 (Summer 1986).

Caralis, P.V., et al., *The Influence of Ethnicity and Race on Attitudes Toward Advance Directives, Life-prolonging Treatments, and Euthanasia*, 4 JOURNAL OF CLINICAL ETHICS 155 (1993).

Carrese, Joseph A. & Lorna A. Rhodes, *Western Bioethics on the Navajo Reservation: Benefit or Harm?*, 274 JOURNAL OF AMERICAN MEDICAL ASSOCIATION 826 (1995).

Centers for Disease Control, *Changes in the Cigarette Brand Preferences of Adolescent Smokers--United States, 1989-1993*, 43 MORBIDITY & MORTALITY WEEKLY REPORT 577 (1994).

Centers for Disease Control, *Cigarette Brand Use Among Adult Smokers--United States, 1986*, 39 MORBIDITY & MORTALITY WEEKLY REPORT 665 (1990).

Centers for Disease Control, *Cigarette Smoking Among Blacks and Other Minority Populations*, 36 MORBIDITY & MORTALITY WEEKLY REPORT 405 (1987).

Centers for Disease Control, *Smoking-Attributable Mortality and Years of Potential Life Lost--United States, 1988*, 40 MORBIDITY & MORTALITY WEEKLY REPORT 62 (1991).

Chang, Pancho H. & Julia Puebla Fortier, *Language Barriers to Health Care: An Overview*, 9 JOURNAL OF HEALTH CARE FOR THE POOR AND UNDERSERVED (1998).

Chin, Jean Lau, *Culturally Competent Health Care*, 115 PUBLIC HEALTH REPORT 25 (2000).

Clancy, Carolyn M. & Bruce E. Hillner, *Physicians as Gatekeepers: The Impact of Financial Incentives*, 149 ARCHIVES INTERNAL MEDICINE. 917 (1989).

Clark, J., *Targeting Blacks in Cigarette Billboard Advertising: Results from Down South*, 2 NURSING SCAN IN ONCOLOGY 12 (1993).

Collie, Tim, *Black Teen-Age Girls Refuse to Follow the Smoking Pack*, Sun-Sentinel (Fort Lauderdale, Florida), January 12, 1998, at 1A.

Cooper, R. & B.E. Simmons, *Cigarette Smoking and Ill Health Among Black Americans*, 85 NEW YORK STATE MEDICAL JOURNAL 344 (1985).

Cooper, R.M., et. al., *Improved Mortality Among United States Africans, 1968-1978, The Role of Anti-Racist Struggle*, 11 INTERNATIONAL JOURNAL OF HEALTH SERVICES 511 (1981).

Cooper, Richard & Brian E. Simmons, *Cigarette Smoking and Ill Health among Black Americans*, 83(7) NEW YORK STATE JOURNAL OF MEDICINE 344 (1985).

Cotton, Paul, *Tobacco Foes Attack Ads that Target Women, Minorities, Teens, and the Poor*, 26 JOURNAL OF THE AMERICAN MEDICAL ASSOCIATION 1505 (1990).

Coultas, David B. et al., *Respiratory Diseases in Minorities of the United States*, 149 AMERICAN JOURNAL OF RESPIRATORY & CRITICAL CARE MEDICINE S93-S97 (1994) (erratum published in 150 American Journal of Respiratory & Critical Care Medicine 290 (1994)).

Council on Ethical and Judicial Affairs, *Black-White Disparities in Health Care*, 263 JOURNAL OF THE AMERICAN MEDICAL ASSOCIATION 2344 (1990).

Cummings, K. Michael et al., *Cigarette Advertising and Black-White Differences in Cigarette Brand Preference*, 102 PUBLIC HEALTH REPORT 698 (1987).

Dallek, Geraldine & Judith Waxman, *"Patient Dumping": A Crisis in Emergency Medical Care for the Indigent*, 19 CLEARINGHOUSE REVIEW 1413 (1986).

Darity, William A. & Castellano B. Turner, *Family Planning, Race Consciousness and the Fear of Race Genocide*, 62 AMERICAN JOURNAL OF PUBLIC HEALTH 1454 (1972).

Davidson, Jaime A., *Diabetes Care in Minority Groups: Overcoming Barriers to Meet These Patients' Special Needs*, 90 POSTGRADUATE MEDICINE 153 (1991).

Davis, Angela Y., *Surrogates and Outcast Mothers: Racism and Reproductive Politics*, in "IT JUST AIN'T FAIR": THE ETHICS OF HEALTH CARE FOR AFRICAN AMERICANS 41-55 (Annette Dula & Sara Goering eds. 1994).

Davis, Karen & Diane Rowland, *Uninsured and Underserved: Inequalities in Health Care in the United State*, 61 MILBANK MEMORIAL FUND QUARTERLY 149 (1983).

Davis, Ronald M., *Current Trends in Cigarette Advertising and Marketing*, 316 NEW ENGLAND JOURNAL OF MEDICINE 725 (1987).

Diaz, Robyn Whipple, *Unequal Access: The Crisis of Health Care Inequality for Low-income African-American Residents of the District of Columbia*, 107 JOURNAL OF HEALTH CARE LAW AND POLICY 120 (2004).

Dimsdale, Joel E., *Stalked by the Past: The Influence of Ethnicity on Health*, 62 PSYCHOSOMATIC MEDICINE 161 (2000).

Dorn, Stan & Judith Waxman, *States Take the Lead in Preventing Patient Dumping*, 22 CLEARINGHOUSE REVIEW 136 (1988).

Dorn, Stan, et al, *Anti-Discrimination Provisions and Health Care Access: New Slants on Old Approaches*, 20 CLEARINGHOUSE REVIEW 439 (Special Issue, Summer 1986).

Dutt, Hans R. et al., *The Financial Implications of HMOs' Partial County Carve-Out Option*, 14 MANAGED CARE INTERFACE 46 (2001).

Emanuel, Ezekiel J. & Linda L. Emanuel, *Preserving Community in Health Care*, 22 JOURNAL OF HEALTH POLITICS, POLICY AND THE LAW 147 (1997).

Emanuel, Ezekiel J., & Linda L. Emanuel, *Four Models of the Physician-Patient Relationship*, 267 JOURNAL OF AMERICAN MEDICAL ASSOCIATION 2221 (1992).

Eubanks, D.C., *Black Mortality and Health Before 1940*, HEALTH POLICIES AND BLACK AMERICANS.

Fauci, Cara A., *Racism and Health Care in America: Legal Responses to Racial Disparities in the Allocation of Kidneys*, 21 BOSTON COLLEGE THIRD WORLD LAW JOURNAL 35 (Winter, 200).

Fine, Max W. & Jonathan H. Sunshine, *Malpractice Reform Through Consumer Choice and Consumer Education: Are New Concepts Marketable?*. 49 LAW AND CONTEMPORARY PROBLEMS 213 (Spring 1986).

Finley, Randy, *In War's Wake: Health Care and Arkansas Freedmen*, 1863-1868, 51 Arkansas History Quarterly 135 (1992).

Fiore, Michael C. et al., *Trends in Cigarette Smoking in the United States: The Changing Influence of Gender and Race*, 261 JOURNAL OF THE AMERICAN MEDICAL ASSOCIATION 49 (1989).

*Food and Drug Administration Loosened its Rules, Poppleton Residents Say Facility Should Publicize Test More*, BALTIMORE SUN, April 19, 1997 at 1B.

Fox, Renée C., *The Evolution of American Bioethics: A Sociological Perspective*, in SOCIAL SCIENCE PERSPECTIVES ON MEDICAL ETHICS 201 (George Weisz ed 1990).

Frost, F. et. al., *Racial Misclassification of Native Americans in Surveillance Epidemiology and End Results Cancer Registry*, 84 JOURNAL OF NATIONAL CANCER INSTITUTE 957 (1992).

Garrett, Joanne Mills et al., *Life-sustaining Treatments During Terminal Illness: Who Wants What?*, 8 JOURNAL OF GENERAL INTERNAL MEDICINE 361(1993).

Geiger, H. Jack, *Race and Health Care: An American Dilemma?*, 335 NEW ENGLAND JOURNAL OF MEDICINE 815 (September 12, 1996).

Ginzburg, Eli & Miriam Ostow, *Beyond Universal Health Insurance to Effective Health Care*, 265 JOURNAL OF THE AMERICAN MEDICAL ASSOCIATION 2559 (1991).

Gnessin, A., *Liability in the Managed Care Organization Setting*, in MANAGED CARE ORGANIZATION HEALTH CARE 471:405 (PLI Commercial Law and Handbook Series)(September 1, 1986).

Gornick, Marian, et al., *Effects of Race and Income on Mortality and Use of Services Among Medicare Beneficiaries*, 335 NEW ENGLAND JOURNAL OF MEDICINE 791 (1996).

Gostin, Larry, *Genetic Discrimination: The Use of Genetically Based Diagnostic and Prognostic Tests by Employers and Insurers*, 17 AMERICAN JOURNAL OF LAW & MEDICINE 109 (1991).

Greene, Leonard, *Blacks Fight Back Against Lure of Tobacco Giants*, BOSTON HERALD, May 28, 1997.

Grim, C.E., J.P. Henry & H. Myep, *High Blood Pressure in Blacks: Salt, Slavery, Survival, Stress and Racism*, in J.H. Laragh & B.M. Brenner, eds. HYPERTENSION: PATHOPHYSIOLOGY, DIAGNOSIS AND MANAGEMENT, 2d Ed. 171 (1995).

Hadeley, Jack et. al., *Comparison of Uninsured and Privately Insured Hospital Patients*, 265 JOURNAL OF THE AMERICAN MEDICAL ASSOCIATION 376 (1991).

Hancock, Trevor, *Beyond Health Care: From Public Health Policy to Healthy Public Policy*, 76 AMERICAN JOURNAL OF PUBLIC HEALTH 9 (Supplement 1985).

Harris, R.E. et al., *Race and Sex Differences in Lung Cancer Risk Associated with Cigarette Smoking*, 22 INTERNATIONAL JOURNAL OF EPIDEMIOLOGY 592 (1993).

Harwood, Alan H, *Guidelines for Culturally Appropriate Health Care*, in ETHNICITY AND MEDICAL CARE (1981).

Harwood, Alan, *Mainland Puerto Rican*, in ETHNICITY AND MEDICAL CARE (1981).

Haywood, J.L, *Coronary Heart Disease Mortality/Morbidity and Risk in Africans. II Access to Medical Care*, 3 AMERICAN HEART ASSOCIATION JOURNAL 794 (1984).

Hazony, Orly, *Increasing the Supply of Cadaver Organs for Transplantation: Recognizing That the Real Problem is Psychological Not Legal*, 3 HEALTH MATRIX 219 (1993).

Heller, Jean, *Syphilis Victims in U.S.: Study Went Untreated for 40 Years*, NEW YORK TIMES, July 26, 1972, at A1.

Henry J. Kaiser Family Fund, KEY FACTS, RACE, ETHNICITY & MEDICAL CARE, 16 (1999), at Http://www.kff.org/content/1999/19991014a/ (Last Visited: October 30, 2002)

Herbert, J.R. et al., *Menthol Cigarette Smoking and Esophageal Cancer*, 18 INTERNATIONAL JOURNAL OF EPIDEMIOLOGY 37 (1989).

Hillman, A.L, *Financial Incentives for Physicians in HMOs – Is There a Conflict of Interest?* 317 NEW ENGLAND JOURNAL OF MEDICINE 1743 (1987).

Hilts, Philip J., *Health Chief Assails a Tobacco Producer for Aiming at Blacks*, NEW YORK TIMES, Jan. 19, 1990, at A1.

Hinden, Richard A. & Douglas L. Elden, *Liability Issues for Managed Care Organization Entities*,14(1) SETON HALL LEGISLATIVE JOURNAL 1 (Summer 1990).

Hinton IV, Ladson & Arthur Kleinman, *Cultural Issues and International Psychiatric Diagnosis*, in INTERNATIONAL REVIEW OF PSYCHIATRY 111 (Jorge Alberto, Costa E. Silva, & Carol Nadelson eds. 1993).

Hoffman, Diane E. & Anita J. Tarzian, *The Girl Who Cried Pain: A Bias Against Women in the Treatment of Pain*, 29 JOURNAL OF LAW, MEDICINE AND ETHICS 13 (Spring 2001).

Hoffman-Goetz, Laurie et al., *Cancer Coverage and Tobacco Advertising in African American Popular Magazines*, 22 JOURNAL OF COMMUNITY HEALTH 261.

Hubert, Cynthia, *African Americans Breaking Silence on Reality of AIDS*, SACRAMENTO BEE, January 2, 1996, at A1.

Hudson, Kathy L. et al., *Genetic Discrimination and Health Insurance: An Urgent Need for Reform*, SCIENCE, Oct. 20, 1995, at 391.

Husted, Amanda, *Shortage of African Dentists Has Ill Effect in Community*, ATLANTA JOURNAL & CONSTITUTION, Aug 19, 1991, at B3.

Jackson, Derrick, *Let Blacks Rethink Tobacco Underwriting*, MILWAUKEE JOURNAL & SENTINEl, July 12, 1997.

Jackson, Derrick, *Why Blacks Are Losing Tobacco War*, DALLAS MORNING NEWS, June 3, 1997.

Jackson, J.J., *Urban Black Americans*, in A. Harewood eds., ETHNICITY AND MEDICAL CARE 37 (1981).

Jarvik, M.E. et al., *Nonmentholated Cigarettes Decrease Puff Volume of Smoke and Increase Carbon Monoxide Absorption*, 56 PHYSIOLOGY & BEHAVIOR 563 (1994).

Johnson, Danny R., *Tobacco Stains*, 56 PROGRESSIVE 26 (1992).

Johnson, Paula C., *Danger in the Diaspora: Law, Culture and Violence Against Women of African Descent in the United States and South Africa*, 1 JOURNAL OF GENDER RACE & JUSTICE 471 (Spring 1998).

Judicial Council, *Ethical Guidelines for Organ Transplantation*, 205 JOURNAL OF AMERICAN MEDICAL ASSOCIATION 341 (1968).

Kabat, Geoffrey C. & James R. Hebert, *Use of Mentholated Cigarettes and Lung Cancer Risk*, 51 CANCER RESOURCE 6510 (1991).

Kamer, M.D., Russell S. et Al., *Effect of New York State's Do-Not-Resuscitate Legislation on In-Hospital Cardiopulmonary Resuscitation Practice*, 88 AMERICAN JOURNAL OF MEDICINE 108 (1990).

Kasiske, Bertram L. et al., *The Effect of Race on Access and Outcome in Transplantation*, 324 NEW ENGLAND JOURNAL OF MEDICINE 302 (1991).

Kass, Leon R., *Practicing Ethics: Where's the Action?*, HASTINGS CENTER REPORT 5., January-February 1990.

Kennedy, R.D. & R.D. Deapen, *Differences Between Oklahoma and Indian Infant Mortality and Other Races*, 106 PUBLIC HEALTH REPORT 97 (1991).

Kimmelman, Donald, *Poverty and Norplant: Can Contraception Reduce the Underclass?*, PHILADELPHIA INQUIRER, December 12, 1990, at A18.

Kindig, David A., et. al., *Trends in Physician Availability in 10 Urban Areas from 1963 to 1980*, 24 INQUIRY 136 (1987).

Kleinman, Arthur & Joan Kleinman, *Suffering and its Professional Transformation: Toward an Ethnography of Interpersonal Experience*, 15 CULTURAL MEDICINE. & PSYCHIATRIC 275 (1991).

Koenig, Barbara A. & Jan Gate-Williams, *Understanding Cultural Difference in Caring for Dying Patients*, 163 WESTERN JOURNAL OF MEDICINE 244 (1995).

Kreiger, Nancy, *Embodying Inequality: a Review of Concepts, Measures and Methods for Studying Health Consequences of Discrimination*, 29 INTERNATIONAL JOURNAL OF HEALTH SERVICES 295 1999).

Laguerre, Michael S., *Haitian Americans*, in ETHNICITY AND MEDICAL CARE 198 (1981).

Larimer, Tim, *High School Offers Birth Control Implant, African Americans Disagree on Merits of Program*, DALLAS MORNING NEWS, March 17, 1993, at A37.

Laveist, Thomas A., *Segregation, Poverty and Empowerment: Health Consequences for African Americans*, 71 MILBANK QUARTERLY 41 (1993).

Lavizzo-Mourey, Risa, et al., *The Perceptions of African American Physicians Concerning Their Treatment by Managed Care Organization s*, 88 JOURNAL OF THE NATIONAL MEDICAL ASSOCIATION 210 (1996).

Lee, Felicia R. & Rachel B. Gold, *Empty Womb*, ESSENCE, at 51 (May 1990).

Levy, David R., *White Doctors and Black Patients: Influence of Race on the Doctor-Patient Relationship*, 75 PEDIATRICS 639 (1985).

Lewis, Claude, *Norplant Editorial Was Offensive: The Thrust of the Editorial was Aimed at the African American Underclass, Unjustly So*, PHILADELPHIA INQUIRER, December 21, 1990, at A19.

Lloyd, J. William, *Long-term Mortality Study of Steelworkers: Respiratory Cancer in Coke Plant Workers*, 13 JOURNAL OF OCCUPATIONAL MEDICINE 53 (1971).

Lock, Margaret, *The Concept of Race: An Ideological Construct*, 30 TRANSCULTURAL PSYCHIATRIC RESEARCH REVIEW 203 (1993).

Long, Stephen, *Public Versus Employment-Related Health Insurance: Experience and Implications for Black and NonBlack Americans*, in HEALTH POLICIES AND BLACK AMERICANS 200 (David P. Willis ed., 1989).

Lowe, Robert A. et al., *Effect of Ethnicity on Denial of Authorization for Emergency Department Care by Managed Care Organization Gatekeepers*, 8 ACADEMY OF EMERGENCY MEDICINE 259 (2001).

Lucey, Daniel R. et. al., *Comparison by Search Term Begin Race Search Term End of Total Serum Igg, Iga, and Igm with Cd4+ T-cell Counts in North American Persons Infected with the Human Immunodeficiency Virus Type*, 5(4) JOURNAL OF ACQUIRED IMMUNE DEFICIENCY SYNDROMES 325 (April 1992).

Macer, Darryl, *Whose Genome Project?*, 5 BIOETHICS 183 (1991).

Manning, W.G., A. Leibowitz, G.A. Goldber, et al., *A Controlled Trial on the Effect of a Prepaid Group Practice on the Use of Services*, 310 NEW ENGLAND JOURNAL OF MEDICINE 1505 (1984).

Martin, Rachel Vander et al., *Ethnicity and Smoking: Differences in White, Black, Hispanic, and Asian Medical Patients Who Smoke*, 6 AMERICAN JOURNAL OF PREVENTIVE MEDICINE 194 (1990).

May, Jude Thomas, *The Medical Care of Blacks in Louisiana During Occupation and Reconstruction, 1862-1868: Its Social and Political Background* (1970).

McCraven, Marilyn, *Hospital's Experiment Draws Worry, Shock Trauma Plans Trial of New Therapy Without Subjects' Ok, Research Conducted Without Patients' Consent, Study of Blood Substitute is Halted When Death Rates Exceed Projections*, BALTIMORE SUN, January 18, 1999 at 3A

McGregor, Deborah K., SEXUAL SURGERY AND THE ORIGINS OF GYNECOLOGY: J. MARION SIMS, HIS HOSPITAL, AND HIS PATIENTS (1989).

McMichael, A.J. et. al., *Mortality Among Rubber Workers: Relationship to Specific Jobs*, 17 JOURNAL OF OCCUPATIONAL MEDICINE 178 (1976).

*Medicaid, A Cooperative State-Federal Program, Provides Health Insurance to Eligible Individuals and Families*, 42 UNITED STATES CODE § 1396 (1992).

*Medicare Program: Swing-Bed Program*, 54 Federal Regulation. 37 (September 7, 1989).

Menzel, P., *Medical Costs, Moral Choices: A Philosophy of Health Care Economics*, in AMERICA 85 (1983).

Mettger, Wendy & Vicki S. Freimuth, *Is There a Hard-to-Reach Audience?*, 105 PUBLIC HEALTH REPORTS 232 (1990).

Miller, G.E. et al., *Cigarette Mentholation Increase Smokers' Exhaled Carbon Monoxide Levels*, 2 EXPERIMENTAL & CLINICAL PSYCHOPHARMACOLOGY 154 (1994).

Miller, Robert H., *Healthcare Managed Care Organization and Change: Implications for Access to Care and Its Measurement*, 33 HEALTH SERVICES RESEARCH 653 (1998).

Moore, D.J. et al., *Target Marketing of Tobacco and Alcohol-Related Products to Ethnic Minority Groups in the United States*, 6 ETHNICITY & DISEASE 83 (1996).

Morain, Claudia, *Kiss of Death: African Americans and the Tobacco Industry*, AMERICAN MEDICAL NEWS, Nov. 15, 1993, at 13.

Morreim, E.H., *The MD and The DRG*, 15 HASTINGS CENTER REPORT 34-5 (1985).

Moy, E. & B.A. Bartman, *Physician Race and Care of Minority and Medically Indigent Patients*, 272 JOURNAL OF THE AMERICAN MEDICAL ASSOCIATION 1515 (May 17, 1995).

Nightingale, Elena et al., *Apartheid Medicine: Health and Human Rights in South Africa*, 264 JOURNAL OF THE AMERICAN MEDICAL ASSOCIATION 2097 (1990).

Noah, Barbara A., *Racist Health Care?*, 35 SAN DIEGO LAW Review 135 (1998).

Nsiah-Jefferson, Laurie, *Reproductive Laws, Women of Color, and Low-Income Women*, in REPRODUCTIVE LAWS FOR THE 1990S 23 (Sherrill Cohen & Nadine Taubs eds 1988).

Orleans, Carole Tracy et al., *A Survey of Smoking and Quitting Patterns among Black Americans*, 79 AMERICAN JOURNAL OF PUBLIC HEALTH 176 (1989).

Orona, Celia J., et al., *Cultural Aspects of Nondisclosure*, 3 CAMBRIDGE QUARTERLY HEALTHCARE ETHICS 338 (1994).

Pappas, Gregory et.al., *The Increasing Inequity in Mortality Between Socioeconomic Groups in the United States, 1960 and 1986*, 329 NEW ENGLAND JOURNAL OF MEDICINE 103 (1993).

Patrick, D.L. & J. Elinson, METHODS OF SOCIOMEDICAL RESEARCH, IN HANDBOOK OF MED. SOC. 437 (H. Freeman et al. eds., 1979).

Perez, Luis M. et al., *Organ Donation in Three Major American Cities With Large Latino and African American Populations*, 46 TRANSPLANT PROCEDURES 555 (1988).

Perez-Stable, Eliseo J. et.al. *Nicotine Metabolism and Intake in Black and White Smokers*, 280(2) THE JOURNAL OF THE AMERICAN MEDICAL ASSOCIATION 152b (July 8, 1998).

Perkins, Henry S., *Cultural Differences and Ethical Issues in the Problem of Autopsy Requests*, 87 THE JOURNAL OF TEXAS MEDICINE (1991).

Perry, Tony, *New Camel Cigarette Draws Protest Smoking*, LOS ANGELES TIMES, Mar. 16, 1997, at A2.

Pollak, Susan, *Melancholia and Depression: From Hippocratic Times to Modem Times*, 22 PSYCHOLOGY TODAY 73 (1988).

Quesada, Gustavo M., *Language and Communication Barriers for Health Delivery to Minority Group*, 10 SOCIAL SCIENCE & MEDICINE 323(1976).

Ramirez, Anthony, *A Cigarette Campaign Under Fire*, NEW YORK TIMES, Jan. 12, 1990, at D1.

Ramirez, Anthony, *Reynolds, After Protests, Cancels Cigarette Aimed at Black Smokers*, NEW YORK TIMES, Jan. 20, 1990, at A1.

Rasell, Edith, Jared Bernstein & Kainan Tang, *The Impact of Health Care Financing on Family Budgets*, 24 INTERNATIONAL JOURNAL OF HEALTH SERVICES 691 (1994).

Raymond, Janice G., *Women as Wombs: International Traffic in Reproduction*, MS. MAGAZINE, May/June 1991, at 28.

Reich, Kenneth, *Panel Hears Horrors of Health Care Crisis*, Los Angeles TIMES, January 12,1992, at B1.

Richardson, Terri, *African American Smokers and Cancers of the Lung and of the Upper Respiratory and Digestive Tracts: Is Menthol Part of the Puzzle?*, 166 WORLD JOURNAL OF MEDICINE 189 (1997).

Roberts, Alma, *The Evolution of a Community Hospital: Improving Access to Ensure Political and Financial Viability*, in "IT JUST AIN'T FAIR": THE ETHICS OF HEALTH CARE FOR AFRICAN AMERICANS 195-200 (Annette Dula & Sara Goering eds 1994).

Roberts, Leslie, *One Worked: the Other Didn't*, 247 SCIENCE 18 (1990).

Romano, Michael, *In the Physician's Practice: Minority Docs Find Racism Continues to Infect Many American Hospitals*, 31 MODERN HEALTHCARE 12 (August 27, 2001).

Rosenberg, Charles E., *Disease in History: Frames and Framers*, 67 MILBANK QUARTERLY 1 (1989).

Ross, Miriam, *Societal/Cultural Views Regarding Death and Dying*, TOPICS IN CLINICAL NURSING 5 (1981).

Rowley, H., *Prescription from Canada: Would Universal Health Care Work in this Country?*, CHICAGO TRIBUNE, May 31, 1992.

Royce, Jacqueline M. et al., *Smoking Cessation Factors Among Americans and Whites*, 83 AMERICAN JOURNAL OF PUBLIC HEALTH 220 (1993).

Rutkow, Ira M., Ira & Jeffrey M. Lipton, *Some Negative Aspects of State Health Departments' Policies Related to Screening for Sickle Cell Anemia*, 64 AMERICAN JOURNAL OF PUBLIC HEALTH 217 (1974).

Ryan, Robyn Pforr, *Should Combat Troops Be Given the Option of Refusing Investigational Drug Treatment?*, 52 Food and Drug Law Journal 377 (1997).

Sanders, Cheryl J., *Problems and Limitations of an African American Perspective* in Eds. BIOMEDICAL ETHICS: A THEOLOGICAL VIEW, IN AFRICAN AMERICAN PERSPECTIVES ON BIOMEDICAL ETHICS, 165 (Harley E. Flack & Edmund D. Pellegrino eds 1992).

Savitt, Todd L. & Morton F. Goldberg, *Herrick's 1910 Case Report of Sickle Cell Anemia: The Rest of the Story*, 261 JOURNAL OF THE AMERICAN MEDICAL ASSOCIATION 266 (1989).

Schiff, Robert L. et. al., *Transfers to the Public Hospital: A Prospective Study of 467 Patients*, 314 NEW ENGLAND JOURNAL OF MEDICINE 552 (1986).

REFERENCES • 189

Schneider, Eric C., Alan M. Zaslavsky, & Arnold M. Epstein, *Racial Disparities in the Quality of Care for Enrollees in Medicare Managed Care Organization Care*, 287 JOURNAL OF THE AMERICAN MEDICAL ASSOCIATION 1288 (Mar. 13, 2002).

Schneider, Eric C. et al., *Racial Inequity in Influenza Vaccination: Does Managed Care Organization Narrow the Gap Between African Americans and Whites?*, 286 JOURNAL OF THE AMERICAN MEDICAL ASSOCIATION 1455 (2001).

Schulman, Kevin A. et.al., *The Effect of Race and Sex on Physicians' Recommendations for Cardiac Catherization*, 340 NEW ENGLAND JOURNAL OF MEDICINE 618 (1999).

Scott, *Lawmakers Differ on Measures to Reform Health Care*, MEMPHIS BUSINESS JOURNAL, June 1, 1992, 41.

Scott, Robert B., *Health Care Priority and Sickle Cell Anemia*, 214 JOURNAL OF THE AMERICAN MEDICAL ASSOCIATION 731 (1970).

SENIOR HEALTH DIGEST, No. 91-17 (Sept. 16, 1991).

Sheifer, Stuart E. et al., *Race and Sex Differences in the Management of Coronary Artery Disease*, 139 AMERICAN HEART JOURNAL 848 (2000).

Short, Pamela, et. al., *Health Insurance of Minorities in the United States* 1(2) JOURNAL OF HEALTH CARE FOR THE POOR & UNDERSERVD 9 (1990).

Shreiber, Janet M & John P. Homiak, *Mexican Americans*, in ETHNICITY AND MEDICAL CARE 301 (1981).

Sibert, Anthony & Denise Ji-Alunte Siebert, *Radiation Scandal*, Zmag (May 1994) http://www.zmag.org/ZMag/articles/may94sibert.htm (Last visited: March 25, 2005).

Sidney, Stephen et al., *Mentholated Cigarette Use Among Multiphasic Examinees, 1979-1986*, 79 AMERICAN JOURNAL OF PUBLIC HEALTH 1415 (1989).

Sidney, Stephen et al., *Mentholated Cigarette Use and Lung Cancer*, 155 ARCHIVES OF INTERNAL MEDICINE 727 (1995).

Skolnick, Andrew A., *National Medical Association Unveils Billboard Campaign to Promote Health in Black Communities*, 270 JOURNAL OF THE AMERICAN MEDICAL ASSOCIATION 1166 (1993).

Smedley, Brian D., et. al.., *Unequal Treatment: Confronting Racial and Ethnic Disparities in Health Care*, INSTITUTE OF MEDICINE, COMMITTEE ON UNDERSTANDING AND ELIMINATING RACIAL AND ETHNIC DISPARITIES IN HEALTH CARE ( 2002).

Smith, David Barton, HEALTH. CARE DIVIDED: RACE AND HEALING A NATION (1999).

Smith, David Barton, *The Racial Integration of Health Facilities*, 18 JOURNAL OF HEALTH POLITICS, POLICY AND LAW 851 (Winter 1993).

Soucie, F. J. Michael et al., *Race and Sex Differences in the Identification of Candidates for Renal Transplantation*, 19 AMERICAN JOURNAL OF. KIDNEY DISEASE 414 (1992).

Stellman, S.D. & L. Garfinkel, *Smoking Habits and Tar Levels in a New American Cancer Society Prospective Study of 1.2 Million Men and Women*, 76 JOURNAL OF THE NATIONAL CANCER INSTITUTE 1057 (1986).

Sterling, T.D. & D. Weinkam, *Comparison of Smoking-Related Risk Factors Among Black and White Males*, 15 AMERICAN JOURNAL OF INDUSTRIAL MEDICINE 319 (1989).

Stevens, Carol, *Research: Distrust Runs Deep Medical Community Seeks Solutions*, DETROIT NEWS, December 10, 1995, at A12.

Stevens, Carol St, *Churches Preach the Gospel of Good Health*, DETROIT NEWS, December 11, 1995, at A1.

Stotts, R.C. et al., *Smoking Cessation among Blacks*, 2 JOURNAL OF HEALTH CARE FOR THE POOR AND UNDESERVED 307 (1991).

Temple, J. & D.P. Burkitt, *Towards a New System of Health: The Challenge of Western Disease*, 18 JOURNAL OF COMMUNITY HEALTH 37 (1993).

*The Crisis of the Disappearing African Hospitals*, EBONY, March 1992, at 23-28.

Thomas, Laurence, *The Morally Beautiful,* in AFRICAN AMERICAN PERSPECTIVES ON BIOMEDICAL ETHICS 118 (Harley E. Flack & Edmund D. Pellegrino eds 1992).

Thomas, Stephen B. & Sandra Crouse Quinn, *The Tuskegee Syphilis Study, 1932 to 1972: Implications for HIV Education and Aids Risk Education Programs in the African American Community,* 81 AMERICAN JOURNAL OF PUBLIC HEALTH 499 (1991).

*Tobacco Industry's Ad Assault on Blacks Is Detailed in Records: Newly Released Documents Disclose Broad Scope of Marketing Campaigns,* ST. LOUIS POST-DISPATCH, Feb. 8, 1998, at A14.

Truax, Hawley, *Minorities at Risk,* ENVIRONMENTAL ACTION, January-February, 1990, at 19-20.

Uba, Laura, *Cultural Barriers to Health Care for Southeast Asian Refugees,* 107 PUBLIC. HEALTH REPORTER 544 (1992).

*US Tobacco Documents Show How Industry Targeted Black Community,* AGENCE FRENCH-PRESSE, Feb. 6, 1998.

Voas, Sharon, *Aging African Americans Sick, Scared past Abuses, Tradition Keep Them from Clinic,* PITTSBURGH POST-GAZETTE, Auggust 27, 1995, at B1.

Vorhaus Enthoven, Alain C. & Carol B., *A Vision of Quality in Health Care Delivery,* HEALTH AFFAIRS, May/June 1997.

Wagenknecht, Lynne E. et al., *Racial Differences in Serum Cotinine Levels Among Smokers in the Coronary Artery Risk Development in (Young) Adults Study,* 80 AMERICAN JOURNAL OF PUBLIC HEALTH, 1053 (1990).

Washington, Harriet A., *Tuskegee Experiment Was but One Medical Study That Exploited African Americans [Sic] Infamous Research,* BALTIMORE SUN, March 19, 1995, at 1f.

Waxman, Judith & Molly McNulty, *Access to Emergency Medical Care: Patients' Rights and Remedies,* 22 CLEARINGHOUSE REVIEW 21 (Nov. 1991).

Weinberg, Judith, *Utilization Review as the Practice of Medicine: Scaling the Wall of ERISA,* 9 BOSTON UNIVERSITY PUBLIC INTEREST LAW JOURNAL 89 (Fall, 1999).

Weinstein, Henry & Alissa J. Rubin, *Tobacco Firms Targeted Blacks, Documents Show,* LOS ANGELES TIMES, Feb. 6, 1998, at A1.

Weir, M.R. & E. Saunders, *Pharmacologic Management of Systemic Hypertension in Blacks,* 61 AMERICAN JOURNAL OF CARDIOLOGY 46 (1988).

Whitten, Charles F., *Sickle-cell Programming—an Imperiled Promise,* 288 NEW ENGLAND JOURNAL OF MEDICINE 318 (1973).

Will, George, *Revision of Our Health-care System Should Be High on Nations' Agenda,* ATLANTA JOURNAL & CONSTITUTION, Mar. 9, 1992.

Williams, D.R. and H. Neighbors, *Racism, Discrimination and Hypertension: Evidence and Needed Research,* 11(4) ETHNICITY AND DISEASE 800 (Fall 2001).

Williams, David R. & Toni D. Rucker, *Understanding and Addressing Racial Disparities in Health Care,* 21(4) HEALTH CARE FINANCING REVIEW 75 (Summer 2000).

Williams, David R. Etal ., *The Concept of Race and Health Status in America,* 109 PUBLIC HEALTH REPORT 26 (1994),.

Williams, David R., *Race and Health: Basic Questions, Emerging Directions,* 7 ANNALS OF EPIDEMIOLOGY 322 (July 1997).

Williams, David R., *Race/Ethnicity and Socioeconomic Status: Measurement and Methodological Issues,* 26(3) INTERNATIONAL JOURNAL OF HEALTH SERVICES 483 (1996).

Wilson, Donald, *Minorities and the Medical Profession: A Historical Perspective and Analysis of Current and Future Trends,* 78 JOURNAL OF THE NATIONAL MEDICAL ASSOCIATION,177 (1986).

Wilson, Donald, *Minorities and the Medical Profession: a Historical Perspective and Analysis of Current and Future Trends,* 78 JOURNAL OF THE NATIONAL MEDICAL ASSOCIATION 177 (1986).

Woodlander, S. et al., *Medical Care and Mortality: Racial Differences in Preventable Deaths,* 15 INTERNATIONAL JOURNAL OF HEALTH SERVICES 1 (1985).

Wright, Barnett, *'Liquid Crack': Fortified Beer Pours into Black Community*, PHILADELPHIA TRIBUNE, Apr. 30, 1993, at 1A.


## HEALTH - BOOKS

AFRICAN AMERICAN PERSPECTIVES ON BIOMEDICAL ETHICS (Harley E. Flack & Edmund Pellegrino eds 1992).

Annas, George J., AMERICAN HEALTH CARE LAW 80-81 (1990).

Beauchamp, Tom L. and James F. Childress, PRINCIPLES OF BIOMEDICAL ETHICS (3d Ed. 1989).

Bender, George A., GREAT MOMENTS IN MEDICINE 236-44 (1966).

Bishop, Jerry E. & Michael Waldholz, GENOME: THE STORY OF THE MOST ASTONISHING SCIENTIFIC ADVENTURE OF OUR TIME--THE ATTEMPT TO MAP ALL THE GENES IN THE HUMAN BODY (1990).

Bowman, James E., *Genetic Screening: Toward a New Eugenics?*, in "IT JUST AIN'T FAIR": THE ETHICS OF HEALTH CARE FOR AFRICAN AMERICANS 165-181 (Annette Dula & Sara Goering, eds 1994).

Byrd, W. Michael & Linda A. Clayton, AN AMERICAN HEALTH DILEMMA: A MEDICAL HISTORY OF AFRICAN AMERICANS AND THE PROBLEM OF RACE, BEGINNINGS TO 1900 (2000)

Byrd, W. Michael & Linda A. Clayton, AN AMERICAN HEALTH DILEMMA: A MEDICAL HISTORY OF AFRICAN AMERICANS AND THE PROBLEM OF RACE – 1900 TO 2000 (2002).

Byrd, W. Michael & Linda C. Clayton, RACE AND HEALTH CARE, AFRICAN AMERICAN HEALTH IN THE JACKSONIAN AND ANTEBELLUM PERIODS, 1812-46: GROWTH, CHANGE AND MANIFEST DESTINY (1996) (Unpublished Manuscript).

Caplan, Arthur L., *Informed Consent and Provider/Patient Relationships in Rehabilitation Medicine*, in IF I WERE A RICH MAN COULD I BUY A PANCREAS? 240 (1992).

Cook, Rebecca J., *Feminism and the Four Principles*, in PRINCIPLES OF HEALTH CARE ETHICS 193 (Raanan Gillon & Ann Lloyd eds 1993).

Daniels, Norman, *Health Care Needs and Distributive Justice*, in IN SEARCH OF EQUITY: HEALTH NEEDS AND THE HEALTH CARE SYSTEM 1 (1983

Davis, Karen,CLOSING THE GAP IN HEALTH INSURANCE COVERAGE FOR BLACK AMERICANS (Unpublished).

Davis, Karen et. al., HEALTH CARE FOR AFRICAN AMERICANS: THE PUBLIC SECTOR, HEALTH POLICIES AND BLACK AMERICANS (David Willis ed. 1989).

Davis, Karen, *Health Care for African Americans: The Public Sector* in HEALTH POLICIES AND BLACK AMERICANS (David Willis Ed., 1989).

Department of Health and Human Services, HEALTH STATUS OF MINORITIES AND LOW-INCOME GROUPS: THIRD EDITION (1990).

Department of Health and Human Services, REPORT OF THE SECRETARY'S BLUE RIBBON PANEL ON VIOLENCE PREVENTION (Jan. 15, 1993).

Dowling, William L. and Patricia A. Armstrong. *The Hospital*, in INTRODUCTION TO HEALTH SERVICES 125, 127 (Stephen J. Williams & Paul R. Torrens eds. 2002).

Dula, Annette & Sara Goering eds, "IT JUST AIN'T FAIR": THE ETHICS OF HEALTH CARE FOR AFRICAN AMERICANS ( 1994).

Dula, Annette, *African American Suspicion of the Healthcare System Is Justified: What Do We Do about It?*, CAMBRIDGE QUARTERLY HEALTHCARE ETHICS 347, 347 (1994).

Dula, Annette, *Bioethics: the Need for a Dialogue with African Americans*, in "IT JUST AIN'T FAIR": THE ETHICS OF HEALTH CARE FOR AFRICAN AMERICANS 11 (Annette Dual & Sara Goering eds 1994).

Dula, Annette, *Yes, There Are African American Perspectives on Bioethics*, in AFRICAN AMERICAN PERSPECTIVES ON BIOMEDICAL ETHICS 193 (Harley E. Flack & Edmund D. Pellegrino eds 1992).

Engelhardt, Jr., H. Tristram, BIOETHICS AND SECULAR HUMANISM: THE SEARCH FOR A COMMON MORALITY Xi (1991).

*Forgotten Americans-A Special Report on Medical Care for Blacks*, 9 AMERICAN HEALTH: FITNESS OF BODY AND MIND 52 (1990).

Galton, Francis, *Notes on the Early Days of the Eugenics Education Society*, in WAR AGAINST THE WEAK: EUGENICS AND AMERICA'S CAMPAIGN TO CREATE A MASTER RACE 18 (Edwin Black ed. 2003).

Gamble, Vanessa N., GERMS HAVE NO COLOR LINE: BLACKS AND AMERICAN MEDICINE, 1900-1940 (1989).

Garbarino, Joseph W., HEALTH PLANS AND COLLECTIVE BARGAINING (1960).

Gordon, Linda, WOMAN'S BODY, WOMAN'S RIGHT: A SOCIAL HISTORY OF BIRTH CONTROL IN AMERICA (1976).

Gornick, Marian E., VULNERABLE POPULATIONS AND MEDICARE SERVICES: WHY DO DISPARITIES EXIST? (2000).

Grant, George, GRAND ILLUSIONS: THE LEGACY OF PLANNED PARENTHOOD (2d ed. 1992).

Hall, Mark A., Ira Mark Gellman, & Daniel S. Strouse, HEALTH CARE LAW AND ETHICS IN A NUTSHELL (1990).

Harris, Leonard, *Autonomy Under Duress*, in BLACK PERSPECTIVES ON BIOMEDICAL ETHICS (Harley E. Flack & Edmund D. Pellegrino eds. 1992).

Hatcher, R.G., *Medicine of the Ghetto*, 21 in MEDICINE IN THE GHETTO (J.C. Norman Ed., 1969).

Helman, Cecil, CULTURE, HEALTH AND ILLNESS (1995).

Hertz, Brian, *Toward Successful Urban Perinatal Health Care*, in "IT JUST AIN'T FAIR": THE ETHICS OF HEALTH CARE FOR AFRICAN AMERICANS 201 (Annette Dula & Sara Goering eds 1994).

Holmes, Helen Bequaert & Laura M. Purdy Eds., FEMINIST PERSPECTIVES IN MEDICAL ETHICS (1992).

Howard University, HUMAN EXPERIMENT: AN ANCIENT NOTION IN A MODERN TECHNOLOGY (1974).

Hughes, Dana et al., THE HEALTH OF AMERICA'S CHILDREN: MATERNAL AND CHILD HEALTH DATA BOOK 10 (Children's Defense Fund 1989).

Ingelfinger, Franz J., et. al., *The Poor*, in NATIONAL ACADEMY OF SCIENCE, EXPERIMENTS AND RESEARCH WITH HUMANS: VALUES IN CONFLICT (1975).

Institute of Medicine, UNEQUAL TREATMENT: CONFRONTING RACIAL AND ETHNIC DISPARITIES IN HEALTH CARE, Brian D. Smedley, Y. Stith, & Alan R. Nelson, Editors, Committee on Understanding and Eliminating Racial and Ethnic Disparities in Health Care (2003).

Isaacs, Mareasa R. & Marva P. Benjamin, TOWARDS A CULTURALLY COMPETENT SYSTEM OF CARE, Volume II (1991).

Jones, James H., BAD BLOOD: THE TUSKEGEE SYPHILIS EXPERIMENT (1981).

Jones, Jr., Woodrow & Mitchell F. Rice, *Black Health Care: An Overview, in Health Care Issues* in BLACK AMERICA: POLICIES, PROBLEMS AND PROSPECTS (Woodrow Jones, Jr. & Mitchell F. Rice eds. 1987).

Kagawa-Singer, Marjorie, *Diverse Cultural (Beliefs and Practices About Death and Dying in the Elderly*, in CULTURAL DIVERSITY AND GERIATRIC CARE: CHALLENGES TO THE HEALTH PROFESSIONS (Darryl Wieland et. al. eds 1994).

Kaiser Commission on Key Facts, WELFARE AND WORK: HOW DO THEY AFFECT PARENTS' HEALTH CARE COVERAGE?, (June 17, 2002).

King, Patricia A., *The Past as Prologue: Race, Class, and Gene Discrimination*, in GENE MAPPING: USING LAW AND ETHICS AS GUIDES (George J. Annas & Sherman Elias eds 1992).

Kleinman, Arthur, PATIENTS AND HEALERS IN THE CONTEXT OF CULTURE (1980).

Kravitis, Joanna & John Schneider, *Health Care Need and Actual Use by Age, Race and Income*, EQUITY IN HEALTH SERVICES (1975).

Kunits, Stephen J. & Jerrold E. Levy, *Navajos*, in ETHNICITY AND MEDICAL CARE (1981).

Lantos, John D., *Race, Prenatal Care, and Infant Mortality*, in "IT JUST AIN'T FAIR": THE ETHICS OF HEALTH CARE FOR AFRICAN AMERICANS 67(Annette Dula & Sara Goering eds. 1994).

Larned, Deborah, *The Epidemic in Unnecessary Hysterectomy*, in SEIZING OUR BODIES: THE POLITICS OF WOMEN'S HEALTH 202 (Claudia Dreifus ed. 1977).

Law, Sylvia A., BLUE CROSS: WHAT WENT WRONG? 6 (1974).

Lyons, Albert S. & R. Joseph Petrucelli II, MEDICINE: AN ILLUSTRATED HISTORY 523 (1987).

NAACP Legal Defense & Educational Fund, Inc. AN AFRICAN AMERICAN HEALTH CARE AGENDA: STRATEGIES FOR REFORMING AN UNJUST SYSTEM, RACIAL DISPARITIES IN MEDICAID COVERAGE FOR NURSING HOME CARE (1991).

Nelkin, Dorothy & Laurence Tancredi, DANGEROUS DIAGNOSTICS: THE SOCIAL POWER OF BIOLOGICAL INFORMATION 106 (1994).

Okazawa-Rey, Margo, *Grandparents Who Care: An Empowerment Model of Health Care*, in "IT JUST AIN'T FAIR": THE ETHICS OF HEALTH CARE FOR AFRICAN AMERICANS (Annette Dula & Sara Goering eds 1994).

Pellegrino, Edmund D., *Foreword to* AFRICAN AMERICAN PERSPECTIVES ON BIOMEDICAL ETHICS (Harley E. Flack & Edmund D. Pellegrino eds 1992).

Pellegrino, Edmund D., *Response to Leonard, Harris*, AFRICAN AMERICAN PERSPECTIVES ON BIOMEDICAL ETHICS, 150, (Harley E. Flack & Edmund D. Pellegrino eds. 1992).

Perfecto, Ivette, *Pesticide Exposure of Farm Workers and The International Connection*, in RACE AND THE INCIDENCE OF ENVIRONMENTAL HAZARDS, 180 (Bunyan & Paul Mohai eds. 1992).

Power, G.D. *Allocation of Risk in Managed Care Organization Programs*, in MANAGED CARE ORGANIZATION HEALTH CARE 393:279 (PLI Commercial Law and Practice Handbook Series)(September 25, 1986).

Rene, Antonio A., *Racial Differences in Mortality: Blacks and Whites*, in Woodrow Jones, Jr. & Mitchell F. Rice, BLACK HEALTH CARE: AN OVERVIEW IN HEALTH CARE ISSUES IN BLACK AMERICA: POLICIES PROBLEMS AND PROSPECTS, 3- (1987). at 21

Robert Wood Johnson Foundation, HOW LANGUAGE BARRIERS HINDER ACCESS AND DELIVERY OF QUALITY CARE, www.rwjf.org (Last Visited: June 26, 2001).

Roberts, Dorothy, KILLING THE BLACK BODY (1997).

Rosenberg, Charles E., THE CARE OF STRANGERS: THE RISE OF AMERICA'S HOSPITAL SYSTEM (1995).

Savitt, Todd L., MEDICINE AND SLAVERY: THE DISEASES AND HEALTH CARE OF BLACKS IN ANTEBELLUM VIRGINIA (2002).

Scham, Max, BLACKS AND AMERICAN MEDICAL CARE 20 (1973).

Schlesinger, Mark,*Paying the Price: Medical Care, Minorities and the Newly Competitive Health Care System*, in HEALTH POLICIES AND BLACK AMERICANS 275 (David Willis ed., 1989).

Secundy, Marian Gray, *Response to Kwasi Wiredu*, in AFRICAN AMERICAN PERSPECTIVES ON BIOMEDICAL ETHICS 99, (Harley E. Flack & Edmund D. Pellegrino eds 1992).

Semmes, Clovis E., Racism, HEALTH AND POST-INDUSTRIALIZATION (1996).

Sherwin, Susan, No Longer Patient: Feminist Ethics and Health Care (1992).

Smith, David A., Discrimination in Access to Nursing Homes in Pennsylvania (1991),

Torrens, Paul R., *Historical Evolution and Overview of Health Services in the United States*, in Introduction to Health Services 3 (Stephen J. Williams & Paul R. Torrens eds. 2002).

Twiss, Sumner B., *Problems of Social Justice in Applied Human Genetics*, in Genetic Counseling: Facts, Values, and Norms 255 (Alexander M. Caprom et al. eds. 1979).

U.S. Department of Health and Human Services, Health Status of Minorities and Low Income Groups: Third Edition (1991).

U.S. Department of Health and Human Services, Public Health Services, Health Status of Minorities and Low Income Groups (1985).

United States Department of Health & Human Services, African Americans and Smoking at a Glance: A Report of the Surgeon General (1995).

Weiler, Paul C., Medical Malpractice on Trial 13 (1991).

Weisbord, Robert G., Genocide? Birth Control and the African American (1975).

White, Evelyn C. & Shafia Mawushi Monroe, *Interview: Lay Midwifery and the Traditional Child-Bearing Group*, in "It Just Ain't Fair": The Ethics of Health Care for African Americans 208-20 (Annete Dula & Sara Goering eds 1994).

Wiredu, Kwasi, *The Moral Foundations of African Culture*, in African American Perspectives on Biomedical Ethics 80-81 (Harley E. Flack & Edmund D. Pellegrino eds 1992).

## Health - Other Materials

Agency for Toxic Substances and Disease Registry, Centers for Disease Control, The Nature and Extent of Lead Poisoning in Children in the United States A Report to Congress (1988).

Andersen, Ronald M. et al., Total Survey Error: Applications to Improve Health Surveys (1979).

Basic Indicators of All Member States, World Health Organization Report 2000, Http://www.who.int/whr/2002/annex/en/ (Last Visited: December 6, 2003).

Butts, Cassandra, *The Color of Money: Barriers of Access to Private Health Care Facilities for African Americans*, (Unpublished Manuscript).

Centers for Medicare and Medicaid Services, http://www.cms.hhs.gov/statistics/nhe/historical/t1.asp (Last Visited: March 24, 2005).

*Cigarette Company Considered 'Sweets' to Lure Youngsters.*

Commission for Racial Justice, Toxic Wastes and Race in the United States: A National Report on the Racial and Socio-economic Characteristics of Communities with Hazardous Waste Sites 13 (1987).

Cooke, Michael Anthony, *The Health of Blacks During Reconstruction*, 1862-1870 (1983) (unpublished Ph.D. dissertation, University of Maryland).

*Current Estimates from the National Health Interview Survey, 1985, Series 10, No. 160*, National Center for Health Statistics, Table 3.

Hahn, Lorraine P. et al., *Cigarette Smoking and Cessation Behaviors Among Urban Blacks and Whites*, 105 Public Health Report 290 (1990).

Health Care Financing Administration, End Stage Renal Disease Patient: Profile Tables (1988).

HEALTH, UNITED STATES, 1995,National Center for Health Statistics, U.S. Dept. of Health and Human Services, Public Health Service, Centers for Disease Control, National Center for Health Statistics, Washington, D.C. (1996)

HEALTH, UNITED STATES, 2003, National Center for Health Statistics, U.S. Dept. of Health and Human Services, Public Health Service, Centers for Disease Control, National Center for Health Statistics, Washington, D.C. (2004)

HEALTH, UNITED STATES 2004 National Center for Health Statistics, U.S. Dept. of Health and Human Services, Public Health Service, Centers for Disease Control, National Center for Health Statistics, Washington, D.C. (2005)

http://www.cms.hhs.gov/medicaid/managed care organization care/trends03.pdf (Last Visited: March 24, 2005).

Jones, James H., *The Tuskegee Legacy: AIDs and the Black Community*, 22 HASTINGS CENTER REPORT 38 (1992).

Kaiser Commission on Medicaid and the Uninsured, MEDICAID TODAY: A PROFILE OF THE LOW-INCOME UNINSURED, 5 (1999), Available at Http://www.kff.org/content1999/2158/lowincomunins.pdf. http://kff.org/ (Last Visited: March 25, 2005).

Kaiser Commission on Medicaid and Uninsured, *The Uninsured: A Primer, Key Facts About Americans Without Health Insurance* (November 2004).

MEALEY'S LITIGATION REPORT: *Tobacco, Attorneys General, Tobacco Companies Enter into Historic $368.5 Billion Pact*, July 3, 1997, at 3.

*Medical Technology Assessment: Hearings on House Rule 5496 Before The Subcommittee on Health and The Environment of The Committee on Energy and Commerce*, 98th Congress 2d Session 544 (1984) (Statement of Raymond Dross, Medical Doctor, on Behalf of The Health Insurance Association of America).

*Minority Update: Genocide to Some Vital Choice to Others*, AMERICAN POLITICAL NETWORK: ABORTION REPORT, June 17, 1992.

MORTALITY AMONG BLACK AND WHITE WOMEN BY STATE: UNITED STATES, 1987-1996, Http://www.ced.gov/od/oc/media/fact/mmabww.htm (Last Visited: December 10, 2003).

National Commission on Quality Assurance, HEALTH PLAN AND EMPLOYER DATA INFORMATION SET (Version 3.0 1998).

NATIONAL HEALTH EXPENDITURES AGGREGATE AND PER CAPITA AMOUNTS, PERCENT DISTRIBUTION, AND AVERAGE ANNUAL PERCENT GROWTH, BY SOURCE OF FUNDS: SELECTED CALENDAR YEARS 1980-2003.

*National Minority Cancer Awareness Week – April 17-23, 2000*, 49(15) MORBIDITY AND MORTALITY WEEKLY REPORT 330 (April 21, 2000).

Office of Inspector General, THE DISTRIBUTION OF ORGANS FOR TRANSPLANTATION: EXPECTATIONS AND PRACTICES 8 (1991).

Office of Minority Health, CHARACTERISTICS OF MINORITY HEALTH ENTITIES BY STATE (Table 1) (Unpublished).

Office of Smoking & Health, United States Department Health & Human Services, TOBACCO USE IN 1986: METHODS AND BASIC TABULATIONS FROM ADULT USE OF TOBACCO SURVEY (1986).

Office of Technology Assessment, MAPPING OUR GENES--THE GENOME PROJECTS: HOW BIG, HOW FAST? 24 United States Congressional Publication Number Ota-ba-373 (1988).

Office of Technology Assessment, MEDICAL TECHNOLOGY AND COSTS OF THE MEDICARE PROGRAM 45-61(1984).

Office of the United Nations High Commissioner for Human Rights, STATUS OF RATIFICATIONS OF THE PRINCIPAL HUMAN RIGHT TREATIES, STATUS AS OF JUNE 17, 2002, Available at Http://www.unhchr.ch/html/menu3/b/d_icerd.htm (Last Visited: June 26, 2002).

Office on Smoking & Health, United States Department of Health & Human Services, THE IMPACT OF CIGARETTE SMOKING ON MINORITY POPULATIONS (1987) .

President's Commission for the Study of Ethical Problems in Medicine and Biomedical and Behavioral Research, THE ETHICAL AND LEGAL IMPLICATIONS OF INFORMED CONSENT IN THE PATIENT-PRACTITIONER RELATIONSHIP 7 (1982).

Public Health Services, Department Health & Human Services, PREVENTING TOBACCO USE AMONG YOUNG PEOPLE: A REPORT OF THE SURGEON GENERAL (1994).

*Racial Disparities in Medicaid Coverage for Nursing Home Care* (1991) (Unpublished Data).

Raphael, Alan, *Health and Medical Care of Black People in the United States During Reconstruction* (1972) (unpublished Ph.D. dissertation, University of Chicago).

Sager, Alan, *The Closure of Hospitals That Serve the Poor: Implications for Health Planning*, A Statement to the Subcommittee on Health and Environment, Committee on Energy and Commerce, United States House of Representatives, 2 (April 30, 1982).

Sanger, Margaret, Planned Parenthood, http://www.plannedparenthood.org/about/thisispp/sanger.html (Last Visited: March 25, 2005).

The Commonwealth Fund, DIVERSE COMMUNITIES, COMMON CONCERNS: ASSESSING HEALTH CARE QUALITY FOR MINORITY AMERICANS, www.cmwf.org. (Last Visited: June 26, 2001).

The National Commission for the Protection of Human Subjects of Biomedical and Behavioral Research, THE BELMONT REPORT: ETHICAL GUIDELINES FOR THE PROTECTION OF HUMAN SUBJECTS OF RESEARCH (1978).

The Partnership for Organ Donation and the Annenberg Washington Program, SOLVING THE DONOR SHORTAGE BY MEETING FAMILY NEEDS: A COMMUNICATIONS MODEL 4 (Oct. 30-31, 1990).

U.S. Dept. Of Health & Human Services, MINORITIES & WOMEN IN THE HEALTH FIELDS (1990).

United States Department of Health & Human Services, HEALTH STATUS OF MINORITIES AND LOW-INCOME GROUPS 147 tbl. 9 (1990).

United States Department of Health & Human Services, 1 EXECUTIVE SUMMARY REPORT OF THE SECRETARY'S TASK FORCE ON BLACK & MINORITY HEALTH 88 (1985).

United States Department Of Health & Human Services, MINORITY & WOMEN IN THE HEALTH FIELDS, Table 3 (1990).

United States Department Of Health & Human Services, SECRETARY'S TASKFORCE REPORT ON MINORITY HEALTH (1986).

United States General Accounting Office, SITING OF HAZARDOUS WASTE LANDFILLS AND THEIR CORRELATION WITH RACIAL AND ECONOMIC STATUS OF SURROUNDING COMMUNITIES (Jun. 1, 1983), Available at Http://www.gao.gov/ (Last Visited: August 8, 2002).

United States House of Representative, Committee on Ways and Means, 1991. GREEN BOOK, BACKGROUND MATERIAL AND DATE ON PROGRAMS WITHIN THE JURISDICTION OF THE COMMITTEE ON WAYS AND MEANS, Washington, D.C.: United States Government Printing Office, May 7 (1991).

United States. Dept. of Health and Human Services, Healthy people 2010 / U.S. Department of Health and Human Services (2001)

Washington State Department Of Health, DATA REPORT ON PEOPLE OF COLOR 33.

Whiteis, D.G., *Hospital and Community Characteristics in Closures of 1980-87*, 107(4) PUBLIC HEALTH REPORTS 409-416 (1992).

Wolf, Susan M., *Health Care Reform and the Future of Physician Ethics*, HASTINGS CENTER REPORT, March-April 1994, at 28.

*Women: African Americans "No Longer Silent" on Abortion*, AMERICAN POLITICAL NETWORK: ABORTION REPORT, Aug. 25, 1992.

## LEGAL PRIMARY SOURCE

### CONSTITUTION

United States Constitution Article. II, Clause 2.

### COURT CASES

*Alexander v. Choate*, 469 U.S. 287 (1985).
*Alexander v. Sandoval*, 532 United States 275 (2001).
*American Hospital Association v. Schweiker*, 721 F.2d 170 (7th Cir. 1983).
*Anna J. v. Mark C.*, 286 California Reporter 369, 380-81 (California Court of Appeals 1991).
*Baumgartner v Harrisburg Housing Authority*, 21 Federal 3d 541(3rd Circuit 1994).
*Brown v. Board of Education*, 347 United States. 483 (Supreme Court 1954).
*Bryan v. Koch*, 627 Federal 2d 612 (1980).
*Buck v. Bell*, 274 United States 200 (1927).
*Byran v. Koch*, 627 F.2d. 612 (1980).
*Cox v. Stanton*, 529 Federal 2d 47 (4th Circuit 1975).
*Cruzan v. Director, Missouri Department of Health*, 497 United States 261(1990).
*Desnick v. American Broadcasting*, 44 Federal Reports3d 1345 (1995).
*Havens Realty Corporation v. Coleman*. 455 United States 363 (1982).
*Howe v. Hull*, 874 Federal Supplement 779, 789 (Northern District Ohio 1994).
*Johnson v. University of Chicago Hospitals*, 982 F.2d. 230 (1992).
*Lesley v. Chie*, 250 Federal3d 47 (1st Circuit 2001).
*Linda R.S. v. Richard D.*, 410 United States 614 (1973)
*Linton v. Carney*, 77 Federal Supplement 925 (M.d. Tennessee 1990).
*Lynn V. Regents of University of California*, 656 Federal2d 1337 (California Attorney General 1981).
*Madison-Hughes v. Shalala*, 80 Federal3d 1121, at 1123 (6th Circuit 1996).
*Marbley v Bane*, 57 Federal3d 224, 234 (2nd Circuit 1995).
*NAACP v. Wilmington Medical Ctr., Inc.* 657 F.2d. 1322 (1981).
*National Association for the Advancement of Colored People v. Wilmington Medical Center*, 657 Federal2d 1322 (1981).
*Plessy v. Ferguson*, 163 United States 538, 6 Supreme Court 1138 (1896)
Regents of the University of California v. Bakke, 438 U.S. 265 (1978).
*Relf v. Weinberger*, 372 Federal Supplement 1196, 1199 (District Court of the District of Columbia, 1974).
*Schloendorff v. Society of New York Hospital.*, 105 N.E. 92 (N.Y. 1914).
*Stanton v Southern Berkshire Regional School District*, 197 Federal3d 574 (1st Circuit 1999).
*The Civil Rights Cases*, 109 United States. 3, 3 Supreme Court 18 (1883).
*United Automobile Workers v. Johnson Controls, Inc*, 499 United States 187 (1991).
*United States v. the La Jeune Eugenie*, 2 Mason 409, 26 F.Cas. 832, No. 15,551 (C.C.D.Mass. May Term 1822
*Walker v.. Pierce*, 560 Federal 2d 609, 613 (4th Circuit 1977).

### STATUTES

2 United States Code § 1395.
42 United State Code § 1395x
42 United State Code § 1396(a) (30).
42 United State Code § 1396a(a)(28).

42 United State Code § 1396c(d) (1988).
42 United State Code Annotated § 1395 dd(a)-(d) (West Supp. 1992).
42 United State Codes § 3604.
42 United States Code § 291 A(1).
42 United States Code § 291-2910 (2002).
42 United States Code Annotated § 2000d-4 (1981).
42 United States Code Annotated § 1395 Dd(a) (West Supplement 1992).
42 United States Code Annotated § 1395 Dd(a)-(D) (West Supplement 1992).
42 United States Code Annotated § 2000d-1 (1981).
42 United States Code § 1396d(i) (1988).
Arizona Review Statute Annotated §11-297.01 1-3d (1956).
Civil Rights Act of 1875, 18 Statute 335.
CIVIL RIGHTS ACT OF 1965 (Public Law 88-352)
CIVIL RIGHTS ACTS OF 1964.
Social Security Amendments of 1965, Public Law Number 89-97, 87 Statute
286.
SOCIAL SECURITY AMENDMENTS OF 1965, PUBLIC LAW NUMBER 89-97, 79
Statute 286 (Codified as Amended in Scattered Sections of 42 United States Code).
SUMMARY RECORD OF THE 1475TH MEETING: UNITED STATE OF AMERICA
22/08/2001/cerd/c/sr1475 (Summary Record).
Title III, "Reduction in Underage Tobacco Use" Senate 1530, 105th Congress
300-317 (1997).
TITLE VI OF THE 1964 CIVIL RIGHTS ACT, Public Law Number 99-352, 378
252 (Codified at 42 United States Code Section 2000d-200d-4 (1982).
OHIO REVISED CODE ANNOTATED. §§ 2151.03(A).
Public Law Number 103-43, 107 Statute 122 (codified in scattered sections of
8 and 42 United States Code (1994 & Supplement II 1996).
Public Law Number 79-725, 60 Statute 1040 (1946) (codified at 42 United
States Code §§ 291291o (1976).
Public Law Number. 103-43, 107 Statute 122 (Codified in Scattered Sections
Of 8 and 42 United States Code (1994 & Supplement II 1996)
VOTING RIGHTS ACT OF 1965.

## REGULATIONS

28 Code of Federal Regulations § 42.406(a) (1992).
42 Code of Federal Regulation § 440.150 (1991)
42 Code of Federal Regulation § 441.257 (1991) (informed consent).
42 Code of Federal Regulation § 441.258 (1991) (consent form requirements).
42 Code of Federal Regulation §§ 441.250-259 (1991) (sterilizations).
42 Code of Federal Regulation. § 59.5(a)(1) (1995).
42 Code of Federal Regulations § 456.271 and 456.372.
42 Code of Federal Regulations § 440.40 (1991).
42 Code of Federal Regulations § 441.253 (1994).
42 Code of Federal Regulations §§ 441.202-.203 (1994).
45 Code of Federal Regulations ' 80.3(b)(2) (1991).
45 Code of Federal Regulations § 80.13(i) (1991).
45 Code of Federal Regulations § 80.3(b)(1)(i) (1991).
45 Code of Federal Regulations § 80.3(b)(1)-(3) (1991).
45 Code of Federal Regulations § 80.3(b)(6)(i) (1991).
45 Code of Federal Regulations § 80.3(b)(I)(Vii)(2) (1991).
45 Code of Federal Regulations § 80.6(3) (1991), ' 80.3(b) (1991).
45 Code of Federal Regulations § 80.6(b) (1991).

## LEGAL SECONDARY SOURCES

### LEGAL SECONDARY - ARTICLES

978 DIGEST ON UNITED STATES PRACTICE IN INTERNATIONAL LAW 440-46.

Aeschleman, Heather K., *The White World of Nursing Homes: The Myriad Barriers to Access Facing Today's Elderly Minorities*, 8 ELDER LAW JOURNAL 367-391 (2000).

Allen, Jessie, *A Possible Remedy for Unthinking Discrimination*, 61 BROOKLYN LAW REVIEW 1299 (1995).

Asaro, Andrea, *The Judicial Portrayal of the Physician in Abortion and Sterilization Decisions: the Use and Abuse of Medical Discretion*, 6 HARVARD WOMEN'S LAW JOURNAL 51, 93-101 (1983).

Ayres, Ian et al., *Unequal Racial Access to Kidney Transplantation*, 46 VANDERBILT LAW REVIEW 805 (1993).

Ayres, Ian, *Fair Driving: Gender and Race Discrimination in Retail Car Negotiations*, 104 HARVARD LAW REVIEW 817 (1991).

Balkin, Jack M., *History Lesson. Five Supreme Court Justices Think Congress doesn't have the Power to Pass New Laws against Discrimination. They're Forgetting about the Civil Rights Movements of the 19th and 20th Centuries.*, 2002-AUGUST LEGAL AFFAIRS 44 (July/August, 2002).

Barrow, Jackie, *Implications of the Emergency Medical Treatment and Active Labor Act (EMTALA) on Differences Based on Race and Gender in the Treatment of Patients Presenting to a Hospital Emergency Department with Chest Pain*, 15 SAINT LOUIS UNIVERSITY PUBLIC LAW REVIEW 278 (1996).

Beauchamp, Tom L., *Principles and Other Emerging Paradigms in Bioethics*, 69 INDIANA LAW JOURNAL 955 (1994).

Been, Vicki, *Locally Undesirable Land Uses in Minority Neighborhoods: Disproportionate Siting or Market Dynamics?*, 103 YALE LAW JOURNAL 1383 (1994).

Belton, Robert, *Mixed-Motive Cases in Employment Discrimination Law Revisited: A Brief Updated View of the Swamp*, 51 MERCER LAW REVIEW 651(2000).

Berg, Daniel R.,*A History of Health Care for the Indigent in St. Louis: 1904-2001*, 48 SAINT LOUIS UNIVERSITY LAW JOURNAL 191 (Fall 2003).

Bernier, Barbara L., *Class, Race, and Poverty: Medical Technologies and Socio-Political Choices*, 11 HARVARD BLACKLETTER LAW JOURNAL 115 (1994).

Bess, Carol Johann, *Gender Bias in Health Care: A Life or Death Issue for Women with Coronary Heart Disease*, 6 HASTINGS WOMEN'S LAW JOURNAL 41 (Winter 1995).

Black, Derek, *Picking up the Pieces after Alexander V. Sandoval: Resurrecting a Private Cause of Action for Disparate Impact*, 81 NORTH CAROLINA LAW REVIEW 356 (December, 2002).

Bloche, M. Gregg, *Race and Discretion in American Medicine*, 1 YALE JOURNAL OF HEALTH POLICY, LAW AND ETHICS 95 (2001)

Bloche, M.Gregg, *Race and Discretion in American Medicine*, 1 YALE JOURNAL HEALTH POLICY LAW & ETHICS 95 (2001).

Blumstein, James F. *Court Action, Agency Reaction: The Hill-Burton Act as a Case Study*, 69 IOWA LAW REVIEW 1227 (July, 1984).

Bogen, David S., *Precursors of Rosa Parks: Maryland Transportation Cases Between the Civil War and the Beginning of World War*, 63 MARYLAND LAW REVIEW 721 (2004).

Bonnyman, Jr., Gordon, *Unmasking Jim Crow*, 18 JOURNAL OF HEALTH POLITICS, POLICY AND LAW 871 (1993).

Bowser, Rene, *Racial Bias in Medical Treatment*, 105 DICKINSON LAW REVIEW 365 (Spring 2001).

Bowser, Rene, *Racial Profiling in Health Care: An Institutional Analysis of Medical Treatment Disparities*, 7 MICHIGAN JOURNAL OF RACE & LAW 79 (Fall 2001).

Brosnan, James W., *Black Caucus Examines Tobacco Lobby's Sway*, COMMERCIAL

APPEAl (Memphis, Tenn.), Sept. 15, 1996.

Bullard, Robert D., *Environmental Justice: A New Framework for Action*, 5 ENVIRONMENTAL LAW NEWS, Number 1, 3 (1996).

Bullard, Robert D., *The Legacy of American Apartheid and Environmental Racism*, 9 SAINT JOHN'S JOURNAL OF LEGAL COMMENT 445 (1994).

Burrell, Darci Elaine, *The Norplant Solution: Norplant and the Control of African American Motherhood*, 5 University of California at Los Angeles WOMEN'S LAW JOURNAL 401 (1995).

Cantor, Norman L. & George C. Thomas III, *The Legal Bounds of Physician Conduct Hastening Death*, 48 BUFFALO LAW REVIEW 83, 160 (2000).

Capron, Alexander Morgan & Vicki Michel, *Law and Bioethics*, 27 LOYOLA LOS ANGELES LAW REVIEW 25 (1993).

Cate, Fred H., *Emerging Paradigms in Bioethics: Posthumous Autonomy Revisited*, 69 INDIANA LAW JOURNAL 1067 (1994).

Chamallas, Martha, *The Architecture of Bias: Deep Structures in Tort Law*, 146 UNIVERSITY OF PENNSYLVANIA LAW REVIEW 463 (1998).

Cherry, April L., SOCIAL CONTRACT THEORY, WELFARE REFORM, RACE, AND THE MALE SEX-RIGHT, 75 OREGON LAW REVIEW 1037 (Winter, 1996).

Chin, Gabriel J., *The "Voting Rights Act of 1867": The Constitutionality of Federal Regulation of Suffrage During Reconstruction*, 82 NORTH CAROLINA LAW REVIEW 1581 (June 2004).

Coale, David S., *Norplant Bonuses and the Unconstitutional Conditions Doctrine*, 71 TEXAS LAW REVIEW 189 (1992).

Cole, Luke W., *Empowerment as the Key to Environmental Protection: The Need for Environmental Poverty Law*, 19 ECOLOGY LAW QUARTERLY 619 (1992).

Crossley, Mary, *Infected Judgment: Legal Responses to Physician Bias*, 48 VILLANOVA LAW REVIEW 195 (2003).

Davis, Peggy C., *Law as Micro-Aggression*, 98 Yale Law Journal 1559 (1989).

Davis, Thomas J., *More Than Segregation, Racial Identity: The Neglected Question in Plessy V. Ferguson* 10 WASHINGTON AND LEE RACE AND ETHNIC ANCESTRY LAW JOURNAL 1 (Spring 2004).

de la Vega, Connie, *Civil Rights During the 1990s: New Treaty Law Could Help Immensely*, 65 UNIVERSITY OF CINCINNATI LAW REVIEW 423 (1997).

Denny, Marilyn, *Managed Care: Increasing Inequality & Individualism*, 3 QUINNIPIAC LAW REVIEW 59 (1999/2000).

Dudziak, Mary, *Desegregation as a Cold War Imperative*, 41 STANFORD LAW REVIEW 61 (1988).

*Environmental Defense Fund, Inc. v Environmental Protection Agency*, 716 Federal2d 915 (DC Circuit 1983).

Evans, Jill E., *Challenging the Racism in Environmental Racism: Redefining the Concept of Intent*, 40 ARIZONA LAW REVIEW 219 (Winter, 1998).

Farrior, Stephanie, *The Neglected Pillar: The Teaching Tolerance Provision of The International Convention on The Elimination of All Forms of Racial Discrimination*, 5 ILSA JOURNAL OF INTERNATIONAL & COMPARATIVE LAW 291 (1999).

Flagg, Barbara J., *Was Blind, But Now I See: White Race Consciousness and the Requirement of Discriminatory Intent*, 91 MICHIGAN LAW REVIEW 953 (1993).

Fox, Jr., James W., *Democratic Citizenship and Congressional Reconstruction: Defining and Implementing the Privileges and Immunities of Citizenship*, 13 TEMPLE POLITICAL AND CIVIL RIGHTS LAW REVIEW 453 (Spring 2004).

Freeman, Alan D., *Legitimizing Racial Discrimination Through Anti-discrimination Law: A Critical Review of Supreme Court Doctrine*, 62 MINNESOTA LAW REVIEW 1049 (1978).

Gabel, J. and Dan Ermann, et al, *The Emergence and Future of PPOs.*, 11 JOURNAL OF HEALTH POLITICS, POLICY AND LAW 305 (Summer 1986).

Gareis-Smith, Donna, *Environmental Racism: The Failure of Equal Protection to*

*Provide a Judicial Remedy and the Potential of Title VI of the 1964 Civil Rights Act*, 13 TEMPLE ENVIRONMENTAL LAW & TECHNOLOGY JOURNAL 57 (1994).

Ginzberg, Janet F., *Compulsory Contraception as a Condition of Probation: The Use and Abuse of Norplant*, 58 BROOKLYN LAW REVIEW 979 (1992).

Gionis, Thomas A., Carlos A. Camargo, Jr., & Anthony S. Zito, Jr., *The Intentional Tort of Patient Dumping: A New State Cause of Action to Address the Shortcomings of the Federal Emergency Medical Treatment and Active Labor Act (EMTALA)*, 1 AMERICAN UNIVERSITY LAW REVIEW 173 (October, 2002).

Gould, Stephen Jay, *Carrie Buck's Daughter*, 2 CONSTITUTIONAL COMMENT. 331 (1985).

Grosboll, Dick, *Sterilization Abuse: Current State of the Law and Remedies for Abuse*, 10 GOLDEN GATE UNIVERSITY LAW REVIEW 1147 (1980).

Hampton, Daniel K., *Title VI Challenges by Private Parties to the Location of Health Care Facilities: Toward a Just and Effective Action*, 37 BOSTON COLLEGE LAW REVIEW 517 (1996).

Haydons, Stephen E., *A Measure of Our Progress: Testing for Race Discrimination in Public Accommodations*, 44 UNIVERSITY OF CALIFORNIA AT LOS ANGELES LAW REVIEW 1207 (April, 1997).

Higginbotham, Jr., A. Leon, *The Ten Precepts of American Slavery Jurisprudence: Chief Justice Roger Taney's Defense and Justice Thurgood Marshall's Condemnation of the Precept of Black Inferiority*, 17 CARDOZO LAW REVIEW 1695 (May, 1996)

Ifill, Sherrilyn A., *Creating a Truth and Reconciliation Commission for Lynching*, 21 LAW AND INEQUALITY: A JOURNAL OF THEORY AND PRACTICE 263 (Summer 2003).

Ikemoto, Lisa C., *The Fuzzy Logic of Race and Gender in the Mismeasure of Asian American Women's Health Needs*, 65 UNIVERSITY OF CINCINNATI LAW REVIEW 799 (Spring 1997)..

Jennings, James, *The International Convention on The Elimination of All Forms of Racial Discrimination: Implications for Challenging Racial Hierarchy*, 40 HOWARD LAW JOURNAL 597 (1997).

Jensen, Arthur R., *How Much Can We Boost IQ and Scholastic Achievement?*, 39 HARVARD EDUCATION REVIEW 1 (1969).

Johnson, Sandra H., *The Changing Nature of the Bioethics Movement*, 53 MARYLAND LAW REVIEW 1051 (1994).

Johnson, Sheri Lynn, *Unconscious Racism and the Criminal Law*, 73 CORNELL LAW REVIEW 1016 (1988).

Kelly, Deborah, *Tobacco Settlement Attacked Again, Black Physicians' Group Believes Proposal Is Weak*, RICHMOND TIMES-DISPATCH, Aug. 6, 1997, at A10.

Kelly, Kathryn A., *The Target Marketing of Alcohol and Tobacco Billboards to Minority Communities*, 5 UNIVERSITY OF FLORIDA. JOURNAL OF LAW. & PUBLIC POLICY 33 (1992).

Klaben, Mathew J., *Split-Recovery Statutes: The Interplay of the Takings and Excessive Fines Clauses*, 80 CORNELL LAW REVIEW 104 (1994).

Knapp, Kiyoko Kamio, *Language Minorities: Forgotten Victims of Discrimination?*, 11 GEORGETOWN IMMIGRATION LAW JOURNAL 747 (Summer 1997).

Lado, Marianne Engelman, *Breaking the Barriers of Access to Health Care: A Discussion of the Role of Civil Rights Litigation and the Relationship Between Burdens of Proof and the Experience of Denial*, 60 BROOKLYN LAW REVIEW 239 (1994).

Lado, Marianne Engleman, *Unfinished Agenda: The Need for Civil Rights Litigation to Address Race Discrimination and Inequalities in Health Care Delivery*, 6 TEXAS FORUM ON CIVIL LIBERTIES & CIVIL RIGHTS 1 (Summer 2001).

Lado, Marianne Engleman, *Unfinished Agenda: the Need for Civil Rights Litigation to Address Race Discrimination and Inequalities in Health Care Delivery*, 6 TEXAS FORUM ON CIVIL LIBERTIES. & CIVIL RIGHTS 1 (Summer 2001).

Law, Sylvia A., *Addiction, Autonomy and Advertising*, 77 IOWA L. REVIEW 909 (1992).

Lawrence III, Charles, *The Id, The Ego, and Equal Protection: Reckoning with Unconscious Racism*, 39 STANFORD LAW REVIEW 317 (1987).

Leach, Bryan W., *Race as Mission Critical: The Occupational Need Rationale in Military Affirmative Action and Beyond*, 113 YALE LAW JOURNAL 1093 (March, 2004).

Lillquist, Erik & Charles A. Sullivan, *The Law and Genetics of Racial Profiling in Medicine*, 39 HARVARD CIVIL RIGHTS-CIVIL LIBERTIES LAW REVIEW 391 (Summer, 2004).

Lipp, Mary Beth, *Legislators' Obligation to Support a Living Wage: A Comparative Constitutional Vision of Justice*, 75 SOUTHERN CALIFORNIA LAW REVIEW 475 (January 2002).

Lopez, Ian F. Haney, The Social Construction of Race: Some Observations on Illusion, Fabrication, and Choice, 29 HARVARD CIVIL RIGHTS-CIVIL LIBERTIES LAW REVIEW ( Winter, 1994).

Lyons, David, *Corrective Justice, Equal Opportunity, and the Legacy of Slavery and Jim Crow*, 84 BOSTON UNIVERSITY LAW REVIEW 1375 (December, 2004).

Macklin, Ruth, *Women's Health: An Ethical Perspective*, 21 JOURNAL OF LAW, MEDICINE AND ETHICS 23 (1993).

Martinson, Lisa R., *An Analysis of Racism and Resources for African American Female Victims of Domestic Violence in Wisconsin*, 16 WISCONSIN WOMEN'S LAW JOURNAL 259 (Fall 2001).

McDougall, Gay J., *Toward a Meaningful International Regime: The Domestic Relevance of International Efforts to Eliminate All Forms of Racial Discrimination*, 40 HOWARD LAW JOURNAL 571 (1997).

McGinley, Ann C., *Viva La Evolucion!: Recognizing Unconscious Motive in Title VII*, 9 CORNELL JOURNAL OF LAW & PUBLIC POLICY 415 (2000).

Miller, Macon Dandridge, *Catalysts as Prevailing Parties Under the Equal Access to Justice Act*, 69 UNIVERSITY OF CHICAGO LAW REVIEW 1347 (Summer 2002).

Mitchell, Carolyn M., *Environmental Racism: Race as a Primary Factor in the Selection of Hazardous Waste Sites*, 12 NATIONAL BLACK LAW JOURNAL 176 (1993).

Navarro, Alex S., *Bona Fide Damages for Tester Plaintiffs: An Economic Approach to Private Enforcement of the Antidiscrimination Statutes*, 81 Georgia Law Journal 2727 (1993).

Noah, Barbara A., *Racial Disparities in the Delivery of Health Care*, 35 SAN DIEGO LAW REVIEW 135 (1998).

Northern, Kathy Seward, *Battery and Beyond: A Tort Law Response to Environmental Racism*, 21 WILLIAM & MARY ENVIRONMENTAL LAW & POLICY REVIEW 485 (1997).

Oberman, Michelle & Margie Schaps, *Women's Health and Managed Care*, 65 TENNESSEE LAW REVIEW 555 (Winter, 1998).

Oppenheimer, David B.,*Negligent Discrimination*, 141 UNIVERSITY OF PENNSYLVANIA LAW REVIEW 899 (1993).

Pittman, Larry J., *A Thirteenth Amendment Challenge to Both Racial Disparities in Medical Treatments and Improper Physicians' Informed Consent Disclosures*, 48 SAINT LOUIS UNIVERSITY LAW JOURNAL 131 (Fall 2003).

Pogorelec, Jason P., UNDER WHAT CIRCUMSTANCES DID CONGRESS INTEND TO AWARD PUNITIVE DAMAGES FOR VICTIMS OF UNLAWFUL INTENTIONAL DISCRIMINATION UNDER TITLE VII?, 40 BOSTON COLLEGE LAW REVIEW 1269 (September, 1999).

Randall, Vernellia R., *African-Americans, Nursing Home Care, and the Law*, in VULNERABLE POPULATIONS IN THE LONG TERM CARE CONTINUUM, 73- 98 (Paul R. Katz, Mathy D. Mezey, & Marshall B. Kapp eds. 2004).

Randall, Vernellia R. *Does Clinton's Health Care Reform Proposal Ensure (E)qual(ity) of Health Care Ethnic Americans and the Poor*, 60 BROOKLYN LAW REVIEW 167 (Spring 1994).

Randall, Vernellia R., *Eliminating Racial Discrimination in Health Care: A Call for State Health Care Anti-Discrimination Law*, ( 2005).

Randall, Vernellia R., *Eliminating the Slave Health Deficit: Using Reparation to Repair Black Health*, POVERTY & RACE Vol. 11, No. 6, pages 3-8, 14 . (November/December 2002).

Randall, Vernellia R. *Impact of Managed Care Organizations on Ethnic Americans and Underserved Populations*, 5 JOURNAL OF HEALTH CARE FOR THE POOR AND UNDERSERVED 224 (1994).

Randall, Vernellia R., *Managed Care Organization, Utilization Review, and Financial Risk Shifting: Compensating Patients for Health Care Cost Containment Injuries*, 17 PUGET SOUND LAW REVIEW 1 (1993).

Randall, Vernellia R., *Racist Health Care: Reforming an Unjust Health Care System to Meet the Needs of Blacks*, 3 HEALTH MATRIX 127 (Spring 1993).

Randall, Vernellia R., *Slavery, Segregation and Racism: Trusting the Health Care System Ain't Always Easy! An African American Perspective on Bioethics*, 15 SAINT LOUIS UNIVERSITY PUBLIC LAW REVIEW 191 (1996).

Randall, Vernellia R., Smoking, *The African American Community, and the Proposed National Tobacco Settlement*, 29 UNIVERSITY OF TOLEDO LAW REVIEW 677 (Summer, 1998).

Randall, Vernelllia R., *Racial Discrimination in Health Care in the United States as a Violation of the International Convention on the Elimination of All Forms of Racial Discrimination*, 13 UNIVERSITY OF FLORIDA JOURNAL OF LAW & PUBLIC POLICY 45 (Fall, 2002).

Reilly, Phillip, GENETICS, LAW AND SOCIAL POLICY 67 (1977).

Richardson, III, Henry J., *Gulf Crisis and African American Interests Under International Law*, 87 AMERICAN JOURNAL OF INTERNATIONAL LAW 42 (1993).

Roberts, Dorothy E., *Crime, Race and Reproduction*, 67 TULANE LAW REVIEW 1945 (1993).

Roberts, Dorothy E., *Norplant's Threat to Civil Liberties and Racial Justice*, NEW JERSEY LAW JOURNAL, July 26, 1993, at 20.

Roberts, Dorothy E., *Unshackling Black Motherhood*, 95 MICHIGAN LAW REVIEW 938 (February, 1997).

Robertson, John A., *Posthumous Reproduction*, 69 *Indiana Law Journal* 1027 (1994).

Rogers, W. Sherman, *The Black Quest for Economic Liberty: Legal, Historical, and Related Considerations*, 48 HOWARD LAW JOURNAL 1 (Fall 2004).

Rosenblatt, Rand E., *Dual Track Health Care--the Decline of the Medicaid Cure*, 44 UNIVERSITY OF CINCINNATI LAW REVIEW 643 (1975).

Rosenblum, Sara & Joel Teitelbaum, *Civil Rights Enforcement in the Modern Healthcare System: Reinvigorating the Role of the Federal Government in the Aftermath of Alexander V. Sandoval*, 3 YALE JOURNAL OF HEALTH POLICY, LAW & ETHICS 215 (Summer 2003).

Rubin, Seymour J., *Economic and Social Human Rights and the New International Economic Order*, 1 AMERICAN UNIVERSITY JOURNAL OF INTERNATIONAL LAW AND POLICY 67 (1986).

Rutherford, Charlotte, *Reproductive Freedoms and African American Women*, 4 YALE JOURNAL OF LAW & FEMINISM 255 (1992).

Ruttenberg, Miriam H., *A Feminist Critique of Mandatory Arrest: An Analysis of Race and Gender in Domestic Violence Policy*, 2 AMERICAN UNIVERSITY JOURNAL OF GENDER, SOCIAL POLICY & THE LAW 171 (1994).

Schlesinger, Mark, *On Values and Democratic Policy Making: The Deceptively Fragile Consensus Around Market-Oriented Medical Care*, 27 JOURNAL OF HEALTH POLITICS, POLICY AND LAW 889 (December, 2002).

Schmidt, Robert Milton, LAW, MEDICINE AND PUBLIC POLICY : THE SICKLE CELL ANEMIA CONTROL ACT OF 1972, A CASE STUDY (1982).

Schneider, Carl E., *Bioethics With a Human Face*, 69 INDIANA LAW JOURNAL 1075 (1994).

Schneider, Carl E., *Lawyers and Children: Wisdom and Legitimacy in Family Policy*,

84 MICHIGAN LAW REVIEW 919 (1986).

Schneider, Carl E., *Rethinking Alimony: Marital Decisions and Moral Discourse*, 1991 BRIGHAM YOUNG LAW SCHOOL LAW REVIEW 197.

Schneider, Carl E., *Social Structure and Social Control: On the Moral Order of a Suburb*, 24 LAW & SOCIOLOGICAL REVIEW 875 (1990).

Schuck, Peter H., *Rethinking Informed Consent*, 103 YALE LAW JOURNAL 899 (1994).

Sellers-Diamond, Alfreda A., *Disposable Children in Black Faces: the Violence Initiative as Inner-city Containment Policy*, 62 UNIVERSITY OF MISSOURI KANSAS CITY LAW REVIEW 423 (1994).

Selmi, Michael, *Subtle Discrimination: A Matter of Perspective Rather Than Intent*, 34 COLUMBIA HUMAN RIGHTS LAW REVIEW 657, 667 (2003).

Silver, Michael G., *Eugenics and Compulsory Sterilization Laws: Providing Redress for the Victims of a Shameful Era in United States History*, 72 GEORGE WASHINGTON LAW REVIEW 862 (April, 2004).

Smilkstein, Gabriel, *The Cycle of Family Function: A Conceptual Model for Family Medicine*, 11 J. FAMILY PRO 223 (1980).

Smith, Catherine E, *(Un)masking Race-Based Intracorporate Conspiracies Under the Ku Klux Klan Act*, 11 VIRGINIA JOURNAL OF SOCIAL POLICY AND THE LAW 129 (Winter 2004).

Smith, David Barton, *Addressing Racial Disparities in Health Care: Civil Rights Monitoring and Report Cards*, 23 JOURNAL HEALTH POLITICS, POLICY AND THE LAW 75 (1998).

Smith, David Barton, *Healthcare's Hidden Civil Rights Legacy*, 48 SAINT LOUIS UNIVERSITY LAW JOURNAL 37 (Fall 2003).

Smith II, George P., *Genetics, Eugenics, and Public Policy*, 1985 SOUTHERN ILLINOIS UNIVERSITY LAW JOURNAL 435.

Smith, Terry, *Everyday Indignities: Race, Retaliation and the Promise of Title VII*, 34 COLUMBIA HUMAN RIGHTS LAW REVIEW 529 (2003).

Stepanian II, Leo M., *The Feasibility of Full State Extraction of Punitive Damages Awards*, 32 DUQENSE LAW REVIEW 301 (1994).

Stern, J., A. Ostroff, A. Southam, et al. *Health Maintenance Managed Care Organizations: Reconciling Quality of Care With Cost Control*. 9 WHITTIER LAW REVIEW 185 (1987).

Stone, Deborah A., *The Struggle for the Soul of Health Insurance*, 18 Journal of Health Policy & Law 287 (1993).

Sunstein, Cass R. *What the Civil Rights Movement Was and Wasn't (With Notes on Martin Luther King, Jr. and Malcolm X*, 1995 UNIVERSITY OF ILLINOIS LAW REVIEW 191 (1995).

*The Impact of Managed Care Organizations on Doctors Who Serve Poor and Minority Patients*, 108 HARVARD LAW REVIEW 1625 (1995).

United States Department of Health & Human Services, UNDERSTANDING OUR GENETIC INHERITANCE: THE U.S. HUMAN GENOME PROJECT (1992).

Veatch, Robert M., *Ethical Principles in Medical Experimentation*, in ETHICAL AND LEGAL ISSUES OF SOCIAL EXPERIMENTATION 22-24 (Alice M. Rivlin et al, eds 1974).

Villazor, Rose Cuison, *Community Lawyering: An Approach to Addressing Inequalities in Access to Health Care for Poor, of Color and Immigrant Communities*, 8 NEW YORK UNIVERSITY JOURNAL OF LEGISLATION AND PUBLIC POLICY 35 (2004-2005).

Wallace, Steven P., et al., *The Consequences of Color-Blind Health Policy for Older Racial and Ethnic Minorities*, 9 STANFORD LAW & POLICY REVIEW 329 (1998).

Wallace, Steven P., Steven, Vilma Enriquez-Haass, & Kyriakos Markides, *The Consequences of Color-Blind Health Policy for Older Racial and Ethnic Minorities*, 9 STANFORD LAW AND POLICY REVIEW 329 (Spring, 1998).

Walsh, Julia, *Reproductive Rights and the Human Genome Project*, 4 SOUTHERN

CALIFORNIA LAW REVIEW & WOMEN'S STUDIES. 145 (1994).

Watson, Sidney D., *Book Review Essay Health Care Divided: Race and Healing a Nation David Barton Smith*, 21 JOURNAL OF LEGAL MEDICINE 601 (December, 2000).

Watson, Sidney D., *Commercialization of Medicaid*, 45 SAINT LOUIS UNIVERSITY LAW JOURNAL 53 (Winter 2001).

Watson, Sidney D., *Foreword*, 1. 48 SAINT LOUIS UNIVERSITY LAW JOURNAL 1 (Fall 2003).

Watson, Sidney D., *Health Care in the Inner City: Asking the Right Question*, 71 NORTH CAROLINA LAW REVIEW 1647 (June, 1993).

Watson, Sidney D., *Race, Ethnicity and Quality of Care: Inequalities and Incentives*, 27 AMERICAN JOURNAL OF LAW AND MEDICINE 203 (2001).

Watson, Sidney D., *Reinvigorating Title VI: Defending Health Care Discrimination – It Shouldn't Be So Easy*, 58 FORDHAM LAW REVIEW 939 (April 1990).

Wertheimer, Ellen, *Shakespeare In Law: The Use of History in Shattering Student Credulity*, 45 VILLANOVA LAW REVIEW 463 (2000).

Williams, Christian, *Combating the Problems of Human Rights Abuses and Inadequate Organ Supply Through Presumed Donative Consent*, 26 CASE WESTERN RESERVE JOURNAL OF INTERNATIONAL LAW 315, 316 (1994).

Williams, David R., *Race, Health, And Health Care* 48 SAINT LOUIS UNIVERSITY LAW JOURNAL 13 (Fall 2003).

Wing, Kenneth, *American Health Policy in the 1980s*. 36(4) CASE WESTERN RESERVE LAW REVIEW 608-707 (1986).

Wing, Kenneth R., *The Community Service Obligation of Hill-Burton Health Facilities*, 23 BOSTON COLLEGE LAW REVIEW 577, 613-14 (1982).

Wington, Arthur, *A Property of Special and Peculiar Value: The Tennessee Supreme Court and the Law of Manumission*, 44 TENNESSEE HISTORICAL QUARTERLY 302-17 (1985).

Wolf, Susan M., *Shifting Paradigms in Bioethics and Health Law: the Rise of a New Pragmatism*, 20 AMERICAN JOURNAL OF LAW AND MEDICINE 395 (1994).

Wren, J. Thomas, *A Two-Fold Character: The Slave as Person and Property in Virginia Court Cases, 1800-1860*, 24 SOUTHERN STUDIES 417-31 (1985).

Yelnosky, Michael J., *Filling an Enforcement Void: Using Testers to Uncover and Remedy Discrimination in Hiring for Lower-Skilled, Entry-Level Jobs*, 26 UNIVERSITY OF MICHIGAN JOURNAL OF LAW REFORM 403 (1993).

## LEGAL SECONDARY - BOOKS

Amistad Committee, THE AMISTAD REVOLT: STRUGGLE FOR FREEDOM (1993)

Appelbaum, Paul S., et al., INFORMED CONSENT: LEGAL THEORY AND CLINICAL PRACTICE (1987).

Bell Jr., Derrick, RACE, RACISM AND AMERICAN LAW (2d ed. 1980).

Bell Jr., Derrick, AND WE ARE NOT SAVED: THE ELUSIVE QUEST FOR RACIAL JUSTICE (Basic Books, 1987).

Bullard, Robert D., *Anatomy of Environmental Racism and the Environmental Justice Movement*, in CONFRONTING ENVIRONMENTAL RACISM: VOICES FROM THE GRASSROOTS (Robert D. Bullard ed. 1993).

Delgado, Gary, GRASS ROOTS INNOVATIVE POLICY PROGRAM, Applied Research Center (2000).

Ellickson, Robert C., ORDER WITHOUT LAW: HOW NEIGHBORS SETTLE DISPUTES (1991).

Furrow, Barry R. et al., HEALTH LAW: CASES, MATERIALS AND PROBLEMS (2d Ed. 1991).

Hogan, Joseph J., *Reaganomics and Economic Policy*, in THE REAGAN PRESIDENCY: AN INCOMPLETE REVOLUTION? (Dilys M. Hill et al. eds. 1990).

Jones, James M., PREJUDICE AND RACISM (1997).
Knowles, Louis L. & Kenneth Prewitt, INSTITUTIONAL RACISM IN AMERICA (1969).
Law, Sylvia A., AMERICAN CIVIL LIBERTIES UNION, THE RIGHTS OF THE POOR (1973).
Marable, Manning, W.E.B. DU BOIS: BLACK RADICAL DEMOCRAT (1986).
Marshall Kapp ed., LONG TERM HEALTH CARE PROVIDERS AND THE PATIENT SELF-DETERMINATION ACT ( 1994).
RACE AND PUBLIC POLICY: A PROJECT OF THE APPLIED RESEARCH CENTER'S GRASS ROOTS INNOVATIVE POLICY PROGRAM, Applied Research Center.
United States Commission on Civil Rights, ACKNOWLEDGING INEQUITY, CONFRONTING DISCRIMINATION, AND ENSURING EQUALITY, VOLUME II: THE ROLE OF FEDERAL CIVIL RIGHTS ENFORCEMENT (1999).
United States Commission on Civil Rights, FEDERAL TITLE VI ENFORCEMENT TO ENSURE NONDISCRIMINATION IN FEDERALLY ASSISTED PROGRAMS (Washington, D.C, 1996).
United States Commission on Civil Rights, THE HEALTH CARE CHALLENGE: ACKNOWLEDGING INEQUITY, CONFRONTING DISCRIMINATION, AND ENSURING EQUALITY, VOLUME I, THE ROLE OF GOVERNMENTAL AND PRIVATE HEALTH CARE PROGRAMS AND INITIATIVES (Sept., 1999).
United States Commission on Civil Rights, THE HEALTH CARE CHALLENGE: ACKNOWLEDGING INEQUITY, CONFRONTING DISCRIMINATION, AND ENSURING EQUALITY, VOLUME I, THE ROLE OF GOVERNMENTAL AND PRIVATE HEALTH CARE PROGRAMS AND INITIATIVES, 287 No. 902-00062-2 (September 1999).
United States Department of Health & Human Services, National Center for Health Statistics, HEALTH, UNITED STATES, 1998 WITH SOCIOECONOMIC STATUS AND HEALTH CHARTBOOK 50, 92-96 (1998), Available at Http://www.cdc.gov/nchs/data/hus/hus98.pdf

## LEGAL SECONDARY - OTHER

140 Congressional Record S7634 (Daily Edition June 24, 1994).
Bowser, Rene, *Eliminating Racial and Ethnic Disparities in Medical Care*, 30 AMERICAN BAR ASSOCIATION 25 (Summer 2001).California Health & Safety Code §1317.2 (West 1990).
Bouey, Pamela S., *Peer Review in the Managed Care Organization Setting*, in MANAGED CARE ORGANIZATION HEALTH CARE 1988: 471 LEGAL AND OPERATIONAL ISSUES 279-310 (PLI Commercial Law and Practice Course Handbook Series No. 471, 1988),.
Clark, Pamela I. et al., *Effect of Menthol Cigarettes on Biochemical Markers of Smoke Exposure Among Black and White Smokers*, 110 CHEST 1194, 1194 (1996),.
COMMITTEE ON FOREIGN RELATIONS, 96TH CONGRESS (1st Session 1980).
CONCLUDING OBSERVATIONS OF THE COMMITTEE ON THE ELIMINATION OF RACIAL DISCRIMINATION: UNITED STATES OF AMERICA 14/08/2001 A/56/18, 380-407 (Concluding Observations/comments) Committee on the Elimination of Racial Discrimination, 59th Session July 30 - August 17, 2001.
Congressional Caucus for Women's Issues, THE WOMEN'S HEALTH EQUITY ACT OF 1990 18 (1990)).DEFINITION OF DISCRIMINATION (Article 1, Paragraph 1): 22/03/93. CERD General Recommendation. 14 (General Comments).DISADVANTAGED MINORITY HEALTH IMPROVEMENT ACT OF 1990 HOUSE REPORT NUMBER, PUBLIC LAW 101-527, Number 101-804 (October 5, 1990).Hearing Before the Senate Committee On Governmental Affairs, 104th Congress., Testimony of Karen Narasaki, Executive Director of National Asian Pacific American Legal Consortium,.
House of Representative Report 3028, 105th Congress (1997).

House of Representatives Document Number 318, 88th Congress, 2d Session (1964).

House of Representatives Report No. 804.

HUMAN RIGHTS TREATIES: HEARINGS BEFORE THE SENATE COMMITTEE ON FOREIGN RELATIONS, 96TH CONGRESS (1st Session 1980).

Interim Rule section 50.23(d), 55 Federal Regulation 52,817 (December 21, 1990) (codified at 21 Code of Federal Regulations § 50.23 (1996).

INTERNATIONAL CONVENTION ON THE ELIMINATION OF ALL FORMS OF RACIAL DISCRIMINATION, Opened for Signature December 21,1965, 660 United Nations Treaty Series 195 (Entered into Force January 4, 1969)(ICERD).

INTERNATIONAL COVENANT ON CIVIL AND POLITICAL RIGHTS, United Nations General Assembly 21st Session Supplement Number 16, at 52, United Nations Document A/6316 (1966) (Entered into Force March 23, 1976).

Lundy, J., *Health Insurance: The Pro-Competition Proposals* 4, CONGRESSIONAL RESEARCH SERVICE REPORT NO. 81046 (1984).

*Minority Caucuses Seeking Share of Tobacco Deal Money*, Congress Daily, November 18, 1997,

National Sickle Cell Anemia Control Act, Public Law Number 92-294, 86 Statute 136 (1972) (codified as amended at 42 United States Code §§ 300(b)(1) et seq.). \{(The Sickle Cell Act was passed in 1972, as an amendment to the Public Health Service Act, chapter 373, Title I, § 2, 58 Statute 682 (1944) (codified as amended at 42 United States Code §§ 201 et seq.)}.

United Nation General Assembly Resolution, 21st Session Supplement Number 16, United Nation Document A/6316 (1966) (entered into force January 3, 1976).

Senate Report 1414, 105th Congress (1997).

Senate Report 1415, 105th Congress (1997).

Senate Report 1530, 105th Congress (1997).).

Senate Report 1648, 105th Congress (1998).

UNITED NATIONS: CONVENTION ON THE RIGHTS OF THE CHILD, 28 I.l.m1448 (1989)(Entered into Force September 2, 1990)).

United Nations Development Programme, HUMAN DEVELOPMENT REPORT 29-30 (1998).

United States Code " 1681-88 (2002) (Limited to Sex Discrimination in Educational Programs).

UNIVERSAL DECLARATION OF HUMAN RIGHTS, United Nations General Assembly Resolution 217 A(iii) (December 1948).

# MISCELLANEOUS

## MISCELLANEOUS - ARTICLES

Allen, Kia Morgan, *Black Clergy Attack Menthol Joe*, DAYTON DAILY NEWS, Mar. 14, 1997, at 6.

*Another Looked for Ways to Attract Blacks, Say Newly Unveiled Papers*, BALTIMORE SUN, Feb. 6, 1998, at 3A.

Bardack, Michelle A. & Susan H. Thompson, *Model Prenatal' Program of Rush Medical College at St. Basils Free Peoples Clinic*, 108 PUBLIC HEALTH REPORT 161 (1993).

Blum, Alan, *The Blue Collar, Black Target*, WASHINGTON POST, May 18, 1986, at F1.

Briggs, W. Stanley, *Slavery in French Colonial Illinois*, 18 CHICAGO HISTORY 66 (1989-90).

Cary, Lorene, *Why It's Not Just Paranoia: An American History of 'Plans' for Blacks*, NEWSWEEK, Apr. 6, 1992, at 23.

Clark, Cheryl, *The Ghost of Tuskegee*, SAN DIEGO UNION & TRIBUNE, January 28, 1996, at D14.

Cole, E.G., *Empowerment as the Key to Environmental Protection*, *infra* note 34 .

Collins, William J., *Race, Roosevelt, and Wartime Production: Fair Employment in World War II Labor Markets*, 91 American Economic Review 272 (2001).

Dobash, R. Emerson & Russell P. Dobash, WOMEN, VIOLENCE AND SOCIAL CHANGE, 150 (1992).

Feagin, Joe, *Slavery Unwilling to Die: the Background of Black Oppression in the 1980s*, 17 JOURNAL OF BLACK STUDIES 173 (1986)

Fiske, Susan T. & Peter Glick, *Ambivalence and Stereotypes Cause Sexual Harassment: A Theory with Implications for Organizational Change*, JOURNAL OF SOCIOLOGICAL ISSUES 97 (Spring 1995).

Fiske, Susan T., *Controlling Other People: The Impact of Power on Stereotyping*, 48 AMERICAN PSYCHOLOGIST 621 (1993).

Gaertner, Samuel L. et al., *Reducing Intergroup Bias: Elements of Intergroup Cooperation*, 76 JOURNAL OF PERSONALITY AND SOCIAL PSYCHOLOGY 388 (1999).

Gelfand, Donald & Barbara W.K. Yee, *Trends & Forces: Influence of Immigration, Migration, and Acculturation on the Fabric of Aging in America*, 15 GENERATIONS 7 (1991).

Goldstein, Harry, *Billboard Liberation*, 48 UTNE READER, Nov. 1991, at 46.

Havemann, Joel, *A Safety Net Snags on Its Cost: Western Europe's Prized Welfare Programs Follow Citizens from Cradle to Grave. But Tax Rates Are Astronomical by U.S. Standards and Critics Are Gingerly Making Changes*, LOS ANGELES TIMES, April 21, 1992, at A1.

Herbert, Bob, *Tobacco Hush Money for Black Leaders*, 88 BUSINESS & SOCIETY REVIEW 62 (1994).

Hoeffel, John, *Group Says Reynolds Aims Ads at Black Kids*, WINSTON-SALEM JOURNAL (N.C.), Mar. 14, 1997, at A1.

Hutchinson, Earl Ofari, *Joe Camel Symbol of Black America's Smoking Gun*, NEW PITTSBURGH COURIER, July 12, 1997, at A7.

Johnson, Elaine M., *Symposium, Harmful Targeting*, 83 BUSINESS & SOCIETY REVIEW 16 (1992).

Jones, Lovell, *Insidious the Way Cigarette Makers Target Minorities*, HOUSTON CHRONICAL.., Mar. 24, 1996, at 4.

*Killer Billboards*, 83 BUSINESS. & SOCIETY REVIEW 12 (1992).

Klarman, Michael J.,*How Brown Changed Race Relations: The Backlash Thesis*, 81 JOURNAL OF AMERICAN HISTORY 81 (1994).

Lucadamo, John, *Porter, Sullivan Clash at Debate Over Everything But Pension*, CHICAGO TRIBUNE, March 10, 1992.

Macaulay, Stewart, *Non-Contractual Relations in Business: A Preliminary Study*, 28 AMERICAN SOCIOLOGICAL REVIEW 55 (1963).

Mattera, Philip, *RJR Nabisco: Transnational Tobacco Trafficker*, MULTINATIONAL MONITOR, Jan. 1992, at 38, 41.

Rathore, Saif R., et.al, *The Effects of Patient Sex and Race on Medical Student Ratings of Quality of Life*, 108 AMERICAN JOURNAL OF MEDICINE 561 (2000).

Rice, Mitchell F., *On Assessing African Health*, 9 URBAN LEAGUE REVIEW 6, 6-12 (Winter 1985-1986).

Richardson, Henry S., *Specifying Norms as a Way to Resolve Concrete Ethical Problems*, 19 PHILOSOPHY AND PUBLIC AFFAIR 279 (1990).

Sammon, Peter J., *The Living Wage Movement*, AMERICA, Aug. 26, 2000.

Schwartz, William B. & Henry J. Aaron, *Hospital Cost Control: A Bitter Pill to Swallow*, HARVARD BUSINESS REVIEW 160 (Mar-Apr. 1985).

Shen, Fern & Peter Pae, *Calls for Peace Met With Caution*, WASHINGTON POST, January 23, 1995, at D1.

Smith, Mike, *Banner Combines Confederate Flag, Colors of Black Liberation*, ATLANTA JOURNAL & CONSTITUTION, Apr. 23, 1994, at A4.

Spencer, Debra, *Is Racism Killing Us?*, ESSENCE, at 32 (Jan. 1993).

Tai-Seale, Ming, et al., *Racial Disparities in Service Use Among Medicaid Beneficiaries After Mandatory Enrollment in Managed Care Organization Care: A Difference in Differences Approach*, 38 INQUIRY 49 (2001).

*Tobacco Settlement Proposal Not Fair to Minority Communities*, CALL & POST (Cleveland), July 10, 1997, at 1A.

Why Big Tobacco Woos Minorities, 21 ADWEEK'S MARKETING WEEK 20 (1990).

Wilkins, Roger, *Loss of Hospitals in Central City Said to Cause Array of Problems*, New York Times, September 17, 1979, at D4.

Williams, Linda, *Tobacco Companies Target Blacks with Ads, Donations, and Festivals*, WALL STREET JOURNAL, Oct. 6, 1986.

## MISCELLANEOUS - BOOKS

Alderman, Clifford, RUM, SLAVES, AND MOLASSES: THE STORY OF NEW ENGLAND'S TRIANGULAR TRADE (1972)

Armour, Jody David, NEGROPHOBIA AND REASONABLE RACISM: THE HIDDEN COSTS OF BEING BLACK IN AMERICA (1997).

Brace, C. Loring, "RACE" IS A FOUR-LETTER WORD (2005).

Bracey, Jr., John H., August Meier & Elliott Rudwick, AMERICAN SLAVERY: THE QUESTION OF RESISTANCE (1971).

Chu, Daniel & Elliot Skinner, A GLORIOUS AGE IN AFRICA: THE STORY OF THREE GREAT AFRICAN EMPIRES (1990).

Cornish, D.T., THE STABLE ARM: NEGRO TROOPS IN THE UNION ARMY, 1861-1865, 288 (W.W. Norton Company, 1966).

Douglas, HOW INSTITUTIONS THINK (1986).

Du Bois, W.E.B., BLACK RECONSTRUCTION IN AMERICA 3, 219-30 (1935).

Du Bois, W.E.B., *Reconstruction and Its Benefits*, in W.E.B. DU BOIS: A READER 174, 176 (David Levering Lewis, ed., 1995)

ENCYCLOPEDIA OF THE VIETNAM WAR: A POLITICAL, SOCIAL, AND MILITARY HISTORY (Spencer C. Tucker ed., 1998).

Environmental Equity Workgroup, United States Environmental Protection Agency, ENVIRONMENTAL EQUITY: REDUCING RISK FOR ALL COMMUNITIES (1992).

Equiano, Olaudah, THE INTERESTING NARRATIVE OF THE LIFE OF OLAUDAH EQUIANO, OR GUSTAVUS VASSA, THE AFRICAN (1789).

Falconbridge, Alexander, AN ACCOUNT OF THE SLAVE TRADE ON THE COAST OF AFRICA (1788).

Fry, Gladys-Marie, NIGHT RIDERS IN AFRICAN AMERICAN FOLK HISTORY 170-212 (1975).

Gould, Stephen Jay, THE FLAMINGO'S SMILE: REFLECTIONS IN NATURAL HISTORY 281-290 (1985).

Henderson, H. Donald, THE NEGRO MIGRATION OF 1916-1918, at 56 (1921).

Herrnstein, Richard J. and Charles Murray, THE BELL CURVE: INTELLIGENCE AND CLASS STRUCTURE IN AMERICAN LIFE 251 (1996).

Hoage, Edelin, *Toward a Black-American Agenda: an Inward Look*, THE STATE OF BLACK AMERICA, 173, 177-179 (1990).

Hornblum, Allan M., ACRES OF SKIN: HUMAN EXPERIMENTS AT HOLMESBURG PRISON (1998).

Horne, Gerald, BLACK AND RED: W.E.B. DU BOIS AND THE AFRO-AMERICAN RESPONSE TO THE COLD WAR, 1944-63 (1986).

Horton, James Oliver & Lois E. Horton, SLAVERY AND THE MAKING OF AMERICA 14-16 (2005).

Jackson, Vanessa, IN OUR OWN VOICES: BLACK AMERICAN STORIES OF

OPPRESSION, SURVIVAL AND RECOVERY IN THE MENTAL HEALTH SYSTEM, pp 1-36, p. 4-8 http://www.mindfreedom.org/mindfreedom/jackson.shtm.

Jonsen, Albert R. & Stephen Toulmin, THE ABUSE OF CASUISTRY: A HISTORY OF MORAL REASONING (1988).

Jordan, Winthrop D., WHITE OVER BLACK: AMERICAN ATTITUDES TOWARD THE NEGRO 1550-1812 (1968).

Katz, William Loren, THE INVISIBLE EMPIRE: THE KU KLUX KLAN IMPACT ON HISTORY 86-87, 99-102, 107 (1986).

Matusow, Allen J., THE UNRAVELING OF AMERICA: A HISTORY OF LIBERALISM IN THE 1960S, at 97-127 (1984).

Mills, Kay, THIS LITTLE LIGHT OF MINE: THE LIFE OF FANNIE LOU HAMER, 274 (1993).

Myrdal, Gunnar, AN AMERICAN DILEMMA 174 (1944).

National Research Council, A COMMON DESTINY: BLACKS AND AMERICAN SOCIETY 393 (Gerald D. Jaynes & Robin M. Williams eds., 1989).

Paiewonsky, Isidore, EYEWITNESS ACCOUNTS OF SLAVERY IN THE DANISH WEST INDIES (1989).

Pinkney, Alphonso, BLACK AMERICANS 2, 6 (1969) *citing* Woodward, REUNION AND REACTION 246 (1966).

Pollin, Robert & Stephanie Luce, THE LIVING WAGE: BUILDING A FAIR ECONOMY 2 (1998).

RACE AND THE POLITICS OF WELFARE REFORM (Sanford F. Schram et al. eds. 2003).

Rice, Mitchell F. & Woodrow Jones, Jr., PUBLIC POLICY AND THE BLACK HOSPITAL: FROM SLAVERY TO SEGREGATION AND INTEGRATION (1994).

Rudwick, Elliot M., RACE RIOT AT EAST ST. LOUIS JULY 2, 1917, at 23-26 (1964).

Sale, Maggie Montesinos, THE SLUMBERING VOLCANO: AMERICAN SLAVE SHIP REVOLTS AND THE PRODUCTION OF REBELLIOUS MASCULINITY (1997).

Schaefer, Richard T., RACIAL AND ETHNIC GROUPS 76-78 (2000).

Stampp, Kenneth, THE PECULIAR INSTITUTION, 291 (Random House 1956).

Taylor, Charles, MULTICULTURALISM AND "THE POLITICS OF RECOGNITION" (1992).

Thomas, Hugh, THE SLAVE TRADE: THE STORY OF THE ATLANTIC SLAVE TRADE: 1440- 1870, 147 (1997).

Ture, Kwame & Charles Hamilton, BLACK POWER: THE POLITICS OF LIBERATION (1992).

Turner, Patricia A., I HEARD IT THROUGH THE GRAPEVINE: RUMOR IN AFRICAN AMERICAN CULTURE 67-70 (1993).

WEBSTER'S II NEW COLLEGE DICTIONARY 821 (1985).

Wicker, Tom, *Introduction,* in REPORT OF THE NATIONAL ADVISORY COMMISSION ON CIVIL DISORDERS, at VII (1968).


## MISCELLANEOUS-OTHER

Acorn Living Wage Resource Center, THE LIVING WAGE MOVEMENT: BUILDING POWER IN OUR WORKPLACES AND NEIGHBORHOODS, at Http://livingwagecampaign.org (Last Visited: August 18, 2002).

AFRICAN AMERICAN AND WHITE CHILDREN IN AMERICA: KEY FACT 76 (Children's Defense Fund 1985).

Alabama, Georgia, Hawaii, Indiana, Massachusetts, Oregon, South Carolina and Virginia.

*All Things Considered* (National Public Radio, Nov. 14, 1996)(radio broadcast).

Altman, D.G. et al., *Alcohol and Cigarette Advertising on Billboards.*

Bureau of Labor Statistics & Bureau of the Census, CURRENT POPULATION SURVEY, at Http://www.bls.census.gov/cps/cpsmain.htm (Last Visited: August 8, 2002).

Bureau of the Census, United States Department Of Commerce, Series P60, Number 168 CURRENT POPULATION REPORTS, CONSUMER INCOME: MONEY AND POVERTY STATUS IN THE UNITED STATES, 1989 (Nov. 1990).

Bush, President George, *Remarks of President Bush to the San Diego Rotary Club*, FEDERAL NEWS SERVICE (Feb. 7, 1992).

Chicago Commission on Race Relations, *The Negro in Chicago: A Study of Race Relations and a Race Riot in 1919*, at 2 (William Loren Katz ed., Arno Press & New York Times 1968) (1922).

*Equal Access to Health Care: Patient Dumping*, Hearing Before a Subcommittee of the Committee on Government Operations 100 Congress, 1st Session 270-87 (July 22, 1987).

*Fair Housing Council Finds Discrimination Against Hispanics in DC*, 66 Number 40 INTERPRETER RELEASES 1154 (October 16, 1989).

*Great Society Speech, 1964*, PUBLIC PAPERS OF THE PRESIDENTS OF THE UNITED STATES, LYNDON B. JOHNSON, BOOK I.... 704-707 (1963-64).

Jonsen, Albert R., *Of Balloons and Bicycles--or--the Relationship Between Ethical Theory and Practical Judgment*, HASTINGS CENTER REPORT., September-October 1991.

King, Rev. Martin Luther, at *The Second National Convention of the Medical Committee for Human Rights*, Chicago, Illinois, March 25, 1966.

*Law & Order: Sonata for a Solo Organ* (National Broadcast Corporation April 2, 1991) (Television series).

Perla, J., FROM LEFT TO CENTER: THE APPROPRIATION OF ANTI-COMMUNIST RHETORIC BY THE BLACK PRESS AND LEADING BLACK OPINION-MAKERS, 1946 THROUGH 1948, at 95-118 (Apr. 1, 1992) (unpublished honors thesis, University of Colorado (Boulder).

REPORTS SUBMITTED BY STATES PARTIES UNDER ARTICLE 9 OF THE CONVENTION, THIRD PERIODIC REPORTS OF STATES PARTIES DUE IN 1999, ADDENDUM, United States of America (September 21, 2000), Available at Http://www.unhchr.ch/tbs/doc.nsf/(Symbol)/cerd.c.351.add.1.en?opendocument (Last Visited: June 26, 2002).

Simon, Scott, *Sale of Human Organs Thriving in Some Parts of the World* (National Public Radio, Nov. 27, 1993) (Radio broadcast transcription).

*The Terrible Transformation*, AFRICANS IN AMERICA., Public Broadcasting Services, http://pbs.org/wgbh/aia/part1/1p277.html_(Last Visited: March 30, 2005)

Themba-Nixon, Makani Editor., *The Persistence of White Privilege and Institutional Racism*, in U.S. POLICY: A REPORT ON UNITED STATES GOVERNMENT COMPLIANCE WITH THE INTERNATIONAL CONVENTION ON THE ELIMINATION OF ALL FORMS OF RACIAL DISCRIMINATION ( 2001), Available at Http://www.arc.org/trji/ (Last Visited: June 26, 2002).

United Nation High Commissioner for Human Rights, FACT SHEET NO. 12: THE COMMITTEE ON THE ELIMINATION OF RACIAL DISCRIMINATION, available at http://www.unhchr.ch/html/menu6/2/fs12.htm (last visited: June 26, 2002).

# ABOUT THE AUTHOR

Since 1990, Professor Vernellia R. Randall taught at the University of Dayton School of Law. Professor Vernellia Randall wrote extensively on and spoke internationally about race and racism, women, and health care. She was the recipient of the Ohio Commission on Minority Health Chairman's Award, and she was named one of the "Top 10 Most Influential African-Americans" on the 2001 Black Equal Opportunity Employment Journal list.

Professor Randall wasn't always been associated with the study or practice of law. "I grew up during Jim Crow in the South", she said. "If you were a black woman going to college, you either became a nurse or a teacher." She chose nursing and she liked the profession. As a nurse, Professor Randall worked as a nurse practitioner in Seattle; was an itinerant public health nurse in Alaska and served as maternal-child nurse administrator for the state of Alaska.

Involved in public health work for more than 15 years, Professor Randall focused on eliminating inequalities in health care for minorities and the poor. She believed a thorough knowledge of the law would help her become more effective in her mission, so she enrolled in law school. After graduating in 1987 from Lewis and Clark Law School, she became an associate with a Portland, Oregon, law firm specializing in health care law and issues relating to health and disability insurance coverage. She also served as an adjunct faculty member at Lewis and Clark College.

As a faculty member at the University of Dayton she taught health care law, race and racism in American Law, Gender and the Law, Torts, Criminal Law and Remedies. She was also the director of the Academic Excellence Program.

Professor Randall served as a grant reviewer for the National Institute of Health; as an expert witness in the State of Missouri v. Philip Morris trial and was recognized in Who's Who in the World since 1995 and Who's Who in the United States since 1998. Randall was also a co-organizer of the Miami Valley Community Summit on Eliminating Racism In addition, Professor Randall was the editor and webmaster for four academic websites on race, health care, gender, and academic support. She maintains several website:

- Race, Racism and the Law, http://racism.org/

- Race, Health Care and the Law, http://racism.org/healthcare/

- The Whitest Law School Report, http://whitestlawschool.org/

**For speaking engagements and interviews, contact media@sevenprinciplespress.com**

# NOTES

Note to the Reader: Each reference is given in full the first time it appears in a chapter. Thereafter, a shortened form of the reference, including author(s) and abbreviated title is given for all other citations in the chapter. The citations follow the legal citation form except that abbreviations are avoided, titles of journal articles are italicized, and titles of books and journals are small cap.

---

## Chapter One
### RACE, RACISM AND HEALTH

[1]Ian F. Haney Lopez, The Social Construction of Race: Some Observations on Illusion, Fabrication, and Choice, 29 HARVARD CIVIL RIGHTS-CIVIL LIBERTIES LAW REVIEW 1, 7 ( Winter, 1994)

[2]James M. Jones, PREJUDICE AND RACISM, 342-347 (1997); David R. Williams, Race and Health: Basic Questions, Emerging Directions, 7 ANNALS OF EPIDEMIOLOGY 322-333 (July 1997).

[3]Williams, Race and Health, supra note 2.

[4]Daniel R. Lucey, et. al., Comparison by Search Term Begin Race Search Term End of Total Serum Igg, Iga, and Igm with Cd4+ T-cell Counts in North American Persons Infected with the Human Immunodeficiency Virus Type, 5(4) JOURNAL OF ACQUIRED IMMUNE DEFICIENCY SYNDROMES 325-332 (April 1992).

[5]Eliseo J. Perez-Stable, et.al. Nicotine Metabolism and Intake in Black and White Smokers, 280(2) THE JOURNAL OF THE AMERICAN MEDICAL ASSOCIATION 152b (July 8, 1998).

[6]Jones, PREJUDICE AND RACISM, *supra* note 2 at 347-356.

[7]Nancy Kreiger, *Embodying Inequality: a Review of Concepts, Measures and Methods for Studying Health Consequences of Discrimination*, 29 INTERNATIONAL JOURNAL OF HEALTH SERVICES 295-352 (1999).

[8]Vernellia R. Randall, *Racist Health Care: Reforming an Unjust Health Care System to Meet the Needs of Blacks*, 3 HEALTH MATRIX 127-194 (Spring 1993).

[9]*Id.*

[10]*Id.*

[11]United Nations Development Programme, HUMAN DEVELOPMENT REPORT 29-30 (1998); Seymour J. Rubin, *Economic and Social Human Rights and the New International Economic Order*, 1 AMERICAN UNIVERSITY JOURNAL OF INTERNATIONAL LAW AND POLICY 67 (1986); H. Jack Geiger, *Race and Health Care: An American Dilemma?*, 335 NEW ENGLAND JOURNAL OF MEDICINE 815-16 (September 12, 1996).

[12]Buchanan, *The Right to a Decent Minimum of Health Care*, 13 PHILOSOPHY AND PUBLIC AFFAIRS 55, 55 (1984); P. Menzel *Medical Costs, Moral Choices: A Philosophy of Health Care Economics*, in AMERICA 85 (1983); Norman Daniels, *Health Care Needs and Distributive Justice*, in IN SEARCH OF EQUITY: HEALTH NEEDS AND THE HEALTH CARE SYSTEM 1 (1983), 10 PHILOSOPHY AND PUBLIC AFFAIRS 146, 156 (1981).

[13]United States Commission on Civil Rights, THE HEALTH CARE CHALLENGE: ACKNOWLEDGING INEQUITY, CONFRONTING DISCRIMINATION, AND ENSURING EQUALITY, VOLUME I, THE ROLE OF GOVERNMENTAL AND PRIVATE HEALTH CARE PROGRAMS AND INITIATIVES, 287 No. 902-00062-2 (September 1999).

[14]*Id.*

[15]Douglas, HOW INSTITUTIONS THINK 125-26 (1986).

[16]Richard T. Schaefer, RACIAL AND ETHNIC GROUPS 76-78 (2000); Kwame Ture & Charles Hamilton, BLACK POWER: THE POLITICS OF LIBERATION (1992).

[17]Institute of Medicine, UNEQUAL TREATMENT: CONFRONTING RACIAL AND ETHNIC INEQUITIES IN HEALTH CARE, Brian D. Smedley, Y. Stith, & Alan R. Nelson, Editors, Committee on Understanding and Eliminating Racial and Ethnic Inequities in Health Care 9-12 (2003).

[18] Ture & Hamilton, BLACK POWER, *supra* note 16.

[19]See U.S. Department of Health and Human Services, HEALTH STATUS OF MINORITIES AND LOW INCOME GROUPS: THIRD EDITION 5-8 (1991).

[20]Woodrow Jones, Jr. & Mitchell F. Rice, BLACK HEALTH CARE: AN OVERVIEW IN HEALTH CARE ISSUES IN BLACK AMERICA: POLICIES PROBLEMS AND PROSPECTS, 3-4 (1987).

[21]Jones and Rice, BLACK HEALTH CARE, *supra* note 20.

[22]*Id.*

[23]C.E. Grim, J.P. Henry & H. Myep, *High Blood Pressure in Blacks: Salt, Slavery, Survival, Stress and Racism*, in J.H. Laragh & B.M. Brenner, eds. HYPERTENSION: PATHOPHYSIOLOGY, DIAGNOSIS AND MANAGEMENT, 2d Ed. 171-207 (1995); D.R. Williams and H. Neighbors, *Racism, Discrimination and Hypertension: Evidence and Needed Research*, 11(4) ETHNICITY AND DISEASE 800-816 (Fall 2001).

[24]D.L. Patrick & J. Elinson, METHODS OF SOCIOMEDICAL RESEARCH, IN HANDBOOK OF MED. SOC. 437-59 (H. Freeman et al. eds., 1979).

[25]Louis L. Knowles & Kenneth Prewitt, INSTITUTIONAL RACISM IN AMERICA 1 (1969).

[26]National Research Council, A COMMON DESTINY: BLACKS AND AMERICAN SOCIETY 393 (Gerald D. Jaynes & Robin M. Williams eds., 1989).

[27]National Research Council, A COMMON DESTINY, *supra* note 26 at 393.

[28]*Id.*

[29]Ronald M. Andersen. et al., *Black-White Differences in Health Status: Methods or Substance?*, in HEALTH POLICIES AND BLACK AMERICANS 72, 75 (D. Willis, ed. 1989).

[30]Anderson, *Black-White Differences*, *supra* note 29; Ronald M. Anderson et al., TOTAL SURVEY ERROR: APPLICATIONS TO IMPROVE HEALTH SURVEYS (1979).

[31]Anderson et al., *Black-White Differences*, *supra* note 29.

[32]*Id.*; J.J. Jackson, *Urban Black Americans*, in A. Harewood eds., ETHNICITY AND MEDICAL CARE 37-129 (1981).

[33]*On Trends in the Health of Americans*, HEALTH, UNITED STATES 2003, 46 (2003).

[34]*Id.*

[35]Anderson, *Black-Differences*, *supra* note 29.

[36]*Id.*; Richard Cooper & Brian E. Simmons, *Cigarette Smoking and Ill Health among Black Americans*, 83(7) NEW YORK STATE JOURNAL OF MEDICINE 344, 349 (1985).

[37]Health Status of Minorities and Low-income Groups, *supra* note 19 at 90.

[38]Andersen, *Black-Differences*, *supra* note 29 at 85.

[39]*Id.* at 84.

[40]*Id.* at 82.

[41]*Id.* at 80.

[42]*Id.* at 84.

[45]Andersen, *Black-Differences*, *supra* note 29 at 81.

[46]*Id.* at 84.

[47]*Id.* at 80.

[48]*Id.* at 84.

## Chapter Two
### FROM SLAVE HEALTH DEFICIT
### TO BLACK HEALTH INEQUITIES

[1]United States v. the La Jeune Eugenie, 2 Mason 409, 26 F.Cas. 832, No. 15,551 (C.C.D.Mass. May Term 1822); See also, Leon Higginbotham, Jr., *The Ten Precepts of American Slavery Jurisprudence: Chief Justice Roger Taney's Defense and Justice Thurgood Marshall's Condemnation of the Precept of Black Inferiority*, 17 CARDOZO LAW REVIEW 1695 (May, 1996) citing John C. Calhoun, Speech on the Reception of Abolition Petitions (Feb. 6, 1837), in THE WORKS OF JOHN C. CALHOUN 625, 629-33 (Richard K. Cralle ed., 2d ed., D. Appleton & Co.1856).

[2]James Oliver Horton & Lois E. Horton, SLAVERY AND THE MAKING OF AMERICA 14-16 (2005).

[3]Daniel Chu & Elliot Skinner, A GLORIOUS AGE IN AFRICA: THE STORY OF THREE GREAT AFRICAN EMPIRES (1990).

[4]Hugh Thomas, THE SLAVE TRADE: THE STORY OF THE ATLANTIC SLAVE TRADE: 1440- 1870, 147 (1997); Muhammad, *The Trans-Atlantic Slave Trade*, *supra* note 2 at 888.

[5]W. Michael Byrd & Linda A. Clayton, AN AMERICAN HEALTH DILEMMA: A MEDICAL HISTORY OF AFRICAN AMERICANS AND THE PROBLEM OF RACE, BEGINNINGS TO 1900 (2000); James Oliver Horton & Lois E. Horton, SLAVERY, *supra* n. 2 at 17.

[6]W. Michael Byrd & Linda A. Clayton, AN AMERICAN HEALTH DILEMMA, (2000).

[7]*Id.*; Clifford Alderman, RUM, SLAVES, AND MOLASSES: THE STORY OF NEW ENGLAND'S TRIANGULAR TRADE (1972); Hugh Thomas, THE SLAVE TRADE, *supra* n. 4; Isidore Paiewonsky, EYEWITNESS ACCOUNTS OF SLAVERY IN THE DANISH WEST INDIES (1989).

[8]James Oliver Horton and Lois E. Horton, SLAVERY, *supra* 2 AT 17.

[9]*The Terrible Transformation*, AFRICANS IN AMERICA., Public Broadcasting Services, http://pbs.org/wgbh/aia/part1/1p277.html (Last Visited: March 30, 2005); Hugh Thomas, THE SLAVE TRADE, *supra* N. 4; James Oliver Horton & Lois E. Horton, SLAVERY, *supra* N. 2.

[10]*The Terrible Transformation*, *supra* n. 9; Hugh Thomas, THE SLAVE TRADE, *supra* n.4.

[11]Clifford Alderman, RUM, SLAVES, AND MOLASSES, *supra* n.7; Hugh Thomas, THE SLAVE TRADE, *supra* n. 4; Isidore Paiewonsky, EYEWITNESS ACCOUNTS, *supra* n. 7.

[12] *Id.*

[13] *Id.*

[14]Olaudah Equiano, THE INTERESTING NARRATIVE OF THE LIFE OF OLAUDAH EQUIANO, OR GUSTAVUS VASSA, THE AFRICAN (1789).

[15]Clifford Alderman, RUM, SLAVES AND MOLASSES, *supra* n. 7; Hugh Thomas, THE SLAVE TRADE, *supra* n. 4; Isidore Paiewonsky, EYEWITNESS ACCOUNTS, *supra* n. 7.

[16]Clifford Alderman, RUM, SLAVES, AND MOLASSES, *supra* n.15; Hugh Thomas, THE SLAVE TRADE, *supra* n. 4; Isidore Paiewonsky, EYEWITNESS ACCOUNTS, *supra n. 7*.

[17]*Id.*

[18]*Id.*

[19]*Id.*

[20]*Id.*

[21]*Id* .

[22]*Id.*

[23]*Id.*

[24]Amistad Committee, THE AMISTAD REVOLT: STRUGGLE FOR FREEDOM (1993); Maggie Montesinos Sale, THE SLUMBERING VOLCANO: AMERICAN SLAVE SHIP REVOLTS AND THE PRODUCTION OF REBELLIOUS MASCULINITY (1997).

[25]Alexander Falconbridge, AN ACCOUNT OF THE SLAVE TRADE ON THE COAST OF AFRICA (1788).

[26]W. Michael Byrd & Linda A. Clayton, AN AMERICAN HEALTH DILEMMA, *supra* note 5; James Oliver Horton & LOIS E. HORTON, SLAVERY, *supra* note 2.

[27]W. Michael Byrd & Linda A. Clayton, AN AMERICAN HEALTH DILEMMA, *supra* note 5.

[28]*Id.* at 126.

[29]*Id.* at 196.

[30]*Id.*

[31]*Id.*

[32]*Id.*

[33]W. Michael Byrd & Linda A. Clayton, AN AMERICAN HEALTH DILEMMA, *supra* note 5; Todd L. Savitt, MEDICINE AND SLAVERY: THE DISEASES AND HEALTH CARE OF BLACKS IN ANTEBELLUM VIRGINIA (2002).

[34]*Id.*

[35]Kenneth Stampp, THE PECULIAR INSTITUTION, 291 (Random House 1956).

[36]W. Michael Byrd & Linda A. Clayton, AN AMERICAN HEALTH DILEMMA, *supra* note 5 at 196; Todd L. Savitt, MEDICINE AND SLAVERY, *supra* note 33.

[37]*Id.*

[38]*Id.*

[39]*Id.*

[40]*Id.*

[41]*Id.*

[42]W. Michael Byrd & Linda A. Clayton, AN AMERICAN HEALTH DILEMMA, *supra* note 5 at 196.

[43]*Id.* at 282.

[44]*Id.* at 257.

[45]*Id.*

[46]*Id.*

[47]*Id.*

[48]D.C. Eubanks, *Black Mortality and Health Before 1940*, HEALTH POLICIES AND BLACK AMERICANS, 105 Table 1.

[49]W. Michael Byrd 7 Linda A. Clayton, AN AMERICAN HEALTH DILEMMA, *supra* note 5 at 257.

[50]*Id.*

[51]*Id.* at 282.

[52]*Id.*

[53]John H. Bracey, Jr., August Meier & Elliott Rudwick, AMERICAN SLAVERY: THE QUESTION OF RESISTANCE (1971).

[54]*Id.*

[55]*Id.*

[56]*Id.*

[57]*Id.*

[58]*Id.*

[59]D.T. Cornish, THE STABLE ARM: NEGRO TROOPS IN THE UNION ARMY, 1861-1865, 288 (W.W. Norton Company, 1966).

[60]*Id.*

[61]W. Michael Byrd & Linda A. Clayton, AN AMERICAN HEALTH DILEMMA, *supra* note 5 at 328-347.

[62]*Id.* at 347-351.

[63]*Id.*

[64]*Id.*

[65]*Id.*

[66]Clovis E. Semmes, Racism, HEALTH AND POST-INDUSTRIALIZATION 51 (1996).

[67]W. Michael Byrd & Linda A. Clayton, AN AMERICAN HEALTH DILEMMA, *supra* note 5. Volume I at 411.

[68]*Id.*

[69]LIFE EXPECTANCY AT BIRTH, AT 65 YEARS OF AGE, AND AT 75 YEARS OF AGE, ACCORDING TO RACE AND SEX: UNITED STATES SELECTED YEARS 1900-2002, Table 27; Clovis E. Semmes, RACISM, *supra* note 68 at 56.

[70]*Id.*

[71]W. Michael Byrd & Linda A. Clayton, AN AMERICAN HEALTH DILEMMA, *supra* note 5. Volume I, at 357.

[72]W. Michael Byrd & Linda A. Clayton, AN AMERICAN HEALTH DILEMMA, *supra* note 5, Volume II, at 79.

[73]*Id.* at 81.

[74]*Id.*

[75]Clovis E. Semmes, RACISM, *supra* note 68 at 57.

[76]*Id.*

[77]*Id.* at 58.

[78]*Id.* at 83.

[79]*Id.* at 44.

[80]*Id.*, at 154.

[81]*Id.* at 156.

[82]*Id.*

[83]*Id.*

[84]LIFE EXPECTANCY AT BIRTH; Clovis E. Semmes, RACISM, *supra* note 71.

[85]W. Michael Byrd & Linda A. Clayton, AN AMERICAN HEALTH DILEMMA, *supra* note 5 at 231.

[86]*Id.* at 159.

[87]*Id.*

[88]*Id.*

[89]LIFE EXPECTANCY AT BIRTH; Clovis E. Semmes, RACISM, *supra* note 71.

[90]*Id.*

[91]W. Michael Byrd & Linda A. Clayton, AN AMERICAN HEALTH DILEMMA, *supra* note 5, Volume II, at 230.

[92]*Id.* at 357.

[93]*Id.* at 231.

[94]*Id.* at 232.

[95]*Id.* at 376-80.

[96]*Id.* at 524.

[97]*Id.*

[98]*Age Adjusted Death Rates, Selected* Years, HEALTH, UNITED STATES 2003 at 133.

[99]BASIC INDICATORS OF ALL MEMBER STATES, WORLD HEALTH ORGANIZATION REPORT 2000, Http://www.who.int/whr/2002/annex/en/ (Last Visited: December 6, 2003).

[100]*Age Adjusted Death Rates, supra* note 102 at 136.

[101]*Id.* at 133.

[102]*Id.*

[103]*Id.*

[104]*Id.*

[105]Joe Feagin, *Slavery Unwilling to Die: the Background of Black Oppression in the 1980s*, 17 JOURNAL OF BLACK STUDIES 173, 200 (1986); Lonnie R. Bristow, *Mine Eyes Have Seen*, 261 JOURNAL OF THE AMERICAN MEDICAL ASSOCIATION 284, 284-85 (1989).

[106]*Death Rates for All Causes, According to Sex, Race Hispanic Origin, and Age: United States, Selected Years 1950-2001*, HEALTH, UNITED STATES, 2003, 155-156.

[107]*Id.*

[108]*Id.*

[109]*Id.*

[110]*Leading Causes of Death and Number of Deaths 1980 and 2001*, HEALTH UNITED STATES, 2003, 145-147.

[111]Department of Health and Human Services, HEALTH STATUS OF MINORITIES AND LOW-INCOME GROUPS: THIRD EDITION, 26-27 Table 13 and 143 Table 3.

[112]*Death Rates for All Causes, supra* note 110 at 155-158.

[113]*Id.*

[114]*Id.*

[115]*Id.*

[116]*Age-Adjusted Death Rates, Selected Years*, HEALTH, UNITED STATES 2004,144 Table 28.

[117]*Leading Causes of Death and Numbers of Deaths*, HEALTH UNITED STATES, 2003, 144-147.

[118]*Age Adjusted Death Rates, supra* note 102 at 155-156.

[119]HEALTH, UNITED STATES, 1995, 22 National Center for Health Statistics, U.S. Dept. of Health and Human Services, Public Health Service, Centers for Disease Control, National Center for Health Statistics ; Washington, D.C. (1996)

[120]*Id.*

[121]*Id.*

[122]MORTALITY AMONG BLACK AND WHITE WOMEN BY STATE: UNITED STATES, 1987-1996, Http://www.ced.gov/od/oc/media/fact/mmabww.htm (Last Visited: December 10, 2003).

[123]*Id.*

[124]*Id.*

[125]Antonio A. Rene, *Racial Differences in Mortality: Blacks and Whites*, in Woodrow Jones, Jr. & Mitchell F. Rice, BLACK HEALTH CARE: AN OVERVIEW IN HEALTH CARE ISSUES IN BLACK AMERICA: POLICIES PROBLEMS AND PROSPECTS, 3-4 (1987). at 21; HEALTH STATUS OF MINORITIES, *supra* note 115 at 113 Table 14.

[126]HEALTH, UNITED STATES, 2003, 22 National Center for Health Statistics, U.S. Dept. of Health and Human Services, Public Health Service, Centers for Disease Control, National Center for Health Statistics ; Washington, D.C. (2004)

[127]Joe Feagin, *Slavery Unwilling To Die*, *supra* note 109 at 200; Lonnie R. Bristow, *Mine Eyes Have Seen*, *supra* note 109 at 284-85.

[128]Edelin Hoage, *Toward a Black-American Agenda: an Inward Look*, THE STATE OF BLACK AMERICA, 173, 177-179 (1990).

[129]*Low Birth Weight Live Births, According to Mother's Detailed Race, Hispanic Origin, and Smoking Status: United States, Selected Years 1970-2001*, HEALTH, UNITED STATES 2003, 110.

[130]*Current Estimates from the National Health Interview Survey, 1985, Series 10, No. 160*, NATIONAL CENTER FOR HEALTH STATISTICS, Table 3.

[131]*Id.*

[132]*Id.*

[133]*Id.*

[134]HEALTH STATUS OF MINORITIES 9, *supra* note 115 at 154-57.

[135]Ronald M. Andersen, et. al., *Black-White Differences in Health Status: Methods or Substance?*, in HEALTH POLICIES AND BLACK AMERICAS 72, 83 (D. Willis ed. 1989). (Quoting NATIONAL CENTER FOR HEALTH STATISTICS, 1985, Table 67).

[136]*Current Estimates*, *supra* note 135 at Table 69.

[137]*Id.* at 1988d.

[138]Ronald M. Anderson, *Black-White Differences*, *supra* note 140, (Quoting NATIONAL CENTER FOR HEALTH STATISTICS, 1985, Table 69); Ronald M. Andersen, *Black-White Differences*, *supra* note140 at 84.

[139]*Id.* at 82-83

[140]*Id.* at 93 (Quoting National Opinion Research Center, 1985).

[141]Ronald M. Anderson, *supra* note 140.

[142]Ronald M. Anderson, supra note140 at 95; Joanna Kravitis & John Schneider, *Health Care Need and Actual Use by Age, Race and Income*, EQUITY IN HEALTH SERVICES,186 (1975).

[143]House of Representatives Rep. No. 804.

[144]Andersen, *Black-Differences*, supra note 140 at 82.

[145]Knowles and Prewitt, *Institutional Racism*, supra note 25 at 1.

# Chapter Three
## RACIST HEALTH CARE

[1]Trevor Hancock, *Beyond Health Care: From Public Health Policy to Healthy Public Policy*, 76 AMERICAN JOURNAL OF PUBLIC HEALTH 9,11 (Supplement 1985).

[2]Lawrence D. Brown, *The Medically Uninsured: Problems, Policies and Politics*, 15 JOURNAL OF HEALTH POLITICS, POLICY & LAW. 315, 318 (1990); Karen Davis, CLOSING THE GAP IN HEALTH INSURANCE COVERAGE FOR BLACK AMERICANS (Unpublished); Jack Hadely, et. al., *Comparison of Uninsured and Privately Insured Hospital Patients*, 265 JOURNAL OF THE AMERICAN MEDICAL ASSOCIATION 376 (1991).

[3]Jack Hadely, *"Comparison of Uninsured"*, *supra* note 2 at 376.

[5]Vernellia R. Randall, *Racist Health Care: Reforming an Unjust Health Care System to Meet the Needs of Black Americans*, 3 HEALTH MATRIX 127 (Spring 1993).

[6]J. L. Haywood, *Coronary Heart Disease*, *supra* note 4 at 794-96.

[7]Institute of Medicine, UNEQUAL TREATMENT: CONFRONTING RACIAL AND ETHNIC INEQUITIES IN HEALTH CARE, Committee on Understanding and Eliminating Racial and Ethnic Inequities in Health Care (Brian D. Smedley, Adrienne Y. Stith, & Alan R. Nelson eds. 2003); Vernellia R. Randall, *Racist Health Care*, *supra* note 5.

[8]Rene Bowser, *Racial Profiling in Health Care: An Institutional Analysis of Medical Treatment Inequities*, 7 MICHIGAN JOURNAL OF RACE & LAW 79 (Fall 2001); Marianne Lado Engleman, *Unfinished Agenda: The Need for Civil Rights Litigation to Address Race Discrimination and Inequalities in Health Care Delivery*, 6 TEXAS FORUM ON CIVIL LIBERTIES & CIVIL RIGHTS 1 (Summer 2001); Vernellia R. Randall, *Racist Health Care*, *supra* note 5; Vernellia R. Randall, *Slavery, Segregation and Racism: Trusting the Health Care*

*System Ain't Always Easy! A Black American Perspective on Bioethics*, 15 SAINT LOUIS UNIVERSITY PUBLIC LAW JOURNAL 191 (1996).

[9]United States Commission on Civil Rights, THE HEALTH CARE CHALLENGE: ACKNOWLEDGING INEQUITY, CONFRONTING DISCRIMINATION, AND ENSURING EQUALITY, VOLUME I, THE ROLE OF GOVERNMENTAL AND PRIVATE HEALTH CARE PROGRAMS AND INITIATIVES, 287 Pp. Number 902-00062-2 (September 1999); United States Commission on Civil Rights, THE HEALTH CARE CHALLENGE: ACKNOWLEDGING INEQUITY, CONFRONTING DISCRIMINATION, AND ENSURING EQUALITY, VOLUME II, THE ROLE OF FEDERAL CIVIL RIGHTS ENFORCEMENT, 438 Pp. Number 902-00063-1 (September 1999).

[10]Gunnar Myrdal, AN AMERICAN DILEMMA 174 (1944).

[11]Alphonso Pinkney, BLACK AMERICANS 2, 6 (1969) *citing* Woodward, REUNION AND REACTION 246 (1966).

[12]W. Stanley Briggs, *Slavery in French Colonial Illinois*, 18 CHICAGO HISTORY 66-81 (1989-90); Arthur Wington, *A Property of Special and Peculiar Value: The Tennessee Supreme Court and the Law of Manumission*, 44 TENNESSEE HISTORICAL QUARTERLY 302-17 (1985); Woodrow Jones, Jr, and Mitchell F. Rice, *Black Health Care: An Overview*, in HEALTH CARE ISSUES IN BLACK AMERICA: POLICIES, PROBLEMS AND PROSPECTS 6 (Woodrow Jones, Jr. & Mitchell F. Rice eds., 1987); Alphonso Pinkney, BLACK AMERICANS, *supra* note 11 at 26; Mitchell Rice, *On Assessing African Health*, 9 URBAN LEAGUE REVIEW 6, 6-12 (Winter 1985-1986).

[13]Alphonso Pinkney, BLACK AMERICANS, *supra* note 11; W. Michael Byrd & Linda A. Clayton, AN AMERICAN HEALTH DILEMMA: A MEDICAL HISTORY OF BLACK AMERICANS AND THE PROBLEM OF RACE – BEGINNINGS TO 1900 231 (2000).

[14]Alphonso Pinkney, BLACK AMERICANS, *supra* note 11, at 6; Woodrow Jones & Mitchell F. Rice, *Black Health Care*, *supra* note 12 at 6; See also, Mitchell F. Rice, *On Assessing African Health*, *supra* note 12 at 6-12; J. Thomas Wren, *A Two-Fold Character: The Slave as Person and Property in Virginia Court Cases, 1800-1860*, 24 SOUTHERN STUDIES 417-31 (1985); Arthur Wington, *A Property of Special and Peculiar Value supra* note 12 at 17; W. Stanley Briggs, *Slavery in French Colonial Illinois*, *supra* note 12 at 66-81; W. Michael Byrd & Linda A. Clayton, "AN AMERICAN HEALTH DILEMMA I", *supra* note 13 at 231.

[15]Mitchell F. Rice, *On Assessing African Health*, *supra* note 12 at 1985-1986; Todd L. Savitt, MEDICINE AND SLAVERY: THE DISEASES AND HEALTH CARE OF BLACKS IN ANTEBELLUM VIRGINIA (2002).

[16]J. Thomas Wren, *The Slave as Person and Property*, *supra* note 14 at 417-31.

[17]*Id.*; Institute of Medicine, UNEQUAL TREATMENT, *supra* note 7 at 120; Todd L. Savitt, MEDICINE AND SLAVERY, *supra* note 15.

[18]W. Michael Byrd & Linda A. Clayton, AN AMERICAN HEALTH DILEMMA I, *supra* note 13 at 231; Institute of Medicine, UNEQUAL TREATMENT, *supra* note 7 at 120; Todd L. Savitt, MEDICINE AND SLAVERY, *supra* note 15.

[19]*Id.* at 250; Stephen Jay Gould, THE FLAMINGO'S SMILE: REFLECTIONS IN NATURAL HISTORY 281-290 (1985).

[20]*Id.* at 231; Todd L. Savitt, MEDICINE AND SLAVERY, *supra* note 15.

[21]W. Michael Byrd & Linda A. Clayton, AN AMERICAN HEALTH DILEMMA I, *supra* note 13 at 250; Stephen Jay Gould, THE FLAMINGO'S SMILE, *supra* note 19 at 281-290.

[22]*Id.*

[23]*Id.*

[24]*Id.*

[25]*Id.*

[26]W. Michael Byrd & Linda A. Clayton, AN AMERICAN HEALTH DILEMMA I, *supra* note 13 at 239; See also, Winthrop D. Jordan, WHITE OVER BLACK: AMERICAN ATTITUDES TOWARD THE NEGRO 1550-1812 (1968); Todd L. Savitt, MEDICINE AND SLAVERY, *supra* note 15.

[27]*Id.*

[28]*Id.*

[29]*Id.*
[30]*Id.*
[31]*Id.*
[32]*Id.*
[33]*Id.*
[34]Vanessa Jackson, IN OUR OWN VOICES: BLACK AMERICAN STORIES OF OPPRESSION, SURVIVAL AND RECOVERY IN THE MENTAL HEALTH SYSTEM, pp 1-36, p. 4-8 http://www.mindfreedom.org/mindfreedom/jackson.shtm; (Last visited: March 20, 2002).
[35]*Id.*
[36]*Id.*
[37]*Id.*
[38]Institute of Medicine, UNEQUAL TREATMENT, *supra* note 7; Vernellia R. Randall, *Racist Health Care*, supra *note* 5.
[39]*Id.*
[40]*Id.*
[41]W. Michael Byrd & Linda A. Clayton, AN AMERICAN HEALTH DILEMMA I, *supra* note 13 at 322; W.E.B. Du Bois, BLACK RECONSTRUCTION IN AMERICA 3, 219-30 (1935); W.E.B. Du Bois, *Reconstruction and Its Benefits*, in W.E.B. DU BOIS: A READER 174, 176 (David Levering Lewis, ed., 1995) (reprinting an article of the same title from 15 American Historical Review 781 (1910); James W. Fox, Jr., *Democratic Citizenship and Congressional Reconstruction: Defining and Implementing the Privileges and Immunities of Citizenship*, 13 TEMPLE POLITICAL AND CIVIL RIGHTS LAW REVIEW 453, 466-468 (Spring 2004).
[42]W. Michael Byrd & Linda A. Clayton, AN AMERICAN HEALTH DILEMMA I, *supra* note 13 at 322; Institute of Medicine, UNEQUAL TREATMENT, *supra* note 7 at 121; James W. Fox, *Democratic Citizenship and Congressional Reconstruction, supra* note 30 at 466-468.
[43]W. Michael Byrd & Linda A. Clayton, AN AMERICAN HEALTH DILEMMA I, *supra* note 13 at 350; James W. Fox, Jr., *Democratic Citizenship and Congressional Reconstruction, supra* note 30 at 466-468.
[44]W. Michael Byrd & Linda A. Clayton, AN AMERICAN HEALTH DILEMMA I, *supra* note 13 at 350;
[45]*Id.* at 351.
[46]*Id.* at 323.
[47]*Id.* at 323; David Lyons, *Corrective Justice, Equal Opportunity, and the Legacy of Slavery and Jim Crow*, 84 BOSTON UNIVERSITY LAW REVIEW 1375-1404 (December, 2004).
[48]*Id.*
[49]W. Michael Byrd & Linda A. Clayton, AN AMERICAN HEALTH DILEMMA I, *supra* note 13 at 350;.
[50]Clovis E. Semmes, RACISM, HEALTH AND POST-INDUSTRIALISM 51 (1996).
[51]*Id.*
[52]*Id.*
[53]W. Michael Byrd & Linda A. Clayton, AN AMERICAN HEALTH DILEMMA I, *supra* note 13 at 329.
[54]Alphonso Pinkney, BLACK AMERICAN" *supra* note 11 at 26.
[55]W. Michael Byrd & Linda A. Clayton, AN AMERICAN HEALTH DILEMMA I, *supra* note 13 at 349.
[56]Woodrow Jones, *Black Health Care, supra* note 12 at 6.
[57]Randy Finley, *In War's Wake: Health Care and Arkansas Freedmen*, 1863-1868, 51 Arkansas History Quarterly 135 (1992).
[58]W. Michael Byrd & Linda A. Clayton, AN AMERICAN HEALTH DILEMMA I, *supra* note 13 at 351; Michael Anthony Cooke, *The Health of Blacks During Reconstruction*, 1862-1870 (1983) (unpublished Ph.D. dissertation, University of Maryland); Jude Thomas May, *The Medical Care of Blacks in Louisiana During Occupation and Reconstruction,*

*1862-1868: Its Social and Political Background* (1970) (unpublished Ph.D. dissertation, Tulane University) (on file with the Tulane University Library); Alan Raphael, *Health and Medical Care of Black People in the United States During Reconstruction* (1972) (unpublished Ph.D. dissertation, University of Chicago) (on file with the University of Chicago Library).

⁵⁹W. Michael Byrd & Linda A. Clayton, AN AMERICAN HEALTH DILEMMA I, *supra* note 13 at 351.

⁶⁰Civil Rights Act of 1875, 18 Statute 335; *The Civil Rights Cases*, 109 United States. 3, 3 Supreme Court 18 (1883); *Plessy v. Ferguson*, 163 United States 538, 6 Supreme Court 1138 (1896) overruled by *Brown v. Board of Education of Topeka, Shawnee County, Kansas*, 347 United States 483, 74 Supreme Court. 686 (May 17, 1954).

⁶¹W. Michael Byrd & Linda A. Clayton, AN AMERICAN HEALTH DILEMMA I, *supra* note 13 at 351; Derrick Bell, RACE, RACISM AND AMERICAN LAW 29-30, 203 (2d ed. 1980).

⁶²*Id.*
⁶³*Id.*
⁶⁴W. Michael Byrd & Linda A. Clayton, AN AMERICAN HEALTH DILEMMA I, *supra* note 13 at 351-52.

⁶⁵*Id.* at 352; Thomas J. Davis, *More Than Segregation, Racial Identity: The Neglected Question in Plessy V. Ferguson* 10 WASHINGTON AND LEE RACE AND ETHNIC ANCESTRY LAW JOURNAL 1 (Spring 2004).

⁶⁶*Id.*
⁶⁷*The Civil Rights Cases, supra* note 60.
⁶⁸*Plessy v. Ferguson, supra* note 60; Thomas J. Davis, *The Neglected Question in Plessy v. Ferguson, supra* note 65.

⁶⁹W. Michael Byrd & Linda A. Clayton, AN AMERICAN HEALTH DILEMMA I, *supra* note 13 at 352.

⁷⁰*Id.* at 353; Mitchell F. Rice & Woodrow Jones, Jr., PUBLIC POLICY AND THE BLACK HOSPITAL: FROM SLAVERY TO SEGREGATION AND INTEGRATION (1994); Vanessa N. Gamble, GERMS HAVE NO COLOR LINE: BLACKS AND AMERICAN MEDICINE, 1900-1940, 105-18 (1989); David Barton Smith, *Addressing Racial Inequities in Health Care: Civil Rights Monitoring and Report Cards*, 23 JOURNAL HEALTH POLITICS, POLICY AND THE LAW 75 (1998).

⁷¹W. Michael Byrd & Linda A. Clayton, AN AMERICAN HEALTH DILEMMA I, *supra* note 13 at 356; Gabriel J. Chin, *The "Voting Rights Act of 1867": The Constitutionality of Federal Regulation of Suffrage During Reconstruction*, 82 NORTH CAROLINA LAW REVIEW 1581 (June 2004).

⁷²*Id.*
⁷³*Id.*
⁷⁴W. Michael Byrd & Linda A. Clayton, AN AMERICAN HEALTH DILEMMA I, *supra* note 13; Daniel R. Berg, *A History of Health Care for the Indigent in St. Louis: 1904-2001*, 48 SAINT LOUIS UNIVERSITY LAW JOURNAL 191 (Fall 2003).

⁷⁵*Id.*
⁷⁶W. Michael Byrd & Linda A. Clayton, AN AMERICAN HEALTH DILEMMA I, *supra* note 13 at 356; David Barton Smith, HEALTH CARE DIVIDED 201 (1999).

⁷⁷W. Michael Byrd & Linda A. Clayton, AN AMERICAN HEALTH DILEMMA I, *supra* note 13 at 357.

⁷⁸*Id.*
⁷⁹*Id.* at 360; David Lyons, *The Legacy of Slavery and Jim Crow, supra* note 47.
⁸⁰W. Michael Byrd & Linda A. Clayton, AN AMERICAN HEALTH DILEMMA: A MEDICAL HISTORY OF AFRICAN AMERICANS AND THE PROBLEM OF RACE – 1900 TO 2000 at 37 (2002).

⁸¹*Id.* at 38; David Lyons, *The Legacy of Slavery and Jim Crow, supra* note 47.
⁸²*Id.*
⁸³*Id.*

[84]Clovis E. Semmes, RACISM, HEALTH AND POST-INDUSTRIALISM, *supra* note 50; Sherrilyn A. Ifill, *Creating a Truth and Reconciliation Commission for Lynching*, 21 LAW AND INEQUALITY: A JOURNAL OF THEORY AND PRACTICE 263 (Summer 2003).

[85]*Id.*

[86]*Id..*

[87]*Id.*

[88]W. Michael Byrd & Linda A. Clayton, AN AMERICAN HEALTH DILEMMA II, *supra* note 80 at 42-43.

[89]*Id.*

[90]*Id.*; Chicago Commission on Race Relations, *The Negro in Chicago: A Study of Race Relations and a Race Riot in 1919*, at 2 (William Loren Katz ed., Arno Press & New York Times 1968) (1922); Elliot M. Rudwick, RACE RIOT AT EAST ST. LOUIS JULY 2, 1917, at 23-26 (1964); H. Donald Henderson, THE NEGRO MIGRATION OF 1916-1918, at 56 (1921).

[91]W. Michael Byrd & Linda A. Clayton, AN AMERICAN HEALTH II, *supra* note 80 at 43; William Loren Katz, THE INVISIBLE EMPIRE: THE KU KLUX KLAN IMPACT ON HISTORY 86-87, 99-102, 107 (1986); Catherine E Smith, *(Un)masking Race-Based Intracorporate Conspiracies Under the Ku Klux Klan Act*, 11 VIRGINIA JOURNAL OF SOCIAL POLICY AND THE LAW 129, 135-148 (Winter 2004).

[92]W. Michael Byrd & Linda A. Clayton, AN AMERICAN HEALTH DILEMMA II, *supra* note 80 at 44.

[93]*Id.* at 43; Richard J. Herrnstein and Charles Murray, THE BELL CURVE: INTELLIGENCE AND CLASS STRUCTURE IN AMERICAN LIFE 251 (1996).

[94]W. Michael Byrd & Linda A. Clayton, AN AMERICAN HEALTH DILEMMA II, *supra* note 80 at 44.

[95]*Id.* at 97; Sidney D. Watson, *Race, Ethnicity and Quality of Care: Inequalities and Incentives*, 27 AMERICAN JOURNAL OF LAW AND MEDICINE 203 (2001).

[96]W. Michael Byrd & Linda A. Clayton, AN AMERICAN HEALTH DILEMMA II, *supra* note 80 at 97; Sidney D. Watson, *Race, Ethnicity and Quality of Care*, *supra* note 95.

[97]David Barton Smith, *Healthcare's Hidden Civil Rights Legacy*, 48 SAINT LOUIS UNIVERSITY LAW JOURNAL 37, 40-43 (Fall 2003); W. Michael Byrd & Linda A. Clayton, AN AMERICAN HEALTH DILEMMA II, *supra* note 80 at 97; Sidney D. Watson, *Race, Ethnicity and Quality of Care*, *supra* note 95.

[98]*Id.*

[99]*Id.*

[100]W. Michael Byrd & Linda A. Clayton, AN AMERICAN HEALTH DILEMMA II, *supra* note 80 at 102.

[101]W. Michael Byrd & Linda A. Clayton, AN AMERICAN HEALTH DILEMMA II, *supra* note 80 at 132; W. Sherman Rogers, *The Black Quest for Economic Liberty: Legal, Historical, and Related Considerations*, 48 HOWARD LAW JOURNAL 1 (Fall 2004).

[102]*Id.*

[103]*Id.*

[104]*Id.*

[105]*Id.*

[106]W. Michael Byrd & Linda A. Clayton, AN AMERICAN HEALTH DILEMMA II, *supra* note 80 at 133; Stephen Long, *Public Versus Employment-Related Health Insurance: Experience and Implications for Black and NonBlack Americans*, in HEALTH POLICIES AND BLACK AMERICANS 200-12, at 203 (David P. Willis ed., 1989); Vernellia R. Randall, *Racist Health Care*, *supra* note 5 at 167-170.

[107]*Id.*

[108]W. Michael Byrd & Linda A. Clayton, AN AMERICAN HEALTH DILEMMA II, *supra* note 80 at 136.

[109]*Id.* at 137; William J. Collins, *Race, Roosevelt, and Wartime Production: Fair Employment in World War II Labor Markets*, 91 American Economic Review 272, 272 (2001).

[110]W. Michael Byrd & Linda A. Clayton, An American Health Dilemma II, *supra* note 80 at 137; Bryan W. Leach, *Race as Mission Critical: The Occupational Need Rationale in Military Affirmative Action and Beyond*, 113 Yale Law Journal 1093 (March, 2004).

[111]W. Michael Byrd & Linda A. Clayton, An American Health Dilemma II, *supra* note 80 at 195;

[112]*Id.* at 197; Gerald Horne, Black and Red: W.E.B. du Bois and the Afro-American Response to the Cold War, 1944-63 (1986); Mary Dudziak, *Desegregation as a Cold War Imperative*, 41 Stanford Law Review 61 (1988).

[113]W. Michael Byrd & Linda A. Clayton, An American Health Dilemma II, *supra* note 80 at 195; David Barton Smith, *Healthcare's Hidden Civil Rights Legacy*, *supra* note 97.

[114]W. Michael Byrd & Linda A. Clayton, An American Health Dilemma II, *supra* note 80 at 199; Gerald Horne, the Afro-American Response to the Cold War, *supra* note 112; J. Perla, From Left to Center: The Appropriation of Anti-Communist Rhetoric by the Black Press and Leading Black Opinion-Makers, 1946 Through 1948, at 95-118 (Apr. 1, 1992) (unpublished honors thesis, University of Colorado (Boulder); Manning Marable, W.E.B. du Bois: Black Radical Democrat 171-75 (1986).

[115]*Id.*

[116]W. Michael Byrd & Linda A. Clayton, An American Health Dilemma II, *supra* note 80 at 201; Bryan W. Leach, *Race as Mission Critical*, *supra* note 110.

[117]*Brown v. Board of Education*, 347 United States. 483, 494-95 (Supreme Court 1954).

[118]W. Michael Byrd & Linda A. Clayton, An American Health Dilemma II, *supra* note 80 at 201; David S. Bogen, *Precursors of Rosa Parks: Maryland Transportation Cases Between the Civil War and the Beginning of World War*, 63 Maryland Law Review 721 (2004); Michael J. Klarman, *How Brown Changed Race Relations: The Backlash Thesis*, 81 Journal of American History 81, 116 (1994).

[119]W. Michael Byrd & Linda A. Clayton, An American Health Dilemma II, *supra* note 80 at 202; Jack M. Balkin, *History Lesson. Five Supreme Court Justices Think Congress doesn't have the Power to Pass New Laws against Discrimination. They're Forgetting about the Civil Rights Movements of the 19th and 20th Centuries.*, 2002-August Legal Affairs 44 (July/August, 2002); Cass R. Sunstein, *What the Civil Rights Movement Was and Wasn't (With Notes on Martin Luther King, Jr. and Malcolm X*, 1995 University of Illinois Law Review 191 (1995).

[120]*Id.* at 203.

[121]*Brown v. Board of Education*, *supra* note 117 at 494-95; Civil Rights Acts of 1964 and the Voting Rights Act of 1965; Civil Rights Act of 1965 (Public Law 88-352)

[122]Civil Rights Act of 1965, *supra* note 121.

[123]W. Michael Byrd & Linda A. Clayton, An American Health Dilemma II, *supra* note 80 at 293; Allen J. Matusow, The Unraveling of America: A History of Liberalism in the 1960s, at 97-127 (1984);

[124]*Id.*

[125]W. Michael Byrd & Linda A. Clayton, "An American Health Dilemma II, *supra* note 80 at 293.

[126]*Id.*

[127]David Barton Smith, Health Care Divided, *supra* note 76.

[128]*Id.* at 201.

[129]*Id.*

[130]W. Michael Byrd & Linda A. Clayton, An American Health Dilemma II, *supra* note 80 at 312; Vernellia R. Randall, *Managed Care, Utilization Review, and Financial Risk Shifting: Compensating Patients for Health Care Cost Containment Injuries*, 17 University of Puget Sound Law Review 1 (Fall, 1993).

[131]*Id.*

[132]*Id.*

[133]*Id.* at 313; R.G. Hatcher, *Medicine of the Ghetto*, 21-31 in MEDICINE IN THE GHETTO (J.C. Norman Ed., 1969).

[134]*Id.*

[135]W. Michael Byrd & Linda A. Clayton, "An American Health Dilemma II, *supra* note 80 at 293.

[136]*Id.*; ENCYCLOPEDIA OF THE VIETNAM WAR: A POLITICAL, SOCIAL, AND MILITARY HISTORY (Spencer C. Tucker ed., 1998).

[137]*Id.*

[138]*Id.* at 293; *Great Society Speech, 1964*, PUBLIC PAPERS OF THE PRESIDENTS OF THE UNITED STATES, LYNDON B. JOHNSON, BOOK I.... 704-707 (1963-64).

[139]W. Michael Byrd & Linda A. Clayton, "An American Health Dilemma II, *supra* note 80 at 296; Vernellia R. Randall, *Managed Care, Utilization Review, and Financial Risk Shifting, supra* note 130.

[140]*Id.*

[141]*Id.*

[142]*Id.* at 304; Sidney D. Watson, HEALTH CARE IN THE INNER CITY: ASKING THE RIGHT QUESTION 1647 (1993).

[143]W. Michael Byrd & Linda A. Clayton, "An American Health Dilemma II, *supra* note 80 at 304; Sidney D. Watson, *Health Care in the Inner City, supra* note 142.

[144]*Id.*

[145]*Id.* at 304.

[146]Sidney D. Watson, *Commercialization of Medicaid*, 45 SAINT LOUIS UNIVERSITY LAW JOURNAL 53 (Winter 2001); Vernellia R. Randall, *Managed Care, Utilization Review, and Financial Risk Shifting, supra* note 130.

[147]*Id.*; W. Michael Byrd & Linda A. Clayton, "An American Health Dilemma II, *supra* note 80.

[148]*Id.*

[149]*Id.*

[150]*Id.*

[151]*Id.*

[152]Regents of the University of California v. Bakke, 438 U.S. 265 (1978).

[153]*Id.* at 297.

[154]W. Michael Byrd & Linda A. Clayton, "AN AMERICAN HEALTH DILEMMA II, *supra* note 80 at 417; Rene Bowser, *Racial Bias in Medical Treatment*, 105 DICKINSON LAW REVIEW 365 (Spring 2001); Vernellia R. Randall, *Slavery, Segregation and Racism, supra* note 8.

[155]W. Michael Byrd & Linda A. Clayton, "AN AMERICAN HEALTH DILEMMA II, *supra* note 80 at 417; Khiara M. Bridges, *On the Commodification of the Black Female Body: The Critical Implications of the Alienability of Fetal Tissue*, 102 COLUMBIA LAW REVIEW 123 (January, 2002); Dorothy Roberts, *Unshackling Black Motherhood*, 95 MICHIGAN LAW REVIEW 938 (February, 1997).

[156]*Id.*

[157]W. Michael Byrd & Linda A. Clayton, "AN AMERICAN HEALTH DILEMMA II, *supra* note 80 at 454.

[158]*Id.* at 455; Michael G. Silver, *Eugenics and Compulsory Sterilization Laws: Providing Redress for the Victims of a Shameful Era in United States History*, 72 GEORGE WASHINGTON LAW REVIEW 862 (April, 2004).

[159]*Id.*

[160]W. Michael Byrd & Linda A. Clayton, "AN AMERICAN HEALTH DILEMMA II, *supra* note 80 at 481; Joseph J. Hogan, *Reaganomics and Economic Policy*, in THE REAGAN PRESIDENCY: AN INCOMPLETE REVOLUTION? 68-93 (Dilys M. Hill et al. eds. 1990).

[161]*Id.*

[162]*Id.*

[163]*Id.*

[164]*Id.*
[165]*Id.*
[166]*Id.*
[167]*Id.*
[168]*Id.*
[169]*Id.*
[170]W. Michael Byrd & Linda A. Clayton, "AN AMERICAN HEALTH DILEMMA II, *supra* note 80 at 488; Vernellia R. Randall, *Managed Care, Utilization Review, and Financial Risk Shifting, supra* note 130.
[171]Id.
[172]Id.
[173]Id.
[174]Marilyn Denny, *Managed Care: Increasing Inequality & Individualism*, 3 QUINNIPIAC LAW REVIEW 59, 84 (1999/2000); Rose Cuison Villazor, *Community Lawyering: An Approach to Addressing Inequalities in Access to Health Care for Poor, of Color and Immigrant Communities,* 8 NEW YORK UNIVERSITY JOURNAL OF LEGISLATION AND PUBLIC POLICY 35 (2004-2005); Robyn Whipple Diaz, *Unequal Access: The Crisis of Health Care Inequality for Low-income African-American Residents of the District of Columbia*, 10. 7 JOURNAL OF HEALTH CARE LAW AND POLICY 120 (2004); Vernellia R. Randall, *Managed Care, Utilization Review, and Financial Risk Shifting, supra* note 130.
[175]Marilyn Denny, *Managed Care: Increasing Inequality & Individualism, supra* note 174 at 84; Rose Cuison Villazor, *Inequalities in Access to Health Care, supra* note 174. Vernellia R. Randall, *Managed Care, Utilization Review, and Financial Risk Shifting, supra* note 130.
[176]Marilyn Denny, *Managed Care: Increasing Inequality & Individualism, supra* note 174 at 84; Rose Cuison Villazor, *Inequalities in Access to Health Care, supra* note 174; Vernellia R. Randall, *Impact of Managed Care Organizations on Ethnic Americans and Underserved Populations*, 5 JOURNAL OF HEALTH CARE FOR THE POOR AND UNDERSERVED 224-237 (1994); Vernellia R. Randall, *Managed Care, Utilization Review, and Financial Risk Shifting, supra* note 130.
[177]*Id.;* W. Michael Byrd & Linda A. Clayton, AN AMERICAN HEALTH DILEMMA II, *supra* note 80 at 492.
[178]*Id.*
[179]W. Michael Byrd & Linda A. Clayton, AN AMERICAN HEALTH DILEMMA II, *supra* note 80 at 500; David Barton Smith, *The Racial Integration of Health Facilities*, 18 JOURNAL OF HEALTH POLITICS, POLICY AND LAW 851 (Winter 1993).
[180]*Id.*
[181]*Id.*
[182]*Id.*
[183]W. Michael Byrd & Linda A. Clayton, AN AMERICAN HEALTH DILEMMA II, *supra* note 80 at 573; Vernellia R. Randall, *Does Clinton's Health Care Reform Proposal Ensure (E)qual(ity) of Health Care Ethnic Americans and the Poor*, 60 BROOKLYN LAW REVIEW 167-237 (Spring 1994).
[184]*Id.*
[185]*Id.*
[186]*Id.*
[187]*Id.*
[188]*Id.*
[189]*Id.*
[190]*Id.*
[191]Rene Bowser, *Eliminating Racial and Ethnic Inequities in Medical Care*, 30 AMERICAN BAR ASSOCIATION 25 (Summer 2001).
[192]*Id.*
[193]*Id.*

[194]Kaiser Commission on Medicaid and Uninsured, *The Uninsured: A Primer, Key Facts About Americans Without Health Insurance* (November 2004); http://kff.org/ (Last Visited: March 25, 2005).

[195]Sidney D. Watson, *Health Care in the Inner City*, supra note 142 at 1648 Citing John C. Boger, *Race and the American City: The Kerner Commission in Retrospect, An Introduction*, 71 NORTH CAROLINA LAW REVIEW 1289, 1329 (1993).

[196]*Id.*

[197]*Id.*

[198]Kaiser Commission on Key Facts, *The Uninsured*, supra note 194.

[199]Henry J. Kaiser Family Fund, KEY FACTS, RACE, ETHNICITY & MEDICAL CARE, 16 (1999), at Http://www.kff.org/content/1999/19991014a/ (Last Visited: October 30, 2002) Kaiser Commission on Medicaid and the Uninsured, MEDICAID TODAY: A PROFILE OF THE LOW-INCOME UNINSURED, 5 (1999), Available at Http://www.kff.org/content1999/2158/lowincomunins.pdf.

[200]Kaiser Commission on Key Facts, WELFARE AND WORK: HOW DO THEY AFFECT PARENTS' HEALTH CARE COVERAGE?, (June 17, 2002); http://www.kff/org/ (Last Visited: June 26, 2002); RACE AND THE POLITICS OF WELFARE REFORM (Sanford F. Schram et al. eds. 2003); April L. Cherry, SOCIAL CONTRACT THEORY, WELFARE REFORM, RACE, AND THE MALE SEX-RIGHT, 75 OREGON LAW REVIEW 1037 (Winter, 1996).

[201]RACE AND WELFARE REFORM, supra note 200; April L. Cherry, SOCIAL CONTRACT THEORY, WELFARE REFORM, RACE, supra note 200.

[202]*Id.*; See e.g., United States Commission on Civil Rights I, supra note 9, p. 98-105; Mary Anne Bobinski & Phyllis Griffin Epps, *Women, Poverty, Access to Health Care and the Perils of Symbolic Reform*, 5 JOURNAL OF GENDER, RACE & JUSTICE 233 (Spring 2002).

[203]Gary Delgado, GRASS ROOTS INNOVATIVE POLICY PROGRAM, Applied Research Center (2000).

[204]*Id.*

[205]Michael Romano, *In the Physician's Practice: Minority Docs Find Racism Continues to Infect Many American Hospitals*, 31 MODERN HEALTHCARE 12 (August 27, 2001); Woodrow Jones & Mitchell F. Rice, *Black Health Care*, supra note 12 at 6.

[206]Alan Sager, *The Closure of Hospitals That Serve the Poor: Implications for Health Planning*, A Statement to the Subcommittee on Health and Environment, Committee on Energy and Commerce, United States House of Representatives, 2 (April 30, 1982); Mark Schlesinger, *Paying the Price: Medical Care, Minorities and the Newly Competitive Health Care System*, in HEALTH POLICIES AND BLACK AMERICANS 275-76 (David Willis ed., 1989); D.G. Whiteis, *Hospital and Community Characteristics in Closures of 1980-87*, 107(4) PUBLIC HEALTH REPORTS 409-416 (1992); David Williams & Toni D. Rucker, *Understanding and Addressing Racial Inequities in Health Care*, 21(4) HEALTH CARE FINANCING REVIEW 75 (Summer 2000).

[207]*Equal Access to Health Care: Patient Dumping*, Hearing Before a Subcommittee of the Committee on Government Operations 100 Congress, 1st Session 270-87 (July 22, 1987); Robert L. Schiff et. al., *Transfers to the Public Hospital: A Prospective Study of 467 Patients*, 314 NEW ENGLAND JOURNAL OF MEDICINE 552-57 (1986); Debra Spencer, *Is Racism Killing Us?*, ESSENCE, at 32 (Jan. 1993); Judith Waxman & Molly McNulty, *Access to Emergency Medical Care: Patients' Rights and Remedies*, 22 CLEARINGHOUSE REVIEW 21-27 (Nov. 1991).

[208]Michael Romano, *Racism Continues to Infect American Hospitals*, supra note 205 at 12.

[209]Alan Sager, *The Closure of Hospitals*, supra note 206.

[210]Robert L. Schiff, *Transfers to the Public Hospital*, supra note 207 at 552-57.

[211]United States Commission on Civil Rights, THE HEALTH CARE CHALLENGE II, supra note 9; United States Commission on Civil Rights, THE HEALTH CARE CHALLENGE I, supra note 9.

[212]Stan Dorn, et al, *Anti-Discrimination Provisions and Health Care Access: New Slants on Old Approaches*, 20 CLEARINGHOUSE REVIEW 439, 441 (Special Issue, Summer 1986).

[213]*Id.*

[214]*Id.*; Marianne Engelman Lado, *Unfinished Agenda: the Need for Civil Rights Litigation to Address Race Discrimination and Inequalities in Health Care Delivery*, 6 TEXAS FORUM ON CIVIL LIBERTIES AND CIVIL RIGHTS 1 (Summer 2001).

[215]*Id.*

[216]*Id.*

[217]*Id.*

[218]Alan Sager, *The Closure of Hospitals, supra* note 206 at 2; Marianne Engelman Lado, *Unfinished Agenda: the Need for Civil Rights Litigation, supra* note 214.

[219]*NAACP v. Wilmington Medical Ctr., Inc.* 657 F.2d. 1322 (1981); *Byran v. Koch,* 627 F.2d. 612 (1980).

[220]*NAACP v. Wilmington Medical Ctr., Inc., supra* note 219.

[221]*Byran v. Koch, supra* note 219.

[222]Alan Sager, *The Closure of Hospitals, supra* note 206 at 2; Roger Wilkins, *Loss of Hospitals in Central City Said to Cause Array of Problems*, New York Times, September 17, 1979, at D4.

[223]Public Law Number 79-725, 60 Statute 1040 (1946) (codified at 42 United States Code §§ 291291o (1976); George Annas, AMERICAN HEALTH CARE LAW 80-81 (1990).

[224]George Annas, AMERICAN HEALTH CARE LAW, *supra* note 223 at 80-81.

[225]*Id.*; Kenneth R. Wing, *The Community Service Obligation of Hill-Burton Health Facilities*, 23 BOSTON COLLEGE LAW REVIEW 577, 613-14 (1982).

[226]*NAACP v. Wilmington Medical Ctr., Inc., supra* note 219.

[227]George Annas, AMERICAN HEALTH CARE LAW, *supra* note 223 at 75.

[228]*Id.* at 77.

[229]*American Hospital Association v. Schweiker*, 721 F.2d 170, 172 (7th Cir. 1983); George Annas, AMERICAN HEALTH CARE LAW, *supra* note 223 at 80-81; James F. Blumstein, *Court Action, Agency Reaction: The Hill-Burton Act as a Case Study*, 69 IOWA LAW REVIEW 1227 (July, 1984).

[230]Kenneth R. Wing, *"The Community Service Obligation" supra* note 225 at 613-614; Marianne Engelman Lado, *Civil Rights Litigation and Race Discrimination, supra* note 214.

[231]*Id.* at 613-614.

[232]*Id.* at 614-615.

[233]*Id.* at 616.

[234]*Id.* at 618.

[236]*Id.* at 620-621.

[237]*Id.* at 622.

[238]*Id.* at 613-614.

[239]*The Crisis of the Disappearing African Hospitals*, EBONY, March 1992, at 23-28; Mark Schlesinger, *Minorities and the Newly Competitive Health Care System, supra* note 206.

[240]*Id.*

[241]Jackie Barrow, *Implications of the Emergency Medical Treatment and Active Labor Act (EMTALA) on Differences Based on Race and Gender in the Treatment of Patients Presenting to a Hospital Emergency Department with Chest Pain*, 15 SAINT LOUIS UNIVERSITY PUBLIC LAW REVIEW 278 (1996); Geraldine Dallek & Judith Waxman, *"Patient Dumping": A Crisis in Emergency Medical Care for the Indigent*, 19 CLEARINGHOUSE REVIEW 1413 (1986); Judith Waxman & Molly McNulty, *"Access to Emergency Medical Care", supra* note 207 at 21-27.

[242]*Equal Access to Health Care: Patient Dumping, supra* note 207 at 270-87.

[243]Robert L. Schiff, *Transfers to the Public Hospital, supra* note 207 at 552-57.

[244]42 United States Code Annotated Section 1395 Dd(a) (West Supplement 1992).

[245] 42 United States Code Annotated Section 1395 Dd(a)-(D) (West Supplement 1992).

[246] 42 United State Code Annotated §1395 dd(a)-(d) (West Supp. 1992).

[247] Arizona Review Statute Annotated §11-297.01 1-3d (1956).

[248] California Health & Safety Code §1317.2 (West 1990).

[249] Stan Dorn & Judith Waxman, *States Take the Lead in Preventing Patient Dumping*, 22 CLEARINGHOUSE REVIEW 136 (1988).

[250] Judith Waxman & Molly McNulty, *Access to Emergency Medical Care*, *supra* note 207 at 21-27; Thomas A. Gionis, Carlos A. Camargo, Jr., & Anthony S. Zito, Jr., *The Intentional Tort of Patient Dumping: A New State Cause of Action to Address the Shortcomings of the Federal Emergency Medical Treatment and Active Labor Act (EMTALA)*, 1 AMERICAN UNIVERSITY LAW REVIEW 173 (October, 2002).

[251] *Id.*

[252] *Id.*

[253] *Johnson v. University of Chicago Hospitals*, 982 F.2d. 230 (1992).

[254] *Id.*

[255] *Id.*

[256] *Id.*

[257] *Id.*

[258] *Id.* at 232

[259] *Id.*

[280] DISADVANTAGED MINORITY HEALTH IMPROVEMENT ACT, *supra* note 268.

[281] United States Commission on Civil Rights, THE HEALTH CARE CHALLENGE I, *supra* note 9 at 56-60.

[282] See 42 United State Code 1396c(d) (1988); 42 Code of Federal Regulation 440.150 (1991)

[283] *Id.*

[284] *Id.*; 42 Code of Federal Regulations Section 440.40 (1991); 42 United States Code Section 1396d(i) (1988).

[285] Cassandra Butts, *The Color of Money: Barriers of Access to Private Health Care Facilities for African Americans*, (Unpublished Manuscript); David A. Smith, DISCRIMINATION IN ACCESS TO NURSING HOMES IN PENNSYLVANIA (1991),

[286] But see *Linton v. Carney*, 77 Federal Supplement 925, 933 (M.d. Tennessee 1990).

[287] Cassandra Butts, *The Color of Money*, *supra* note 285 at 5-7; SENIOR HEALTH DIGEST, No. 91-17 (Sept. 16, 1991).

[288] *Id.*

[289] 42 Code of Federal Regulations 456.271 and 456.372; 42 United State Code 1396(a) (30).

[290] 42 United State Code 1396(a) (30).

[291] Bureau of the Census, United States Department Of Commerce, Series P60, Number 168 CURRENT POPULATION REPORTS, CONSUMER INCOME: MONEY AND POVERTY STATUS IN THE UNITED STATES, 1989 (Nov. 1990).

[292] NAACP Legal Defense & Educational Fund, Inc. AN AFRICAN AMERICAN HEALTH CARE AGENDA: STRATEGIES FOR REFORMING AN UNJUST SYSTEM, RACIAL INEQUITIES IN MEDICAID COVERAGE FOR NURSING HOME CARE (1991).

[293] *Id.*

[294] See 42 United State Code 1395x and 42 United State Code 1396a(a)(28); *Medicare Program; Swing-Bed Program*, 54 Federal Regulation 37, 270 (September 7, 1989).

[295] 42 United State Code 1395x and 42 United State Code 1396a(a)(28).

[296] *Medicare Program: Swing-Bed Program*, 54 Federal Regulation. 37, 270 (September 7, 1989).

[297] *Racial Inequities in Medicaid Coverage for Nursing Home Care* (1991) (Unpublished Data).

[298] *Id.*

[299]Alphonso Pinkney, AFRICAN AMERICAN, *supra* note 11 at 26; Institute of Medicine, UNEQUAL TREATMENT, *supra* note 7 at 39-52.

[300]Marian Gornick, et al., *Effects of Race and Income on Mortality and Use of Services Among Medicare Beneficiaries*, 335 NEW ENGLAND JOURNAL OF MEDICINE 791 (1996).

[301]United States Commission on Civil Rights, THE HEALTH CARE CHALLENGE I, *supra* note 9 at 82-83.

[302]Gregory Pappas, et.al., *The Increasing Inequity in Mortality Between Socioeconomic Groups in the United States, 1960 and 1986*, 329 NEW ENGLAND JOURNAL OF MEDICINE 103 (1993); Institute of Medicine, UNEQUAL TREATMENT, *supra* note 7; United States Department of Health & Human Services, National Center for Health Statistics, HEALTH, UNITED STATES, 1998 WITH SOCIOECONOMIC STATUS AND HEALTH CHARTBOOK 50, 92-96 (1998), Available at Http://www.cdc.gov/nchs/data/hus/hus98.pdf

[303]United States Commission on Civil Rights, THE HEALTH CARE CHALLENGE I, *supra* note 9 at 78-82.

[304]*Id.*

[305]*Id.*

[337]Institute of Medicine, UNEQUAL TREATMENT, *supra* note 7 at 62-63

[338]*Id.* at 52-57.

[339]*Id.* at 39-52.

[340]*Id.* at 57-58.

[341]*Id.* at 68-70.

[342]*Id.* at 64.

[343]*Id.* at 61-62.

[344]*Id.* at 71-74.

[345]*Id.* at 58-60.

[346]*Id.* at 66-68.

[347]*Id.* at 70-71.

[348]*Id.* at 64-65.

[349]*Id.* at 65-66.

[306]*Id.* at 74-78.

[308]2 United States Code § 1395; 42 United States Code § 1396a(a)(28); *Linton v. Carney*, *supra* note 286 at 931.

[309]Heather K. Aeschleman, *The White World of Nursing Homes: The Myriad Barriers to Access Facing Today's Elderly Minorities*, 8 ELDER LAW JOURNAL 367-391 (2000); Steven P. Wallace, Steven, Vilma Enriquez-Haass, & Kyriakos Markides, *The Consequences of Color-Blind Health Policy for Older Racial and Ethnic Minorities*, 9 STANFORD LAW AND POLICY REVIEW 329 (Spring, 1998).

[310]Sara Rosenblum & Joel Teitelbaum, *Civil Rights Enforcement in the Modern Healthcare System: Reinvigorating the Role of the Federal Government in the Aftermath of Alexander V. Sandoval*, 3 YALE JOURNAL OF HEALTH POLICY, LAW & ETHICS 215 (Summer 2003).

[311]Hans R. Dutt et al., *The Financial Implications of HMOs' Partial County Carve-Out Option*, 14 MANAGED CARE INTERFACE 46 (2001); Sara Rosenblum & Joel Teitelbaum, *Civil Rights Enforcement in the Modern Healthcare System*, *supra* note 323.

[312]Deborah A. Stone, *The Struggle for the Soul of Health Insurance*, 18 Journal of Health Policy & Law 287 (1993); Sara Rosenblum & Joel Teitelbaum, *Civil Rights Enforcement in the Modern Healthcare System*, *supra* note 323.

[313]United States Commission on Civil Rights, THE HEALTH CARE CHALLENGE I, *supra* note 9 at 52-54.

[314]*Id.* 33-36, 39-40, 42-45.

[315]The Commonwealth Fund, DIVERSE COMMUNITIES, COMMON CONCERNS: ASSESSING HEALTH CARE QUALITY FOR MINORITY AMERICANS, www.cmwf.org. (Last Visited: June 26, 2001).

[316]Jean Lau Chin, *Culturally Competent Health Care*, 115 PUBLIC HEALTH REPORT 25, 28 (2000); David R. Levy, *White Doctors and Black Patients: Influence of Race on the Doctor-Patient Relationship*, 75 PEDIATRICS 639 (1985).

[317]David R. Levy, *White Doctors and Black Patients, supra* note 329.

[318]Saif R. Rathore, et.al, *The Effects of Patient Sex and Race on Medical Student Ratings of Quality of Life*, 108 AMERICAN JOURNAL OF MEDICINE 561 (2000); Kevin A. Schulman, et.al., *The Effect of Race and Sex on Physicians' Recommendations for Cardiac Catherization*, 340 NEW ENGLAND JOURNAL OF MEDICINE 618, 624-625 (1999); Institute of Medicine, UNEQUAL TREATMENT, *supra* note 7.

[319]Joel E. Dimsdale, *Stalked by the Past: The Influence of Ethnicity on Health*, 62 PSYCHOSOMATIC MEDICINE 161, 164 (2000).

[320]Kevin A. Schulman, *The Effect of Race and Sex on Physicians' Recommendations, supra* note 320.

[321]United States Commission on Civil Rights, THE HEALTH CARE CHALLENGE I, *supra* note 9 at 53.

[322]Pancho H. Chang & Julia Puebla Fortier, *Language Barriers to Health Care: An Overview*, 9 JOURNAL OF HEALTH CARE FOR THE POOR AND UNDERSERVED (1998); Mareasa R. Isaacs, & Marva P. Benjamin, TOWARDS A CULTURALLY COMPETENT SYSTEM OF CARE, Volume II (1991); Robert Wood Johnson Foundation, HOW LANGUAGE BARRIERS HINDER ACCESS AND DELIVERY OF QUALITY CARE, www.rwjf.org (Last Visited: June 26, 2001).

[323]Hearing Before the Senate Committee On Governmental Affairs, 104th Congress., Testimony of Karen Narasaki, Executive Director of National Asian Pacific American Legal Consortium, Available in Lexis, New Library, Curnws File; Kiyoko Kamio Knapp, *Language Minorities: Forgotten Victims of Discrimination?*, 11 GEORGETOWN IMMIGRATION LAW JOURNAL 747 (Summer 1997).

[324]Lisa C. Ikemoto, *The Fuzzy Logic of Race and Gender in the Mismeasure of Asian American Women's Health Needs*, 65 UNIVERSITY OF CINCINNATI LAW REVIEW 799 (Spring 1997).; United States Commission on Civil Rights, THE HEALTH CARE CHALLENGE I, *supra* note 9 at 47-50

[325]United States Commission on Civil Rights, THE HEALTH CARE CHALLENGE I, *supra* note 9 at 47-50.

[326]*Id.*

[327]Carol Johann Bess, *Gender Bias in Health Care: A Life or Death Issue for Women with Coronary Heart Disease*, 6 HASTINGS WOMEN'S LAW JOURNAL 41 (Winter 1995); Diane E. Hoffmann & Anita J. Tarzian, *The Girl Who Cried Pain: A Bias Against Women in the Treatment of Pain*, 29 JOURNAL OF LAW, MEDICINE AND ETHICS 13 (Spring 2001); Michelle Oberman & Margie Schaps, *Women's Health and Managed Care*, 65 TENNESSEE LAW REVIEW 555 (Winter, 1998).

[328]See e.g., United States Commission on Civil Rights I, *supra* note 9, at 47-50; *National Minority Cancer Awareness Week – April 17-23, 2000*, 49(15) MORBIDITY AND MORTALITY WEEKLY REPORT 330 (April 21, 2000).

[329]*National Minority Cancer Awareness Week – April 17-23, 2000, supra* note 341; United States Commission on Civil Rights, THE HEALTH CARE CHALLENGE I, *supra* note 9 at 47-50

[330]R. Emerson Dobash & Russell P. Dobash, WOMEN, VIOLENCE AND SOCIAL CHANGE, 150-209 (1992); Paula C. Johnson, *Danger in the Diaspora: Law, Culture and Violence Against Women of African Descent in the United States and South Africa*, 1 JOURNAL OF GENDER RACE & JUSTICE 471 (Spring 1998); Lisa R. Martinson, *An Analysis of Racism and Resources for African American Female Victims of Domestic Violence in Wisconsin*, 16 WISCONSIN WOMEN'S LAW JOURNAL 259 (Fall 2001); Miriam H. Ruttenberg, *A Feminist Critique of Mandatory Arrest: An Analysis of Race and Gender in Domestic Violence Policy*, 2 AMERICAN UNIVERSITY JOURNAL OF GENDER, SOCIAL POLICY & THE LAW 171 (1994).

[331]Charlotte Rutherford, *Reproductive Freedoms and African American Women*, 4 YALE JOURNAL OF LAW & FEMINISM 255 (1992).

[332]James D. Shelton, Marcia A. Angle & Roy A. Jocobstein, *Medical Barriers to Access to Family Planning*, 340(8831) THE LANCET 340 1334-1336 (Nov 28, 1992).
[333]Council on Ethical and Judicial Affairs, *Black-White Inequities in Health Care*, 263 JOURNAL OF THE AMERICAN MEDICAL ASSOCIATION 2344 (1990).
[334]Louis L. Knowles & Kenneth Prewitt, INSTITUTIONAL RACISM IN AMERICA 1 (1969) (Quoting St. Clair Drake) at 99.
[335]*Id.* at 98.
[336]*Id.* at 99.

# Chapter Four
## TARGETING THE BLACK COMMUNITY

[1]*Tobacco Settlement Proposal Not Fair to Minority Communities*, CALL & POST (Cleveland), July 10, 1997, at 1A, available in 1997 WL 11584494.
[2]MEALEY'S LITIGATION REPORT: *Tobacco, Attorneys General, Tobacco Companies Enter into Historic $368.5 Billion Pact*, July 3, 1997, at 3.
[3]*Id.*
[4]Senate 1648, 105th Congress (1998); Senate 1530, 105th Congress (1997); House of Representative 3028, 105th Congress (1997); Senate 1414, 105th Congress (1997); Senate 1415, 105th Congress (1997).
[5]Senate 1530, 105th Congress 212 (1997).
[6]Senate1530, 105th Congress 401 (1997).
[7]Senate 1530, 105th Congress 521-22 (1997).
[8]*Id.*
[9]Senate 1530, 105th Congress 501 (1997).
[10]Senate 1530, 105th Congress 256-57 (1997).
[11]Senate 1530, 105th Congress 256 (1997).
[12]Senate 1530, 105th Congress 257(j)(1), (5) (1997).
[13]*Id.* at 257(b).
[14]Senate 1530, 105th Congress 212(a)-(b) (1997) .
[15]Harry Goldstein, *Billboard Liberation*, 48 UTNE READER, Nov. 1991, at 46.
[16]A. Anderson, *Cigarette Brand Use Among Adult Smokers-- United States, 1986*, 39 MORBIDITY & MORTALITY WEEKLY REPORT 665, 673 (1990).
[17]Senate 1530, 105th Congress 522 (1997).
[18]*Id.*
[19]Deborah Kelly, *Tobacco Settlement Attacked Again, Black Physicians' Group Believes Proposal Is Weak*, RICHMOND TIMES-DISPATCH, Aug. 6, 1997, at A10, available in 1997 WL 7625753.
[20]*Tobacco Industry's Ad Assault on Blacks Is Detailed in Records: Newly Released Documents Disclose Broad Scope of Marketing Campaigns*, ST. LOUIS POST-DISPATCH, Feb. 8, 1998, at A14, available in 1998 WL 3318686; *Black Smokers Object to Tobacco Settlement*, BATON ROUGE ADVOCATE, June 6, 1997, at 5A, available in 1997 WL 7250054.
[21]Philip Mattera, *RJR Nabisco: Transnational Tobacco Trafficker*, MULTINATIONAL MONITOR, Jan. 1992, at 38, 41; D.J. Moore et al., *Target Marketing of Tobacco and Alcohol-Related Products to Ethnic Minority Groups in the United States*, 6 ETHNICITY & DISEASE 83, 98 (1996); Sylvia A. Law, *Addiction, Autonomy and Advertising*, 77 IOWA L. REVIEW 909 n.14 (1992); Alan Blum, *The Blue Collar, Black Target*, WASHINGTON POST, May 18, 1986, at F1; Paul Cotton, *Tobacco Foes Attack Ads that Target Women, Minorities, Teens, and the Poor*, 26 JOURNAL OF THE AMERICAN MEDICAL ASSOCIATION 1505 (1990).
[22]Ronald M. Davis, *Current Trends in Cigarette Advertising and Marketing*, 316 NEW ENGLAND JOURNAL OF MEDICINE 725 (1987); Why Big Tobacco Woos Minorities, 21 ADWEEK'S MARKETING WEEK 20 (1990).
[23]D.G. Altman et al., *Alcohol and Cigarette Advertising on Billboards*, 64 HEALTH EDUCATION Res 487 (1991); J. Clark, *Targeting Blacks in Cigarette Billboard Advertising: Results from Down South*, 2 NURSING SCAN IN ONCOLOGY 12 (1993); Lovell Jones,

*Insidious the Way Cigarette Makers Target Minorities*, HOUSTON CHRONICAL., Mar. 24, 1996, at 4, available in 1996 WL 5588921.

[24]Linda Williams, *Tobacco Companies Target Blacks with Ads, Donations, and Festivals*, WALL STREET JOURNAL, Oct. 6, 1986.

[25]K. Michael Cummings et al., *Cigarette Advertising and Black-White Differences in Cigarette Brand Preference*, 102 PUBLIC HEALTH REPORT 698 (1987).

[26]*Killer Billboards*, 83 BUSINESS. & SOCIETY REVIEW 12, 14 (1992); Kathryn A. Kelly, *The Target Marketing of Alcohol and Tobacco Billboards to Minority Communities*, 5 UNIVERSITY OF FLORIDA. JOURNAL OF LAW. & PUBLIC POLICY 33, 59-60 & nn.215-17 (1992).

[27]*Id.*

[28]Barnett Wright, *'Liquid Crack': Fortified Beer Pours into Black Community*, PHILADELPHIA TRIBUNE, Apr. 30, 1993, at 1A.

[29]Elaine M. Johnson, *Symposium, Harmful Targeting*, 83 BUSINESS & SOCIETY REVIEW 16 (1992).

[30]*Id.*

[31]Andrew A. Skolnick, *National Medical Association Unveils Billboard Campaign to Promote Health in Black Communities*, 270 JOURNAL OF THE AMERICAN MEDICAL ASSOCIATION 1166, 1168 (1993).

[32]Sylvia A. Law, *Addiction, Autonomy and Advertising*, *supra* note 21.

[34]David G. Altman, *How an Unhealthy Product Is Sold: Cigarette Advertising in Magazines, 1960-1985*, 37 JOURNAL OF COMMUNITY HEALTH 95-106 (1987); Michael C. Fiore et al., *Trends in Cigarette Smoking in the United States: The Changing Influence of Gender and Race*, 261 JOURNAL OF THE AMERICAN MEDICAL ASSOCIATION 49 (1989); Laurie Hoffman-Goetz et al., *Cancer Coverage and Tobacco Advertising in African American Popular Magazines*, 22 JOURNAL OF COMMUNITY HEALTH 261, available in 1997 WL 10117550.

[33]*Id.*

[35]Derrick Jackson, *Let Blacks Rethink Tobacco Underwriting*, MILWAUKEE JOURNAL & SENTINEL, July 12, 1997, at 10, available in 1997 WL 4810004.

[36]*Id.*

[37]Sylvia A. Law, *Addiction, Autonomy, and Advertising*, *supra* note 21, at 913.

[41]*Id.*

[42]*Id.*

[43]*Id.*

[39]Sylvia A. Law, *Addiction, Autonomy, and Advertising*, *supra* note 21 at 913.

[44]*Id.*

[45]*Id.*

[46]*Id.*

[47]*Id.*; Danny R. Johnson, *Tobacco Stains*, 56 PROGRESSIVE 26 (1992) (discussing how cigarette companies have bought into civil rights groups even though the tobacco-related disease is one of the leading causes of death of African Americans).

[48]Derrick Jackson, *Let Blacks Rethink*, *supra* note 35. Cf. *Million Dollar Gift Helps Restore Abandoned Shaw University Building That Housed First Black Medical School*, NEW YORK BEACON, Oct. 23, 1996, at 35, available in 1996 WL 15800903 (noting the Phillip Morris Companies' one million dollar donation to United Negro College Fund).

[49]Derrick Jackson, *Why Blacks Are Losing Tobacco War*, DALLAS MORNING NEWS, June 3, 1997, at 21A, available in 1997 WL 2674892 .

[50]*Id.*.

[51]*Id.*

[52]Bob Herbert, *Tobacco Hush Money for Black Leaders*, 88 BUSINESS & SOCIETY REVIEW 62 (1994); Morain, *supra* note 41.

[53]Derrick Jackson, *Let Blacks Rethink*, *supra* note 35, at 10.

[54]James W. Brosnan, *Black Caucus Examines Tobacco Lobby's Sway*, COMMERCIAL APPEAl (Memphis, Tenn.), Sept. 15, 1996, at A1, available in 1996 WL 11064351.

[55]*Id.*

236 • Dying While Black

57John Hoeffel, *Group Says Reynolds Aims Ads at Black Kids*, WINSTON-SALEM JOURNAL (N.C.), Mar. 14, 1997, at A1, available in 1997 WL 9361954; Earl Ofari Hutchinson, *Joe Camel Symbol of Black America's Smoking Gun*, NEW PITTSBURGH COURIER, July 12, 1997, at A7, available in 1997 WL 11699804; Anthony Ramirez, *A Cigarette Campaign Under Fire*, NEW YORK TIMES, Jan. 12, 1990, at D1.

58Anthony Ramirez, *A Cigarette Campaign Under Fire*, *supra* note 57, at D1.

59Philip J. Hilts, *Health Chief Assails a Tobacco Producer for Aiming at Blacks*, NEW YORK TIMES, Jan. 19, 1990, at A1.

60Id.

61Anthony Ramirez, *Reynolds, After Protests, Cancels Cigarette Aimed at Black Smokers*, NEW YORK TIMES, Jan. 20, 1990, at A1.

62Earl Ofari Hutchinson, *Joe Camel*, *supra* note 57, at A7.

63Mike Smith, *Banner Combines Confederate Flag, Colors of Black Liberation*, ATLANTA JOURNAL & CONSTITUTION, Apr. 23, 1994, at A4.

64Id.

65Leonard Greene, *Blacks Fight Back Against Lure of Tobacco Giants*, BOSTON HERALD, May 28, 1997, at A8, available in 1997 WL 5401571.

66Id.

67Kia Morgan Allen, *Black Clergy Attack Menthol Joe*, DAYTON DAILY NEWS, Mar. 14, 1997, at 6A, available in 1997 WL 3931006; Tony Perry, *New Camel Cigarette Draws Protest Smoking*, LOS ANGELES TIMES, Mar. 16, 1997, at A26, available in 1997 WL 219172.

68*Tobacco Industry's Ad Assault*, *supra* note 20, at A14.

69Id.

70Id.

71Id.

72Henry Weinstein & Alissa J. Rubin, *Tobacco Firms Targeted Blacks, Documents Show*, LOS ANGELES TIMES, Feb. 6, 1998, at A1, available in 1998 WL 2395899.

73Leonard Greene, *Blacks Fight Back*, *supra* note 65, at A8.

74*US Tobacco Documents Show How Industry Targeted Black Community*, AGENCE FRENCH-PRESSE, Feb. 6, 1998, available in 1998 WL 2216146.

75Id.

76*Cigarette Company Considered 'Sweets' to Lure Youngsters; Another Looked for Ways to Attract Blacks, Say Newly Unveiled Papers*, BALTIMORE SUN, Feb. 6, 1998, at 3A, available in 1998 WL 4950564.

77Henry Weinstein & Alissa J. Rubin, *Tobacco Firms*, *supra* note 72, at A1.

78Id.

79Tony Perry, *New Camel Cigarette*, *supra* note 67, at A26.

80John Hoeffel, *Group Says Reynolds Aims Ads*, *supra* note 57, at A1.

81Karen Grigsby Bates, *Tobacco Pins a Bull's-Eye on Black Kids Smoking: Industry Papers from the 1970s Help Explain the Preponderance of Cigarette Advertising in the Inner City*, LOS ANGELES TIMES, Feb. 20, 1998, at B7, available in 1998 WL 2397287.

82Danny R. Johnson, *Tobacco Stains*, *supra* note 47, at 26-28.

83United States Department of Health & Human Services, HEALTH STATUS OF MINORITIES AND LOW-INCOME GROUPS 147 tbl. 9 (1990).

84R. Cooper & B.E. Simmons, *Cigarette Smoking and Ill Health Among Black Americans*, 85 NEW YORK STATE JOURNAL OF MEDICINE 344-49 (1985); S.D. Stellman & L. Garfinkel, *Smoking Habits and Tar Levels in a New American Cancer Society Prospective Study of 1.2 Million Men and Women*, 76 JOURNAL OF THE NATIONAL CANCER INSTITUTE 1057, 1063 (1986).

85Office on Smoking & Health, United States Department of Health & Human Services, THE IMPACT OF CIGARETTE SMOKING ON MINORITY POPULATIONS (1987) [hereinafter THE IMPACT OF CIGARETTE SMOKING].

86*Black Clergy, Anti-Tobacco Group Campaign Against Camel Brand*, GREENSBORO NEWS & RECORDER (N.C.), Mar. 14, 1997, at B6, available in 1997 WL 4575885.

[87]*Id.* See THE IMPACT OF CIGARETTE SMOKING, *supra* note 85; Office of Smoking & Health, United States Department Health & Human Services, TOBACCO USE IN 1986: METHODS AND BASIC TABULATIONS FROM ADULT USE OF TOBACCO SURVEY (1986); Pamela I. Clark et al., *Effect of Menthol Cigarettes on Biochemical Markers of Smoke Exposure Among Black and White Smokers*, 110 CHEST 1194, 1194 (1996), available in 1996 WL 9033322; Lynne E. Wagenknecht et al., *Racial Differences in Serum Cotinine Levels Among Smokers in the Coronary Artery Risk Development in (Young) Adults Study*, 80 AMERICAN JOURNAL OF PUBLIC HEALTH, 1053, 1056 (1990).

[88]*Id.*

[89]Pamela Clark, *Effects of Menthol Cigarettes*, *supra* note 87, at 1194.

[90]T.D. Sterling & D. Weinkam, *Comparison of Smoking-Related Risk Factors Among Black and White Males*, 15 AMERICAN JOURNAL OF INDUSTRIAL MEDICINE 319, 333 (1989).

[91]Public Health Services, Department Health & Human Services, PREVENTING TOBACCO USE AMONG YOUNG PEOPLE: A REPORT OF THE SURGEON GENERAL 74 (1994).

[92]Carole Tracy Orleans et al., *A Survey of Smoking and Quitting Patterns among Black Americans*, 79 AMERICAN JOURNAL OF PUBLIC HEALTH 176, 178 (1989). See also United States Department of Health & Human Services, AFRICAN AMERICANS AND SMOKING AT A GLANCE: A REPORT OF THE SURGEON GENERAL (1995) [hereinafter SMOKING AT A GLANCE]; Jacqueline M. Royce et al., *Smoking Cessation Factors Among Americans and Whites*, 83 AMERICAN JOURNAL OF PUBLIC HEALTH 220, 224-25 (1993); R.C. Stotts et al., *Smoking Cessation among Blacks*, 2 JOURNAL OF HEALTH CARE FOR THE POOR AND UNDESERVED 307-19 (1991); Rachel Vander Martin et al., *Ethnicity and Smoking: Differences in White, Black, Hispanic, and Asian Medical Patients Who Smoke*, 6 AMERICAN JOURNAL OF PREVENTIVE MEDICINE 194, 197-98 (1990).

[93]SMOKING AT A GLANCE, *supra* note 92.

[97]Terri Richardson, *African American Smokers and Cancer*, *supra* note 94, at 190. See also Jacqueline M. Royce, *Smoking Cessation Factors*, *supra* note 92, at 223.

[98]*Id.* .

[99]Austoker et al., *Smoking and Cancer: Smoking Cessation*, 308 BRITISH MEDICAL JOURNAL 1478, 1482 (1993).

[100]*Id.*

[101]Terri Richardson, *African American Smokers and Cancer*, *supra* note 94, at 190.

[102]M.E. Jarvik et al., *Nonmentholated Cigarettes Decrease Puff Volume of Smoke and Increase Carbon Monoxide Absorption*, 56 PHYSIOLOGY & BEHAVIOR 563, 569 (1994); G.E. Miller et al., *Cigarette Mentholation Increase Smokers' Exhaled Carbon Monoxide Levels*, 2 EXPERIMENTAL & CLINICAL PSYCHOPHARMACOLOGY 154, 160 (1994); Terri Richardson, *African American Smokers and Cancer*, *supra* note 94, at 191.

[104]Jacqueline M. Royce, *Smoking Cessation Factors*, *supra* note 92, at 224. See also CHANGES IN CIGARETTE BRAND PREFERENCES, *supra* note 103, at 578.

[105]*Id.*

[106]D. Sterling & D. Weinkam, *Comparison of Smoking-Related Risk Factors*, *supra* note 90; Jacqueline M. Royce, *Smoking Cessation Factors*, *supra* note 92.

[107]Geoffrey C. Kabat & James R. Hebert, *Use of Mentholated Cigarettes and Lung Cancer Risk*, 51 CANCER RESOURCE 6510, 6510 (1991); Stephen Sidney et al., *Mentholated Cigarette Use and Lung Cancer*, 155 ARCHIVES OF INTERNAL MEDICINE 727, 729 (1995).

[108]K. Michael Cummings, *Cigarette Advertising*, *supra* note 25, at 698; *Killer Billboards*, *supra* note 26, at 14.

[109]*Id.*

[110]J.R. Hebert et al., *Menthol Cigarette Smoking and Esophageal Cancer*, 18 INTERNATIONAL JOURNAL OF EPIDEMIOLOGY 37, 44 (1989); Terri Richardson, *African American Smokers and Cancer*, *supra* note 94, at 191.

[111]HEALTH STATUS OF MINORITIES, *supra* note 83; David R. Williams et al., *The Concept of Race and Health Status in America*, 109 PUBLIC HEALTH REPORT 26 (1994), available in 1994 WL 13504730.

[112]HEALTH STATUS OF MINORITIES, *supra* note 83.

[113]*Id.* at tbl. 1.

[114]*Id.*

[115]Centers for Disease Control, *Smoking-Attributable Mortality and Years of Potential Life Lost--United States, 1988*, 40 MORBIDITY & MORTALITY WEEKLY REPORT 62, 69 (1991).

[116]Centers for Disease Control, *Cigarette Smoking Among Blacks and Other Minority Populations*, 36 MORBIDITY & MORTALITY WEEKLY REPORT 405 (1987); R. Cooper & B.E. Simmons, *Cigarette Smoking and Ill Health Among Black Americans*, 85 NEW YORK STATE MEDICAL JOURNAL 344 (1985).

[117]United States Department of Health & Human Services, 1 EXECUTIVE SUMMARY REPORT OF THE SECRETARY'S TASK FORCE ON BLACK & MINORITY HEALTH 88 (1985).

[118]*Id.*; C.C. Boring et al., *Cancer Statistics For African Americans*, 42 CANCER: CANCER JOURNAL FOR CLINICIANS 7 (1992); R.E. Harris, *Race and Sex Differences, supra* note 95, at 599.

[119]HEALTH STATUS OF MINORITIES, *supra* note 83, at 145 tbl. 7.

[120]*Id.*

[121]*Id.*

[122]*Id.*

[123]R.E. Harris, *Race and Sex Differences, supra* note 95, at 599.

[124]HEALTH STATUS OF MINORITIES, *supra* note 83, at 146 tbl. 8.

[125]*Id.*

[126]Loretta Baines, *Study Claims Black Females at Greater Risk from Smoking*, TRI-STATE DEFENDER, Mar. 22, 1996, at 3A, available in 1996 WL 15887760 (reporting on study conducted by Dr. Henry Glindmeyer, a professor at the Tulane University Medical School)

[127]*Id.*

[128]*Cigarette Smoking Among Blacks and Other Minority Populations, supra* note 116.

[129]*Id.* at 406.

[130]Jacqueline M. Royce, *Smoking Cessation Factors African American, supra* note 92; see also Terri Richardson, *African American Smokers, supra* note 94, at 190-93.

[131]Lorraine P. Hahn et al., *Cigarette Smoking and Cessation Behaviors Among Urban Blacks and Whites*, 105 PUBLIC HEALTH REPORT 290 (1990). See also Terri Richardson, *African American Smokers, supra* note 94 at 193.

[132]Terri Richardson, *African American Smokers, supra* note 94 at 192.


## Chapter Five
### IMPACT OF MANAGED CARE ORGANIZATION ON BLACKS

[1]*The Impact of Managed Care Organizations on Doctors Who Serve Poor and Minority Patients*, 108 HARVARD LAW REVIEW 1625, 1628 & note14 (1995).

[2]*Id.*

[3]*Id.*

[4]Eric C. Schneider et al., *Racial Inequity in Influenza Vaccination: Does Managed Care Organization Narrow the Gap Between African Americans and Whites?*, 286 JOURNAL OF THE AMERICAN MEDICAL ASSOCIATION 1455 (2001).

[5]Robert A. Lowe et al., *Effect of Ethnicity on Denial of Authorization for Emergency Department Care by Managed Care Organization Gatekeepers*, 8 ACADEMY OF EMERGENCY MEDICINE 259 (2001); Stuart E. Sheifer et al., *Race and Sex Differences in the Management of Coronary Artery Disease*, 139 AMERICAN HEART JOURNAL 848 (2000); Eric C. Schneider, Alan M. Zaslavsky, & Arnold M. Epstein, *Racial Inequities in the Quality of Care for*

*Enrollees in Medicare Managed Care Organization Care*, 287 JOURNAL OF THE AMERICAN MEDICAL ASSOCIATION 1288 (Mar. 13, 2002).

[6]NATIONAL HEALTH EXPENDITURES AGGREGATE AND PER CAPITA AMOUNTS, PERCENT DISTRIBUTION, AND AVERAGE ANNUAL PERCENT GROWTH, BY SOURCE OF FUNDS: SELECTED CALENDAR YEARS 1980-2003; Centers for Medicare and Medicaid Services, http://www.cms.hhs.gov/statistics/nhe/historical/t1.asp; (Last Visited: March 24, 2005);

[7]Edith Rasell, Jared Bernstein & Kainan Tang, *The Impact of Health Care Financing on Family Budgets*, 24 INTERNATIONAL JOURNAL OF HEALTH SERVICES 691-714 (1994).

[8]*Id.*

[9]Paul R. Torrens, *Historical Evolution and Overview of Health Services in the United States*, in INTRODUCTION TO HEALTH SERVICES 3, 3 (Stephen J. Williams & Paul R. Torrens eds. 2002).

[10]William L. Dowling and Patricia A. Armstrong. *The Hospital*, in INTRODUCTION TO HEALTH SERVICES 125, 127 (Stephen J. Williams & Paul R. Torrens eds. 2002); Paul R. Torrens, *Historical Evolution, supra* note 9.

[11]Paul R. Torrens, *Historical Evolution, supra* note 9.

[12]*Id.*

[13]*Id.*

[14]William L. Dowling & Patricia A. Armstrong, *The Hospital, supra* note 10; Charles E. Rosenberg, THE CARE OF STRANGERS: THE RISE OF AMERICA'S HOSPITAL SYSTEM (1995).

[15]Charles E. Rosenberg, THE CARE OF STRANGERS, *supra* note 14 .

[16]William L. Dowling & Patricia A. Armstrong, *The Hospital, supra* note 10.

[17]*Id.*

[18]*Id.*; Sylvia A. Law, BLUE CROSS: WHAT WENT WRONG? 6 (1974).

[19]William L. Dowling & Patricia A. Armstrong, *The Hospital, supra* note 10.

[20]Joseph W. Garbarino, HEALTH PLANS AND COLLECTIVE BARGAINING (1960).

[21]J. Lundy, *Health Insurance: The Pro-Competition Proposals* 4, CONGRESSIONAL RESEARCH SERVICE REPORT NO. 81046 (1984); William B. Schwartz & Henry J. Aaron, *Hospital Cost Control: A Bitter Pill to Swallow*, HARVARD BUSINESS REVIEW 160-161 (Mar-Apr. 1985).

[22]42 United States Code Section 1396 (1982).

[23]Social Security Amendments of 1965, Public Law Number 89-97, 87 Statute 286.

[24]Richard A. Hinden & Douglas L. Elden, *Liability Issues for Managed Care Organization Entities*,14(1) SETON HALL LEGISLATIVE JOURNAL 1-63 (Summer 1990).

[25]Alexander M. Capron, *Health Care Costs: Ethical and Legal Implications of Changes in the Methods of Paying Physicians*, 36 CASE WESTERN RESERVE LAW REVIEW 708 (Summer 1986).

[26]Manning, W.G., Leibowitz, A., Goldber, G.A., et al., *A Controlled Trial on the Effect of a Prepaid Group Practice on the Use of Services*, 310 NEW ENGLAND JOURNAL OF MEDICINE 1505 (1984).

[27]Mark A. Hall, Ira Mark Ellman, & Daniel S. Strouse, HEALTH CARE LAW AND ETHICS IN A NUTSHELL (1990).

[28]Max W. Fine & Jonathan H. Sunshine, *Malpractice Reform Through Consumer Choice and Consumer Education: Are New Concepts Marketable?*. 49 LAW AND CONTEMPORARY PROBLEMS 213 (Spring 1986); Kenneth Wing, *American Health Policy in the 1980s*. 36(4) CASE WESTERN RESERVE LAW REVIEW 608-707 (1986).

[29]*Id.*

[30]*Id.*

[31]J. Gabel and Dan Ermann, et al, *The Emergence and Future of PPOs.*, 11 JOURNAL OF HEALTH POLITICS, POLICY AND LAW 305 (Summer 1986).

[32]*Id.*

³³Power, G.D. *Allocation of Risk in Managed Care Organization Programs*, in MANAGED CARE ORGANIZATION HEALTH CARE 393:279-301 (PLI Commercial Law and Practice Handbook Series)(September 25, 1986) available in Westlaw TP-ALL file.
³⁴Mark A. Hall, Ira Mark Ellman, & Daniel S. Strouse, HEALTH CARE LAW, *supra* note 27.
³⁵*The Impact of Managed Care Organizations on Doctors*, *supra* note 1.
³⁶*Id.*
³⁷2003 MEDICAID MANAGED CARE ORGANIZATION ENROLLMENT REPORT, Centers for Medicare and Medicaid Services; http://www.cms.hhs.gov/medicaid/managed care organization care/trends03.pdf (Last Visited: March 24, 2005).
³⁸*Id.*; Robert H. Miller, *Healthcare Managed Care Organization and Change: Implications for Access to Care and Its Measurement*, 33 HEALTH SERVICES RESEARCH 653 (1998).
³⁹Pamela S. Bouey, *Peer Review in the Managed Care Organization Setting*, in MANAGED CARE ORGANIZATION HEALTH CARE 1988: 471 LEGAL AND OPERATIONAL ISSUES 279-310 (PLI Commercial Law and Practice Course Handbook Series No. 471, 1988), available in WESTLAW, TP-All File.
⁴⁰*Id.*; J. Stern, A. Ostroff, A. Southam, et al. *Health Maintenance Managed Care Organizations: Reconciling Quality of Care With Cost Control.* 9 WHITTIER LAW REVIEW 185-200 (1987).
⁴¹Richard A.Hinden & Douglas L. Elden, *Liability Issues for Managed Care Organization Care*, *supra* note 24.
⁴²*Id.*
⁴³Judith Weinberg, *Utilization Review as the Practice of Medicine: Scaling the Wall of ERISA*, 9 BOSTON UNIVERSITY PUBLIC INTEREST LAW JOURNAL 89 (Fall, 1999).
⁴⁴*Id.*
⁴⁵Larry J. Pittman, *A Thirteenth Amendment Challenge to Both Racial Inequities in Medical Treatments and Improper Physicians' Informed Consent Disclosures*, 48 SAINT LOUIS UNIVERSITY LAW JOURNAL 131 (Fall 2003)
⁴⁶*Id.*
⁴⁷M.R. Weir & E. Saunders, *Pharmacologic Management of Systemic Hypertension in Blacks*, 61 AMERICAN JOURNAL OF CARDIOLOGY 46-52 (1988).
⁴⁸Erik Lillquist & Charles A. Sullivan, *The Law and Genetics of Racial Profiling in Medicine*, 39 HARVARD CIVIL RIGHTS-CIVIL LIBERTIES LAW REVIEW 391 (Summer, 2004).
⁴⁹Ana I. Balsa, Naomi Seiler, Thomas G. McGuire, & M. Gregg Bloche, *Clinical Uncertainty and Healthcare Inequities*, 29 AMERICAN JOURNAL OF LAW AND MEDICINE 203 (2003).
⁵⁰*Id.*
⁵¹*Id.*
⁵²*Id.*
⁵³Risa Lavizzo-Mourey, et al., *The Perceptions of African American Physicians Concerning Their Treatment by Managed Care Organization s*, 88 JOURNAL OF THE NATIONAL MEDICAL ASSOCIATION 210 (1996); *All Things Considered* (National Public Radio, Nov. 14, 1996)(radio broadcast).
⁵⁴René Bowser, *Racial Profiling in Health Care: an Institutional Analysis of Medical Treatment Inequities*, 7 MICHIGAN JOURNAL OF RACE AND LAW 79 (Fall 2001)
⁵⁵M.R. Weir & E. Saunders, *Hypertension in Blacks*, *supra* note 47.
⁵⁶Rene Bowser, *Eliminating Racial and Ethnic Inequities in Medical Care*, 30 SUMMER BRIEF 25, 26 (2001); Norman L. Cantor & George C. Thomas III, *The Legal Bounds of Physician Conduct Hastening Death*, 48 BUFFALO LAW REVIEW 83, 160 (2000); Ellen Wertheimer, *Shakespeare In Law: The Use of History in Shattering Student Credulity*, 45 VILLANOVA LAW REVIEW 463, 470 (2000); Steven P. Wallace, et al., *The Consequences of Color-Blind Health Policy for Older Racial and Ethnic Minorities*, 9 STANFORD LAW & POLICY REVIEW 329, 334 (1998); Ezekiel J. Emanuel & Linda L. Emanuel, *Preserving Community*

*in Health Care*, 22 JOURNAL OF HEALTH POLITICS, POLICY AND THE LAW 147, 168 (1997); Anna I. Balsa, Naomi Seiler, Thomas G. McGuire, & M. Gregg Bloche, *Clinical Uncertainty and Healthcare Inequities, supra* note 49.

[57]Larry J. Pittman, *A Thirteenth Amendment Challenge, supra* note 45; Anna I. Balsa,, Naomi Seiler, Thomas G. McGuire, & M. Gregg Bloche, *Clinical Uncertainty and Healthcare Inequities, supra* note 49.

[58]Carolyn M. Clancy & Bruce E. Hillner, *Physicians as Gatekeepers: The Impact of Financial Incentives*, 149 ARCHIVES INTERNAL MEDICINE. 917, 917 (1989); Ana I. Balsa, Naomi Seiler, Thomas G. McGuire, & M. Gregg Bloche, *Clinical Uncertainty and Healthcare Inequities, supra* note 49.

[59]Alexander M. Capron, *Health Care Costs, supra* note 25; A.L. Hillman, *Financial Incentives for Physicians in HMOs – Is There a Conflict of Interest?* 317 NEW ENGLAND JOURNAL OF MEDICINE 1743-8 (1987); E.H. Morreim, *The MD and The DRG*, 15 HASTINGS CENTER REPORT 34-5 (1985).

[60]A.L. Hillman, *Financial Incentives for Physicians in HMOs—Is There a Conflict of Interest?, supra* note 59.

[61]Gnessin, A., *Liability in the Managed Care Organization Setting*, in MANAGED CARE ORGANIZATION HEALTH CARE 471:405-479 (PLI Commercial Law and Handbook Series)(September 1, 1986) available in Westlaw: TP-ALL file.

[62]*Id.*

[70]Larry J. Pittman, *A Thirteenth Amendment Challenge, supra* note 45.

[71]Eric C. Schneider, Alan M. Zaslavsky, & Arnold M. Epstein, *Racial Inequities in the Quality of Care, supra* note 5; Ming Tai-Seale, et al., *Racial Inequities in Service Use Among Medicaid Beneficiaries After Mandatory Enrollment in Managed Care Organization Care: A Difference in Differences Approach*, 38 INQUIRY 49 (2001).

[72]Ana I. Balsa, Naomi Seiler, Thomas G. McGuire, & M. Gregg Bloche, *Clinical Uncertainty and Healthcare Inequities, supra* note 49.; Larry J. Pittman, *A Thirteenth Amendment Challenge, supra* note 45.

[73]Larry J. Pittman, *A Thirteenth Amendment Challenge, supra* note 45.

[74]Ana I Balsa, Naomi Seiler, Thomas G. McGuire, & M. Gregg Bloche, *Clinical Uncertainty and Healthcare Inequities, supra* note 49.

[75]*Id.*

[76]M. Gregg Bloche, *Race and Discretion in American Medicine*, 1 YALE JOURNAL OF HEALTH POLICY, LAW AND ETHICS 95, 97-99 (2001)

[77]Eric C. Schneider, Alan M. Zaslavsky, & Arnold M. Epstein, *Racial Inequities in the Quality of Care, supra* note 5.

[78]Larry J. Pittman, *A Thirteenth Amendment Challenge*, supra note 45; Mark Schlesinger, *On Values and Democratic Policy Making: The Deceptively Fragile Consensus Around Market-Oriented Medical Care*, 27 JOURNAL OF HEALTH POLITICS, POLICY AND LAW 889 (December, 2002).

## Chapter Six
### SLAVERY, SEGREGATION AND RACISM: TRUSTING THE HEALTH CARE SYSTEM AIN'T ALWAYS EASY!

[1]Annette Dula, *African American Suspicion of the Healthcare System Is Justified: What Do We Do about It?*, CAMBRIDGE QUARTERLY HEALTHCARE ETHICS 347, 347 (1994); Carol Stevens, *Research: Distrust Runs Deep; Medical Community Seeks Solutions*, DETROIT NEWS, December 10, 1995, at A12; Cheryl Clark, *The Ghost of Tuskegee*, SAN DIEGO UNION & TRIBUNE, January 28, 1996, at D14.

[2]Barbara A. Koeing & Jan Gate-Williams, *Understanding Cultural Difference in Caring for Dying Patients*, 163 WESTERN JOURNAL OF MEDICINE 244 (1995); Carol Stevens, *Churches Preach the Gospel of Good Health*, DETROIT NEWS, December 11, 1995, at A1; Clark, *The Ghost of Tuskegee, supra* note 1; Cynthia Hubert, *African Americans Breaking Silence on Reality of AIDS*, SACRAMENTO BEE, January 2, 1996, at A1; Sharon

Voas, *Aging African Americans Sick, Scared past Abuses, Tradition Keep Them from Clinic,* Pittsburgh Post-Gazette, August 27, 1995, at B1.

[3]Tom L. Beauchamp, *Response to Jorge Garcia,* in Black Perspectives on Bioethics 67, 72 (Harley E. Flack & Edmund D. Pellegrino eds., 1992).

[4]Webster's II New College Dictionary 821 (1985).

[5]Arthur Kleinman & Joan Kleinman, *Suffering and its Professional Transformation: Toward an Ethnography of Interpersonal Experience,* 15 Cultural Medicine. & Psychiatric 275 (1991); Arthur Kleinman, Patients and Healers in the Context of Culture (1980); Cecil Helman, Culture, Health and Illness (1995); Celia J Orona, et al., *Cultural Aspects of Nondisclosure,* 3 Cambridge Quarterly Healthcare Ethics 338 (1994); Charles Taylor, Multiculturalism and "The Politics of Recognition" 6077 (1992); James H. Jones, Bad Blood: the Tuskegee Syphilis Experiment 216 (1981); Judith Barker, *Cultural Diversity— Changing the Context of Medical Practice,* 157 West Journal of Medicine 248 (1992); Ladson Hinton IV & Arthur Kleinman, *Cultural Issues and International Psychiatric Diagnosis,* in International Review of Psychiatry 111 (Jorge Alberto, Costa E. Silva, & Carol Nadelson eds. 1993); Leonard Harris, *Autonomy Under Duress,* in Black Perspectives on Biomedical Ethics 133, 134-35 (Harley E. Flack & Edmund D. Pellegrino eds. 1992); Margaret Lock, *The Concept of Race: An Ideological Construct,* 30 Transcultural Psychiatric Research Review 203 (1993); Marjorie Kagawa-Singer, *Diverse Cultural (Beliefs and Practices About Death and Dying in the Elderly,* in Cultural Diversity and Geriatric Care: Challenges to the Health Professions (Darryl Wieland et. al. eds 1994); Nancy Adler, et Al., *Socioeconomic Inequalities in Health: No Easy Solution,* 269 Journal of the American Medical Association 3140 (1993); P.V. Caralis, et al., *The Influence of Ethnicity and Race on Attitudes Toward Advance Directives, Life-prolonging Treatments, and Euthanasia,* 4 Journal of Clinical Ethics 155 (1993).

[6]Edmund D. Pellegrino, *Response to Leonard, Harris,* African American Perspectives on Biomedical Ethics, 150, 151 (Harley E. Flack & Edmund D. Pellegrino eds. 1992); Harris, *Autonomy Under Duress, supra* note 5 at 134-35.

[7]Edmund D. Pellegrino, *Response to Leonard, Harris, supra* note 6.

[8]Leonard Harris, *Autonomy under Duress, supra* note 5 at 134-35.

[9]Annette Dula, *Yes, There Are African American Perspectives on Bioethics,* in African American Perspectives on Biomedical Ethics 193, 194 (Harley E. Flack & Edmund D. Pellegrino eds 1992).

[10]Marian Gray Secundy, *Response to Kwasi Wiredu,* in African American Perspectives on Biomedical Ethics 99, 101 (Harley E. Flack & Edmund D. Pellegrino eds 1992) (Citing Mechal Sobel, Trabelin' On: the Slave Journey to an Afro-Baptist Faith 219 (1988)..

[11]Kwasi Wiredu, *The Moral Foundations of African Culture,* in African American Perspectives on Biomedical Ethics 80-81 (Harley E. Flack & Edmund D. Pellegrino eds 1992); Marian Gray Secundy, *Response to Kwasi Wiredu, supra* note 10 at 103.

[12]Kwasi Wiredu, *The Moral Foundations of African Culture, supra* note 11 at 83-84.

[13]Marian Gray Secundy, *Response to Kwasi Wiredu, supra* note 10 at 103; Kwasi Wiredu, *The Moral Foundations of African Culture, supra* note 11 at 89.

[14]Cheryl J. Sanders, *Problems and Limitations of an African American Perspective* in Eds. Biomedical Ethics: a Theological View, in African American Perspectives on Biomedical Ethics, 165, 167-70 (Harley E. Flack & Edmund D. Pellegrino eds 1992); Marian Gray Secundy, *Response to Kwasi Wiredu, supra* note 10 at 102.

[15]Annette Dula, *African American Suspicion, supra* note 1 at 347-357.

[16]*Id.*

[17]*Id.*

[18]W. Michael Byrd & Linda C. Clayton, RACE AND HEALTH CARE, AFRICAN AMERICAN HEALTH IN THE JACKSONIAN AND ANTEBELLUM PERIODS, 1812-46: GROWTH, CHANGE AND MANIFEST DESTINY (1996) (Unpublished Manuscript).

[19]*Id.*

[20]Annette Dula, *African American Suspicion*, *supra* note 1 at 347-357; Todd L. Savitt, MEDICINE AND SLAVERY: THE DISEASES AND HEALTH CARE OF AFRICAN AMERICANS IN ANTEBELLUM VIRGINIA 282 (1978).

[21]Todd L. Savitt, *supra* note 20.

[22]*Id.* at 285.

[23]*Id.* at 286 .

[24]W. Michael Byrd & Linda C. Clayton, AFRICAN AMERICAN HEALTH, *supra* note 18.

[25]Annette Dula, *African American Suspicion*, *supra* note 1 at 347-357; Todd L. Savitt, MEDICINE AND SLAVERY, *supra* note 20; W. Michael Byrd & Linda C. Clayton, AFRICAN AMERICAN HEALTH, *supra* note 18.

[26]Annette Dula, *African American Suspicion*, supra note 1 at 347-357; Gladys-Marie Fry, NIGHT RIDERS IN AFRICAN AMERICAN FOLK HISTORY 170-212 (1975); Todd L. Savitt, MEDICINE AND SLAVERY, *supra* note 20; Patricia A. Turner, I HEARD IT THROUGH THE GRAPEVINE: RUMOR IN AFRICAN AMERICAN CULTURE 67-70 (1993).

[27]Annette Dula, *African American Suspicion*, *supra* note 1 at 347-357; Gladys-Marie Fry, NIGHT RIDERS, *supra* note 26; Todd L. Savitt, MEDICINE AND SLAVERY, *supra* note 20; Patricia A. Turner, I HEARD IT THROUGH THE GRAPEVINE, *supra* note 26.

[28]Todd L. Savitt, MEDICINE AND SLAVERY, *supra* note 20.

[29]Annette Dula, *African American Suspicion*, *supra* note 1 at 347-357.

[30]*Id.*

[31]Todd L. Savitt, MEDICINE AND SLAVERY, *supra* note 20.

[32]*Id.* at 300; W. Michael Byrd & Linda C. Clayton, AFRICAN AMERICAN HEALTH, *supra* note 18.

[33]Todd L. Savitt, MEDICINE AND SLAVERY, *supra* note 20. at 298-99.

[34]*Id.* at 301.

[35]W. Michael Byrd & Linda C. Clayton, AFRICAN AMERICAN HEALTH, *supra* note 18; Diana E. Axelson, *Women as Victims of Medical Experimentation: J. Marion Sims' Surgery on Slave Women, 1845-1850*, 2 SAGE 10-13 (1985).

[36]W. Michael Byrd & Linda C. Clayton, AFRICAN AMERICAN HEALTH, *supra* note18.

[37]*Id.*

[38]*Id.*

[39]Albert S. Lyons & R. Joseph Petrucelli II, MEDICINE: AN ILLUSTRATED HISTORY 523, 531 (1987); W. Michael Byrd & Linda C. Clayton, AFRICAN AMERICAN HEALTH, *supra* note 18.; Deborah K. McGregor, SEXUAL SURGERY AND THE ORIGINS OF GYNECOLOGY: J. MARION SIMS, HIS HOSPITAL, AND HIS PATIENTS (1989); George A. Bender, GREAT MOMENTS IN MEDICINE 236-44 (1966).

[40]Annette Dula *African American Suspicion*, *supra* note 1 at 347-357; Stephen B. Thomas & Sandra Crouse Quinn, *The Tuskegee Syphilis Study, 1932 to 1972: Implications for HIV Education and Aids Risk Education Programs in the African American Community*, 81 AMERICAN JOURNAL OF PUBLIC HEALTH 499 (1991).

[41]Annette Dula, *African American Suspicion*, *supra* note 1 at 347-357.

[42]*Id.*

[43]*Id.*; Jean Heller, *Syphilis Victims in U.S.: Study Went Untreated for 40 Years*, NEW YORK TIMES, July 26, 1972, at A1.

[44]Stephen B. Thomas & Sandra Crouse Quinn, *The Tuskegee Syphilis Study*, *supra* note 40; James H. Jones, BAD BLOOD, *supra* note 5.

[45]Stephen B. Thomas & Sandra Crouse Quinn, *The Tuskegee Syphilis Study*, *supra* note 40.

[46]James H. Jones, BAD BLOOD, *supra* note 5.

[47]*Id.*
[48]*Id.* at 217.
[49]*Id.*
[50]*Id.*
[51]*Id.*
[52]Anthony Sibert & Denise Ji-Alunte Siebert, *Radiation Scandal,* Zmag (May 1994) http://www.zmag.org/ZMag/articles/may94sibert.htm (Last visited: March 25, 2005)(copy on file with author).
[53]*Id.*
[54]*Id.*
[55]*Id.*
[56]*Id.*
[57]*Id.*
[58]*Id.*
[59]*Id.*
[60]*Id.*
[61]*Id.*
[62]Harriet A. Washington, *Tuskegee Experiment Was but One Medical Study That Exploited African Americans [Sic] Infamous Research,* BALTIMORE SUN, March 19, 1995, at 1f; Anthony Sibert & Denise Ji-Alunte Siebert, *Radiation Scandal, supra* note 52.
[63]*Id.*
[64]*Id.*
[65]*Id.*
[66]*Id.*
[67]Marilyn McCraven, *Hospital's Experiment Draws Worry; Shock Trauma Plans Trial of New Therapy Without Subjects' Ok; Food and Drug Administration Loosened its Rules; Poppleton Residents Say Facility Should Publicize Test More,* BALTIMORE SUN, April 19, 1997 at 1B.
[68]*Research Conducted Without Patients' Consent; Study of Blood Substitute is Halted When Death Rates Exceed Projections,* BALTIMORE SUN, January 18, 1999 at 3A.
[69]Barbara L. Bernier, *Class, Race, and Poverty: Medical Technologies and Socio-Political Choices,* 11 HARVARD BLACKLETTER LAW JOURNAL 115, 116- 25 (1994); Cara A. Fauci, *Racism and Health Care in America: Legal Responses to Racial Inequities in the Allocation of Kidneys,* 21 BOSTON COLLEGE THIRD WORLD LAW JOURNAL 35 (Winter, 200); Harriet A. Washington, *Tuskegee Experiment, supra* note 73.
[70]Harriet A. Washington, *Tuskegee Experiment, supra* note 73.
[71]*Id.*
[72]*Id.*
[73]*Id.*
[74]Larry J. Pitman, *A Thirteenth Amendment Challenge to Both Racial Inequities in Medical Treatments and Improper Physicians' Informed Consent Disclosures,* 48 Saint Louis University Law Journal 131 (Fall 2003); Cara A. Fauci, *Legal Responses to Racial Inequities, supra* note 65 Harriett A. Washington, *Tuskegee Experiment, supra* note 73; Howard University, HUMAN EXPERIMENT: AN ANCIENT NOTION IN A MODERN TECHNOLOGY 9-10 (1974); Barbara L. Bernier, *Class, Race, and Poverty, supra* note 65
[75]Larry J. Pittman, *A Thirteenth Amendment Challenge, supra* note 66 ; Cara A. Fauci, *Legal Responses to Racial Inequities, supra* note 65; Harriet A. Washington, *Tuskegee Experiment,* supra note 73; Howard University, HUMAN EXPERIMENT, *supra* note 66 Barbara L. Bernier, *Class, Race, and Poverty, supra* note 65
[76]*Id.*
[77]Andrea Asaro, *The Judicial Portrayal of the Physician in Abortion and Sterilization Decisions: the Use and Abuse of Medical Discretion,* 6 HARVARD WOMEN'S LAW JOURNAL 51, 93-101 (1983); Deborah Larned, *The Epidemic in Unnecessary Hysterectomy,* in SEIZING OUR BODIES: THE POLITICS OF WOMEN'S HEALTH 202 (Claudia Dreifus ed. 1977); Dick Grosboll, *Sterilization Abuse: Current State of the Law and Remedies for Abuse,* 10 GOLDEN GATE UNIVERSITY LAW REVIEW 1147, 1153-56 (1980).

[78]Harriet A, Washington, *Tuskegee Experiment, supra* note 73.

[79]*Id.*

[80]*Id.*

[81]*Id.*

[82]*Id.*

[83]*Id.*

[84]*Id.*

[85]*Id.*

[86]*Id.*

[87]*Id.*; Robyn Pforr Ryan, *Should Combat Troops Be Given the Option of Refusing Investigational Drug Treatment?*, 52 Food and Drug Law Journal 377 (1997); Interim Rule section 50.23(d), 55 Federal Regulation 52,817 (December 21, 1990) (codified at 21 Code of Federal Regulations § 50.23 (1996).

[88]Allan M. Hornblum, ACRES OF SKIN: HUMAN EXPERIMENTS AT HOLMESBURG PRISON (1998).

[89]*Id.* .

[90]*Id.*

[91]*Id.*

[92]James H. Jones, BAD BLOOD, *supra* note 5; Franz J. Ingelfinger, et. al., *The Poor*, in NATIONAL ACADEMY OF SCIENCE, EXPERIMENTS AND RESEARCH WITH HUMANS: VALUES IN CONFLICT 150 (1975); Robert M. Veatch, *Ethical Principles in Medical Experimentation*, in ETHICAL AND LEGAL ISSUES OF SOCIAL EXPERIMENTATION 22-24 (Alice M. Rivlin et al, eds 1974).

[93]Annette Dula, *African American Suspicion, supra* note 1 at 347-357; Leslie Roberts, *One Worked: the Other Didn't*, 247 SCIENCE 18 (1990).

[94]Annette Dual, *African American Suspicion, supra* note 1 at 347-357; Robert B. Scott, *Health Care Priority and Sickle Cell Anemia*, 214 JOURNAL OF THE AMERICAN MEDICAL ASSOCIATION 731, 731-34 (1970); Todd L. Savitt & Morton F. Goldberg, *Herrick's 1910 Case Report of Sickle Cell Anemia: The Rest of the Story*, 261 JOURNAL OF THE AMERICAN MEDICAL ASSOCIATION 266, 266-71 (1989).

[95]National Sickle Cell Anemia Control Act, Public Law Number 92-294, 86 Statute 136 (1972) (codified as amended at 42 United States Code §§ 300(b)(1) et seq.). \{(The Sickle Cell Act was passed in 1972, as an amendment to the Public Health Service Act, chapter 373, Title I, § 2, 58 Statute 682 (1944) (codified as amended at 42 United States Code §§ 201 et seq.)}; Robert Milton Schmidt, LAW, MEDICINE AND PUBLIC POLICY : THE SICKLE CELL ANEMIA CONTROL ACT OF 1972, A CASE STUDY (1982); Dorothy Roberts, KILLING THE BLACK BODY 257 (1997); Annette Dula, *African American Suspicion, supra* note 1 at 347-357

[96]Robert Milton Schmidt, THE SICKLE CELL ANEMIA CONTROL ACT OF 1972, *supra* note 95; Dorothy Roberts, KILLING THE BLACK BODY, *supra* note 95; Annette Dula, *African American Suspicion, supra* note 1 at 347-357.

[97]*Id.*

[98]Charles F. Whitten, *Sickle-cell Programming—an Imperiled Promise*, 288 NEW ENGLAND JOURNAL OF MEDICINE 318, 318-19 (1973); Annette Dula, *African American Suspicion, supra* note 1 at 347-357; Ira M. Rutkow, Ira & Jeffrey M. Lipton, *Some Negative Aspects of State Health Departments' Policies Related to Screening for Sickle Cell Anemia*, 64 AMERICAN JOURNAL OF PUBLIC HEALTH 217, 217-21 (1974); Phillip Reilly, GENETICS, LAW AND SOCIAL POLICY 67-68, 77-78 (1977).

[99]Annette Dula, *African American Suspicion, supra* note 1 at 347-357; Ira M. Rutkow & Jeffrey M. Lipton, *Some Negative Aspects of State Health Departments' Policies, supra* note 98.

[100]*Id.*; Larry Gostin, *Genetic Discrimination: The Use of Genetically Based Diagnostic and Prognostic Tests by Employers and Insurers*, 17 AMERICAN JOURNAL OF LAW & MEDICINE 109, 138-39 (1991); Lori B. Andrews, *Confidentiality of Genetic Information in the Workplace*, 17 AMERICAN JOURNAL OF LAW AND MEDICINE 75, 107-08 (1991).

[101]Annette Dula, *African American Suspicion, supra* note 1 at 347-357; James E. Bowman, *Genetic Screening Programs and Public Policy*, 38 PHYLON 117, 117-42 (1977).

[102]Kay Mills, THIS LITTLE LIGHT OF MINE: THE LIFE OF FANNIE LOU HAMER, 274 (1993); Robert G. Weisbord, GENOCIDE? BIRTH CONTROL AND THE AFRICAN AMERICAN (1975); William A. Darity & Castellano B. Turner, *Family Planning, Race Consciousness and the Fear of Race Genocide*, 62 AMERICAN JOURNAL OF PUBLIC HEALTH 1454, 1454-56 (1972).

[103]Linda Gordon, WOMAN'S BODY, WOMAN'S RIGHT: A SOCIAL HISTORY OF BIRTH CONTROL IN AMERICA 281-83, 332-33 (1976); Margaret Sanger, Planned Parenthood, http://www.plannedparenthood.org/about/thisispp/sanger.html (Last Visited: March 25, 2005).

[104]Dorothy E. Roberts, *Crime, Race and Reproduction*, 67 TULANE LAW REVIEW 1945, 1970-71 (1993); Linda Gordon, WOMAN'S BODY, WOMAN'S RIGHT, *supra* note 103 at 332.

[105]Charlotte Rutherford, *Reproductive Freedoms and African American Women*, 4 YALE JOURNAL OF LAW & FEMINISM 255, 273 (1992); George Grant, GRAND ILLUSIONS: THE LEGACY OF PLANNED PARENTHOOD 63, 65 (2d ed. 1992).

[106]Charlotte Rutherford, *Reproductive Freedoms, supra* note 105.

[107]Francis Galton, *Notes on the Early Days of the Eugenics Education Society*, in WAR AGAINST THE WEAK: EUGENICS AND AMERICA'S CAMPAIGN TO CREATE A MASTER RACE 18 (Edwin Black ed. 2003); Stephen Jay Gould, *Carrie Buck's Daughter*, 2 CONSTITUTIONAL COMMENT. 331, 332 (1985).

[108]George P. Smith II, *Genetics, Eugenics, and Public Policy*, 1985 SOUTHERN ILLINOIS UNIVERSITY LAW JOURNAL 435, 439-44.

[109]*Buck v. Bell*, 274 United States 200 (1927).

[110]*Id.*

[111]Annette Dula, *African American Suspicion, supra* note 1 at 347-357.

[112]*Id.*

[113]Laurie Nsiah-Jefferson, *Reproductive Laws, Women of Color, and Low-income Women*, 11 WOMEN'S RIGHTS LAW REPORTER 15, 30-31 (1989); Dorothy E. Roberts, *Crime, Race and Reproduction, supra* note 104; *Walker v.. Pierce*, 560 Federal 2d 609, 613 (4th Circuit 1977) *Certiorari Denied*, 434 United States 1075 (1978).

[114]*Cox v. Stanton*, 529 Federal 2d 47 (4th Circuit 1975); Dorothy E. Roberts, *Crime, Race and Reproduction, supra* note 104.

[115]*Relf v. Weinberger*, 372 Federal Supplement 1196, 1199 (District Court of the District of Columbia, 1974), Vacated, 565 Federal 2d 722 (District of Columbia Circuit 1977).

[116]Annette Dula, *African American Suspicion, supra* note 1 at 347-357.

[117]Laurie Nsiah-Jefferson, *Reproductive Laws and Women of Color, supra* note 113.

[118]*Id.*

[119]*Id.*

[120]Dorothy E. Roberts, *Crime, Race and Reproduction, supra* note 104.

[121]42 Code of Federal Regulations Section 441.253 (1994) with 42 Code of Federal Regulations Sections 441.202-.203 (1994); Charlotte Rutherford, *Reproductive Freedoms and African American Women, supra* note 105.

[122]W. Michael Byrd & Linda C. Clayton, AFRICAN AMERICAN HEALTH, *supra* note 18; C. Loring Brace, "RACE" IS A FOUR-LETTER WORD (2005).

[124]*Id.*

[125]*Id.*

[126]*Id.*

[123]*Id.*

[127]*Abortion Surveillance, 1984-1985*, 38 MORBIDITY AND MORTALITY WEEKLY REPORT (19/1/89); *Abortion Surveillance --- United States, 2001*, 53 MORBIDITY AND MORTALITY WEEKLY REPORT (11/26/2004 ).

[128]*Id.*

[129]*Id.*

[130]Table 16. *Legal abortions and legal abortion ratios, according to selected patient characteristics: United States, selected years 1973-2001,* HEALTH UNITED STATES, 2004.

[131]John D. Lantos, *Race, Prenatal Care, and Infant Mortality,* in "IT JUST AIN'T FAIR": THE ETHICS OF HEALTH CARE FOR AFRICAN AMERICANS 67, 67-74 (Annette Dula & Sara Goering eds. 1994).

[132]Fern Shen & Peter Pae, *Calls for Peace Met With Caution,* WASHINGTON POST, January 23, 1995, at D1; Kay Mills, THE LIFE OF FANNIE LOU HAMER, *supra* note 102 at 274; *Minority Update: Genocide to Some; Vital Choice to Others,* AMERICAN POLITICAL NETWORK: ABORTION REPORT, June 17, 1992; Felicia R. Lee & Rachel B. Gold, *Empty Womb,* ESSENCE, at 51 (May 1990); Robert G. Weisbord, GENOCIDE? BIRTH CONTROL, *supra* note 102; William A. Darity & Castellano B. Turner, *Race Consciousness and the Fear of Race Genocide, supra* note 102, at 1454-56.

[133]*Women: African Americans "No Longer Silent" on Abortion,* AMERICAN POLITICAL NETWORK: ABORTION REPORT, Aug. 25, 1992, available in WESTLAW 08/25/92 APN-AB13; Felicia R. Lee & Rachel B. Gold, *Empty Wound supra* note 132 at 51-53.

[134]*Minority Update: Genocide to Some, supra* note 132;

[135]Jerry E. Bishop & Michael Waldholz, GENOME: THE STORY OF THE MOST ASTONISHING SCIENTIFIC ADVENTURE OF OUR TIME--THE ATTEMPT TO MAP ALL THE GENES IN THE HUMAN BODY (1990); Julia Walsh, *Reproductive Rights and the Human Genome Project,* 4 SOUTHERN CALIFORNIA LAW REVIEW & WOMEN'S STUDIES. 145, 145-47 (1994). United States Department of Health & Human Services, UNDERSTANDING OUR GENETIC INHERITANCE: THE U.S. HUMAN GENOME PROJECT (1992); Darryl Macer, Whose Genome Project?, 5 BIOETHICS 183, 184, 188 (1991).

[136]Julia Walsh, *Reproductive Rights, supra* note 135 at 147.

[137]*Id.*at 147-48; Office of Technology Assessment, MAPPING OUR GENES-- THE GENOME PROJECTS: HOW BIG, HOW FAST? 24 United States Congressional Publication Number Ota-ba-373 (1988).

[138]Julia Walsh, *Reproductive Rights, supra* note 136 at 151-53; Sumner B. Twiss, *Problems of Social Justice in Applied Human Genetics,* in GENETIC COUNSELING: FACTS, VALUES, AND NORMS 255, 255-62 (Alexander M. Caprom et al. eds. 1979); James E. Bowman, *Genetic Screening: Toward a New Eugenics?,* in "IT JUST AIN'T FAIR": THE ETHICS OF HEALTH CARE FOR AFRICAN AMERICANS 165-181 (Annette Dula & Sara Goering, eds 1994).

[139]Julia Walsh, *Reproductive Rights, supra* note 136.

[140]*Id.* at 157-58; Sumner B. Twiss, *Problems of Social Justice, supra* note 138 at 257.

[141]Dorothy Nelkin & Laurence Tancredi, DANGEROUS DIAGNOSTICS: THE SOCIAL POWER OF BIOLOGICAL INFORMATION 106-32 (1994).

[142]*Id.*

[143]Kathy L. Hudson et al., *Genetic Discrimination and Health Insurance: An Urgent Need for Reform,* SCIENCE, Oct. 20, 1995, at 391; Larry Gostin, *Genetic Discrimination, supra* note 100 at 117-19.

[144]Patricia A. King, *The Past as Prologue: Race, Class, and Gene Discrimination,* in GENE MAPPING: USING LAW AND ETHICS AS GUIDES 94 (George J. Annas & Sherman Elias eds 1992).

[145]*Id.*

[146]*Id.*

[147]Alfreda A. Sellers-Diamond, *Disposable Children in Black Faces: the Violence Initiative as Inner-city Containment Policy,* 62 UNIVERSITY OF MISSOURI KANSAS CITY LAW REVIEW 423, 459-60 (1994) (Citing Samuel F. Yette, THE CHOICE: THE ISSUE OF BLACK SURVIVAL IN AMERICA 82, 249 (1971)).

[148]*Id.*

[149]Patricia A. King, *Race, Class, and Gene Discrimination, supra* note 144.

[150]*Id.*

[151]*Id.*

[152]*Id.* at 460 (citing Arthur R. Jensen, *How Much Can We Boost IQ and Scholastic Achievement?*, 39 HARVARD EDUCATION REVIEW 1 (1969)).

[153]*Id.*

[154]Office of Technology Assessment, *supra* note 137, at 84. Susan Rae Peterson, *The Politics of Prenatal Diagnosis: A Feminist Ethical Analysis*, in THE CUSTOM-MADE CHILD? WOMEN-CENTERED PERSPECTIVES 95, 101-02 (Helen B. Holmes et al. eds 1981).

[155]Office of Inspector General, THE DISTRIBUTION OF ORGANS FOR TRANSPLANTATION: EXPECTATIONS AND PRACTICES 8 (1991); Ian Ayres et al., *Unequal Racial Access to Kidney Transplantation*, 46 VANDERBILT LAW REVIEW 805 (1993); Bertram L. Kasiske et al., *The Effect of Race on Access and Outcome in Transplantation*, 324 NEW ENGLAND JOURNAL OF MEDICINE 302-308 (1991).

[156]Health Care Financing Administration, END STAGE RENAL DISEASE PATIENT: PROFILE TABLES (1988); Ian Ayres, *Unequal Racial Access*, *supra* note 155 at 810.

[157]Ian Ayres, *Unequal Racial Access*, *supra* note 155 at 810.

[158]Institute of Medicine, Committee on Understanding and Eliminating Racial and Ethnic Inequities in Health Care, UNEQUAL TREATMENT: CONFRONTING RACIAL AND ETHNIC INEQUITIES IN HEALTH CARE at 58-60 (Brian D. Smedley, Adrienne Y. Stith, & Alan R. Nelson eds 2003).

[159]*Id.*

[160]Office of Inspector General, DISTRIBUTION OF ORGANS FOR TRANSPLANTATION, supra note 155 at 11; Clive O. Callender, *Organ Donation in the African American Population: Where Do We Go From Here?*, 19 TRANSPLANTATION PROC. 36 (1987); Luis M. Perez et al., *Organ Donation in Three Major American Cities With Large Latino and African American Populations*, 46 TRANSPLANT PROCEDURES 555 (1988).

[161]Clive O. Callender, *Organ Donation in the African American Population*, *supra* note 160.

[162]F. J. Michael Soucie et al., *Race and Sex Differences in the Identification of Candidates for Renal Transplantation*, 19 AMERICAN JOURNAL OF. KIDNEY DISEASE 414 (1992).

[163]Ian Ayres, *Unequal Racial Access*, *supra* note 155 at 810.

[164]*Id.*

[165]*Id.* (citing Clive O. Callender et al., *Attitudes Among African Americans Toward Donating Kidneys for Transplantation: A Pilot Project*, 74 NATIONAL MEDICAL ASSOCIATION JOURNAL 807 (1982); The Partnership for Organ Donation and the Annenberg Washington Program, SOLVING THE DONOR SHORTAGE BY MEETING FAMILY NEEDS: A COMMUNICATIONS MODEL 4 (Oct. 30-31, 1990); Orly Hazony, *Increasing the Supply of Cadaver Organs for Transplantation: Recognizing That the Real Problem is Psychological Not Legal*, 3 HEALTH MATRIX 219 (1993).

[166]*Law & Order: Sonata for a Solo Organ* (National Broadcast Corporation April 2, 1991) (Television series).

[167]W. Michael Byrd & Linda C. Clayton, AFRICAN AMERICAN HEALTH, *supra* note 18.

[168]*Id.*

[169]*Id.*

[170]Harriet A. Washington, *Tuskegee Experiment*, *supra* note 73.

[171]Scott Simon, *Sale of Human Organs Thriving in Some Parts of the World* (National Public Radio, Nov. 27, 1993) (Radio broadcast transcription available in 1993 West Law 9415778); Anthony Boadle, *Film Exposes Black Market in Body Parts From Humans*, SEATTLE TIMES, November 12, 1993, at A14.

[172]*Id.*

[173]Christian Williams, *Combating the Problems of Human Rights Abuses and Inadequate Organ Supply Through Presumed Donative Consent*, 26 CASE WESTERN RESERVE JOURNAL OF INTERNATIONAL LAW 315, 316 (1994).

[174]*Id.*

[175]Charlotte Rutherford, *Reproductive Freedoms and African American Women*, *supra* note 105; Angela Y. Davis, *Surrogates and Outcast Mothers: Racism and Reproductive Politics*, in "IT JUST AIN'T FAIR": THE ETHICS OF HEALTH CARE FOR AFRICAN AMERICANS 41-55 (Annette Dula & Sara Goering eds. 1994).

[176]Charlotte Rutherford, *Reproductive Freedoms and African American Women*, *supra* note 105; Christian Williams, *Human Rights Abuses and Inadequate Organ Supply*, *supra* note 173.

[177]*Id.*

[178]*United Automobile Workers v. Johnson Controls, Inc*, 499 United States 187 (1991).

[179]*Id.* at 211.

[180]Charlotte Rutherford, *Reproductive Freedoms and African American Women*, *supra* note 105 at 277-78.

[181]Dana Hughes et al., THE HEALTH OF AMERICA'S CHILDREN: MATERNAL AND CHILD HEALTH DATA BOOK 10 (Children's Defense Fund 1989).

[182]AFRICAN AMERICAN AND WHITE CHILDREN IN AMERICA: KEY FACT 76 (Children's Defense Fund 1985).

[183]Darci Elaine Burrell, *The Norplant Solution: Norplant and the Control of African American Motherhood*, 5 University of California at Los Angeles WOMEN'S LAW JOURNAL 401 (1995).

[184]Donald Kimmelman, *Poverty and Norplant: Can Contraception Reduce the Underclass?*, PHILADELPHIA INQUIRER, December 12, 1990, at A18; Claude Lewis, *Norplant Editorial Was Offensive: The Thrust of the Editorial was Aimed at the African American Underclass, Unjustly So*, PHILADELPHIA INQUIRER, December 21, 1990, at A19.

[185]David S. Coale, *Norplant Bonuses and the Unconstitutional Conditions Doctrine*, 71 TEXAS LAW REVIEW 189, 189-90 (1992); Dorothy E. Roberts, *Norplant's Threat to Civil Liberties and Racial Justice*, NEW JERSEY LAW JOURNAL, July 26, 1993, at 20.

[186]Tim Larimer, *High School Offers Birth Control Implant, African Americans Disagree on Merits of Program*, DALLAS MORNING NEWS, March 17, 1993, at A37.

[187]Janet F. Ginzberg, *Compulsory Contraception as a Condition of Probation: The Use and Abuse of Norplant*, 58 BROOKLYN LAW REVIEW 979 (1992); Deborah Ann Bailey, *Maternal Substance Abuse: Does Ohio Have an Answer?*, 17 UNIVERSITY OF DAYTON LAW REVIEW 1019, 1032-33 (1992); OHIO REVISED CODE ANNOTATED. §§ 2151.03(A);

[188]Darci Elaine Burrell, *Norplant and the Control of African American Motherhood*, *supra* note 183 at 404.

[189]*Id.* at 416.

[190]42 Code of Federal Regulation §§ 441.250-259 (1991) (sterilizations); 42 Code of Federal Regulation § 441.257 (1991) (informed consent); 42 Code of Federal Regulation § 441.258 (1991) (consent form requirements).

[191]Laurie Nsiah-Jefferson, *Reproductive Laws, Women of Color, and Low-Income Women*, in REPRODUCTIVE LAWS FOR THE 1990S 23, 46 (Sherrill Cohen & Nadine Taubs eds 1988).

[192]But see Charlotte Rutherford, *Reproductive Freedoms and African American Women*, *supra* note 105, at 267.

[193]*Id.*; U.S. Department of Health and Human Services, Public Health Services, HEALTH STATUS OF MINORITIES AND LOW INCOME GROUPS 58 (1985).

[194]*Id.* at 268 note 56.

[195]*Id.* at 268 citing Congressional Caucus for Women's Issues, THE WOMEN'S HEALTH EQUITY ACT OF 1990 18 (1990)).

[196]42 Code of Federal Regulation. § 59.5(a)(1) (1995).

[197]Charlotte Rutherford, *Reproductive Freedoms and African American Women*, *supra* note 105 at 268-69.

[198]Angela Y. Davis, *Racism and Reproductive Politics*, *supra* note 175 at 41-55.

[199]Charlotte Rutherford, *Reproductive Freedoms and African American Women*, *supra* note 105 at 268-69.

[200]*Id.*

[201]*Id.* at 269.

[202]*Id.*

[203]*Id.*

[204]Janice G. Raymond, *Women as Wombs: International Traffic in Reproduction*, MS. MAGAZINE, May/June 1991, at 28, 31.

[205]Charlotte Rutherford, *Reproductive Freedoms and African American Women*, supra note 105 at 269-70.

[206]*Anna J. v. Mark C.*, 286 California Reporter 369, 380-81 (California Court of Appeals 1991).

[207]Charlotte Rutherford, *Reproductive Freedoms and African American Women*, supra note 105 at 272 note 86 (citing Angela Y. Davis, WOMEN, RACE AND CLASS 6-8 (1983).

[208]*Id.*

[209]Alfreda A. Sellers-Diamond, *Disposable Children*, supra note 147.

[210]*Id.* at 424.

[211]Department of Health and Human Services, REPORT OF THE SECRETARY'S BLUE RIBBON PANEL ON VIOLENCE PREVENTION (Jan. 15, 1993); Peter R. Breggin, & Ginger R. Breggin, *The Federal Violence Initiative: Threats to African American Children (And Others)* 24 PSYCHIATRY DISCOURSE 8 (1993).

[212]Alfreda A. Sellers-Diamond, *Disposable Children*, supra note 147 at 425 citing Dr. Frederick K. Goodwin, *Address at the Meeting of the National Mental Health Advisory Council* 115, 117 (Feb. 11, 1992).

[213]*Id.*

[214]Alfreda A. Sellers-Diamond, *Disposable Children*, supra note 147 at 424.

[215]*Id.* at 429.

[216]*Id.*

[217]*Id.* at 431.

[218]*Id.*

[219]*Id.*

[220]*Id.* at 453-54 (citation omitted).

[220]*Id.* at 453-54 (citation omitted).

[221]Alexander Morgan Capron & Vicki Michel, *Law and Bioethics*, 27 LOYOLA LOS ANGELES LAW REVIEW 25, 25 (1993) citing John D. Arras, *Nancy Rhoden: Exploring the Dark Side of Biomedical Technology*, 68 NORTH CAROLINA LAW REVIEW 835, 835 (1990); Sandra H. Johnson, *The Changing Nature of the Bioethics Movement*, 53 MARYLAND LAW REVIEW 1051, 1051-52 (1994).

[222]Alexander Morgan Capron & Vicki Michel, *Law and Bioethics*, supra note 221.

[223]*Id.* at 25, 27.

[224]*Id.* at 28; Tom L. Beauchamp and James F. Childress, PRINCIPLES OF BIOMEDICAL ETHICS (3d Ed. 1989); The National Commission for the Protection of Human Subjects of Biomedical and Behavioral Research, THE BELMONT REPORT: ETHICAL GUIDELINES FOR THE PROTECTION OF HUMAN SUBJECTS OF RESEARCH (1978); Susan M. Wolf, *Shifting Paradigms in Bioethics and Health Law: the Rise of a New Pragmatism*, 20 AMERICAN JOURNAL OF LAW AND MEDICINE 395 (1994); but see Albert R. Jonsen & Stephen Toulmin, THE ABUSE OF CASUISTRY: A HISTORY OF MORAL REASONING (1988); H. Tristram Engelhardt, Jr., BIOETHICS AND SECULAR HUMANISM: THE SEARCH FOR A COMMON MORALITY XI (1991); but see also "IT JUST AIN'T FAIR": THE ETHICS OF HEALTH CARE FOR AFRICAN AMERICANS (Annete Dula & Sara Goering eds 1994); AFRICAN AMERICAN PERSPECTIVES ON BIOMEDICAL ETHICS (Harley E. Flack & Edmund Pellegrino eds 1992); Helen Bequaert Holmes & Laura M. Purdy Eds., FEMINIST PERSPECTIVES IN MEDICAL ETHICS (1992); Susan Sherwin, NO LONGER PATIENT: FEMINIST ETHICS AND HEALTH CARE (1992); John D. Arras, *Getting Down to Cases: The Revival of Casuistry in Bioethics*, 16 JOURNAL OF MEDICINE AND PHILOSOPHY 29 (1991); Albert R. Jonsen, *Of Balloons and Bicycles--or--the Relationship Between Ethical Theory and Practical Judgment*, HASTINGS CENTER REPORT.,

September-October 1991, at 14; Henry S. Richardson, *Specifying Norms as a Way to Resolve Concrete Ethical Problems*, 19 PHILOSOPHY AND PUBLIC AFFAIR 279 (1990).

[225]Tom L. Beauchamp, *Principles and Other Emerging Paradigms in Bioethics*, 69 INDIANA LAW JOURNAL 955, 956 (1994).

[226]Rebecca J. Cook, *Feminism and the Four Principles*, in PRINCIPLES OF HEALTH CARE ETHICS 193 (Raanan Gillon & Ann Lloyd eds 1993); But see Ruth Macklin, *Women's Health: An Ethical Perspective*, 21 JOURNAL OF LAW, MEDICINE AND ETHICS 23 (1993).

[227]Fred H. Cate, *Emerging Paradigms in Bioethics: Posthumous Autonomy Revisited*, 69 INDIANA LAW JOURNAL 1067, 1072 (1994); Susan M. Wolf, *Shifting Paradigms in Bioethics and Health Law, supra* note 224.

[228]Laurence Thomas, *The Morally Beautiful*, in AFRICAN AMERICAN PERSPECTIVES ON BIOMEDICAL ETHICS 118, 123-25 (Harley E. Flack & Edmund D. Pellegrino eds 1992).

[229]*Id.*

[230]*Id.*

[231]*Id.*

[232]Susan M. Wolf, *Shifting Paradigms in Bioethics and Health Law, supra* note 224 at 402.

[233]*Id.*

[234]Laurence Thomas, *The Morally Beautiful, supra* note 228 at 123-25.

[235]Susan M. Wolf, *Shifting Paradigms in Bioethics and Health Law, supra* note 224.

[236]*Id.*

[237]*Id.* At 408; Susan M. Wolf, *Health Care Reform and the Future of Physician Ethics*, HASTINGS CENTER REPORT, March-April 1994, at 28; Renée C. Fox, *The Evolution of American Bioethics: A Sociological Perspective*, in SOCIAL SCIENCE PERSPECTIVES ON MEDICAL ETHICS 201 (George Weisz ed 1990); Joseph A. Carrese & Lorna A. Rhodes, *Western Bioethics on the Navajo Reservation: Benefit or Harm?*, 274 JOURNAL OF AMERICAN MEDICAL ASSOCIATION 826 (1995); President's Commission for the Study of Ethical Problems in Medicine and Biomedical and Behavioral Research, THE ETHICAL AND LEGAL IMPLICATIONS OF INFORMED CONSENT IN THE PATIENT-PRACTITIONER RELATIONSHIP 74-76 (1982).

[238]Tom L. Beauchamp, *Emerging Paradigms in Bioethics, supra* note 225 at 956-57.

[239]Susan M. Wolf, *Shifting Paradigms in Bioethics and Health Law, supra* note 224 at 396-415.

[240]Joanne Mills Garrett et al., *Life-sustaining Treatments During Terminal Illness: Who Wants What?*, 8 JOURNAL OF GENERAL INTERNAL MEDICINE 361, 364 (1993).

[241]P.V. Caralis, et al., *Attitudes Toward Advance Directives supra* note 5.

[242]Carl E. Schneider, *Bioethics With a Human Face*, 69 INDIANA LAW JOURNAL 1075, 1076 (1994); Leon R. Kass, *Practicing Ethics: Where's the Action?*, HASTINGS CENTER REPORT 5., January-February 1990; Judicial Council, *Ethical Guidelines for Organ Transplantation*, 205 JOURNAL OF AMERICAN MEDICAL ASSOCIATION 341, 341 (1968); Arthur L. Caplan, *Informed Consent and Provider/Patient Relationships in Rehabilitation Medicine*, in IF I WERE A RICH MAN COULD I BUY A PANCREAS? 240, 245 (1992); Ezekiel J. Emanuel, & Linda L. Emanuel, *Four Models of the Physician-Patient Relationship*, 267 JOURNAL OF AMERICAN MEDICAL ASSOCIATION 2221, 2225 (1992).

[243]Paul S. Appelbaum, et al., INFORMED CONSENT: LEGAL THEORY AND CLINICAL PRACTICE 46 (1987); Paul C. Weiler, MEDICAL MALPRACTICE ON TRIAL 13 (1991); Barry R. Furrow et al., HEALTH LAW: CASES, MATERIALS AND PROBLEMS 187 (2d Ed. 1991); Arthur L. Caplan, *Can Autonomy Be Saved?, supra* note 242 at 261; Russell S. Kamer, M.d. et Al., *Effect of New York State's Do-Not-Resuscitate Legislation on In-Hospital Cardiopulmonary Resuscitation Practice*, 88 AMERICAN JOURNAL OF MEDICINE 108, 109-10 (1990).

[244]Robert C. Ellickson, ORDER WITHOUT LAW: HOW NEIGHBORS SETTLE DISPUTES 40-64 (1991); Stewart Macaulay, *Non-Contractual Relations in Business: A Preliminary Study*, 28 AMERICAN SOCIOLOGICAL REVIEW 55 (1963); Carl E. Schneider,

*Lawyers and Children: Wisdom and Legitimacy in Family Policy*, 84 MICHIGAN LAW REVIEW 919, 940 (1986); Carl E. Schneider, *Rethinking Alimony: Marital Decisions and Moral Discourse*, 1991 BRIGHAM YOUNG LAW SCHOOL LAW REVIEW 197, 203-09; Carl E. Schneider, *Social Structure and Social Control: On the Moral Order of a Suburb*, 24 LAW & SOCIOLOGICAL REVIEW 875 (1990).

²⁴⁵Carl E. Schneider, *Social Structure and Social Control, supra* note 244 at 1078-80; Peter H. Schuck, *Rethinking Informed Consent*, 103 YALE LAW JOURNAL 899, 957-58 (1994).

²⁴⁶*Cruzan v. Director, Missouri Department of Health*, 497 U.S 261, 278 (990); *Schloendorff v. Society of New York Hospital.*, 105 N.E. 92, 93 (N.Y. 1914); Tom L. Beauchamp, *Emerging Paradigms in Bioethics, supra* note 225 at 956-57 at 956; George J. Annas, *Life, Liberty and Death*, 12 HEALTH MANAGEMENT QUARTERLY 5, 5 (1990); John A. Robertson, *Posthumous Reproduction*, 69 *Indiana Law Journal* 1027, 1028 (1994).

²⁴⁷Tom L. Beauchamp, *Emerging Paradigms in Bioethics, supra* note 225 at 956-57 at 956.

²⁴⁸*Id.*

²⁴⁹*Id.*

²⁵⁰Edmund D. Pellegrino, *Foreword to* AFRICAN AMERICAN PERSPECTIVES ON BIOMEDICAL ETHICS at V, Vi (Harley E. Flack & Edmund D. Pellegrino eds 1992); Rand E. Rosenblatt, *Dual Track Health Care--the Decline of the Medicaid Cure*, 44 UNIVERSITY OF CINCINNATI LAW REVIEW 643 (1975); Sylvia A. Law, AMERICAN CIVIL LIBERTIES UNION, THE RIGHTS OF THE POOR 80-110 (1973); Annette Dula, *Bioethics: the Need for a Dialogue with African Americans*, in "IT JUST AIN'T FAIR": THE ETHICS OF HEALTH CARE FOR AFRICAN AMERICANS 11-23 (Annette Dual & Sara Goering eds 1994).

²⁵¹Laurence Thomas, *The Morally Beautiful, supra* note 228 at 123-25.

²⁵²Cheryl J. Sanders, *African American Perspective, supra* note 14; Annette Dula, *Yes, There Are African American Perspectives on Bioethics, supra* note 9.

²⁵³Annette Dula, *African American Suspicion of the Healthcare System Is Justified, supra* note 1.

²⁵⁴Annette Dula, *A Dialogue with African Americans, supra* note 250.

²⁵⁵Alma Roberts, *The Evolution of a Community Hospital: Improving Access to Ensure Political and Financial Viability*, in "IT JUST AIN'T FAIR": THE ETHICS OF HEALTH CARE FOR AFRICAN AMERICANS 195-200 (Annette Dula & Sara Goering eds 1994).

²⁵⁶Brian Hertz, *Toward Successful Urban Perinatal Health Care*, in "IT JUST AIN'T FAIR": THE ETHICS OF HEALTH CARE FOR AFRICAN AMERICANS 201-07 (Annete Dula & Sara Goering eds 1994).

²⁵⁷Evelyn C. White & Shafia Mawushi Monroe, *Interview: Lay Midwifery and the Traditional Child-Bearing Group*, in "IT JUST AIN'T FAIR": THE ETHICS OF HEALTH CARE FOR AFRICAN AMERICANS 208-20 (Annete Dula & Sara Goering eds 1994).

²⁵⁸Margo Okazawa-Rey, *Grandparents Who Care: An Empowerment Model of Health Care*, in "IT JUST AIN'T FAIR": THE ETHICS OF HEALTH CARE FOR AFRICAN AMERICANS (Annete Dula & Sara Goering eds 1994).

²⁵⁹Annette Dula, *A Dialogue with African Americans, supra* note 250 at 11-23.

²⁶⁰Cheryl J. Sanders, *African American Perspective, supra* note 14 at 171 citing Preston N. Williams, *Ethics and Ethos in the Black Experience*, 31 CHRISTIANITY & CRISIS 104 (1971).

## Chapter Seven
### BLACK HEALTH STATUS AND HEALTH CARE
### AS A VIOLATION OF INTERNATIONAL HUMAN RIGHTS

[1]Brian D. Smedley, et. al.., *Unequal Treatment: Confronting Racial and Ethnic Inequities in Health Care*, INSTITUTE OF MEDICINE, COMMITTEE ON UNDERSTANDING AND ELIMINATING RACIAL AND ETHNIC INEQUITIES IN HEALTH CARE,( 2002); United States Commission on Civil Rights, THE HEALTH CARE CHALLENGE: ACKNOWLEDGING INEQUITY, CONFRONTING DISCRIMINATION, AND ENSURING EQUALITY, VOLUME I, THE ROLE OF GOVERNMENTAL AND PRIVATE HEALTH CARE PROGRAMS AND INITIATIVES 287 (1999)

[2]United States Commission on Civil Rights, THE HEALTH CARE CHALLENGE I, *supra* note 1; W. Michael Byrd & Linda A. Clayton, AN AMERICAN HEALTH DILEMMA: A MEDICAL HISTORY OF AFRICAN AMERICANS AND THE PROBLEM OF RACE: BEGINNINGS TO 1900 (2000).

[3]United States Commission on Civil Rights, ACKNOWLEDGING INEQUITY, CONFRONTING DISCRIMINATION, AND ENSURING EQUALITY, VOLUME II: THE ROLE OF FEDERAL CIVIL RIGHTS ENFORCEMENT 438 (1999); United States Commission on Civil Rights, THE HEALTH CARE CHALLENGE I, *supra* note 1.

[4]*Id.*

[5]United States Commission on Civil Rights, THE HEALTH CARE CHALLENGE II, *supra* note 3.

[6]*Id.*

[7]*Id.*

[8]Gay J. McDougall, *Toward a Meaningful International Regime: The Domestic Relevance of International Efforts to Eliminate All Forms of Racial Discrimination*, 40 HOWARD LAW JOURNAL 571 (1997); Henry J. Richardson, III, *Gulf Crisis and African American Interests Under International Law*, 87 AMERICAN JOURNAL OF INTERNATIONAL LAW 42, 71-72 (1993).

[9]INTERNATIONAL CONVENTION ON THE ELIMINATION OF ALL FORMS OF RACIAL DISCRIMINATION, Opened for Signature December 21,1965, 660 United Nations Treaty Series 195 (Entered into Force January 4, 1969)(ICERD).

[10]UNITED NATIONS: CONVENTION ON THE RIGHTS OF THE CHILD, 28 I.l.m1448 (1989)(Entered into Force September 2, 1990)).

[11]Stephanie Farrior, *The Neglected Pillar: The Teaching Tolerance Provision of The International Convention on The Elimination of All Forms of Racial Discrimination*, 5 ILSA JOURNAL OF INTERNATIONAL & COMPARATIVE LAW 291 (1999); INTERNATIONAL COVENANT ON CIVIL AND POLITICAL RIGHTS, United Nations General Assembly 21st Session Supplement Number 16, at 52, United Nations Document A/6316 (1966) (Entered into Force March 23, 1976); UNIVERSAL DECLARATION OF HUMAN RIGHTS, United Nations General Assembly Resolution 217 A(iii) (December 1948).

[12]Stephanie Farrior, *The Teaching Tolerance, supra* note 11.

[13]UNIVERSAL DECLARATION OF HUMAN RIGHTS, United Nations General Assembly Resolution 217 A(III) (December 1948).

[14]United Nation General Assembly Resolution, 21st Session Supplement Number 16, United Nation Document A/6316 (1966) (entered into force January 3, 1976).

[15]*Id.* At 52.

[16]Gay J. McDougall, *The Domestic Relevance of International Efforts, supra* note 8.; Office of the United Nations High Commissioner for Human Rights, STATUS OF RATIFICATIONS OF THE PRINCIPAL HUMAN RIGHT TREATIES, STATUS AS OF JUNE 17, 2002, Available at Http://www.unhchr.ch/html/menu3/b/d_icerd.htm (Last Visited: June 26, 2002).

[17]140 Congressional Record S7634 (Daily Edition June 24, 1994).

[18]James Jennings, *The International Convention on The Elimination of All Forms of Racial Discrimination: Implications for Challenging Racial Hierarchy*, 40 HOWARD LAW JOURNAL 597 (1997).

[19]*Id.*

[20]United States Constitution Article. II, Clause 2.

[21]ICERD, *supra* note 9.

[22]*Id.* at Article 1.

[23]*Id.*

[24]*Id.*

[25]*Id.* at Article 2(1)(C).

[26]1978 DIGEST ON UNITED STATES PRACTICE IN INTERNATIONAL LAW 440-46; COMMITTEE ON FOREIGN RELATIONS, 96TH CONGRESS (1st Session 1980); HUMAN RIGHTS TREATIES: HEARINGS BEFORE THE SENATE COMMITTEE ON FOREIGN RELATIONS, 96TH CONGRESS (1st Session 1980).

[27]Connie de la Vega, *Civil Rights During the 1990s: New Treaty Law Could Help Immensely*, 65 UNIVERSITY OF CINCINNATI LAW REVIEW 423, 452 (1997).

[28]*Id.*

[29]*Id.*

[30]*Id.*.

[31]ICERD, *supra* note 9, Article 9(1).

[32]REPORTS SUBMITTED BY STATES PARTIES UNDER ARTICLE 9 OF THE CONVENTION, THIRD PERIODIC REPORTS OF STATES PARTIES DUE IN 1999, ADDENDUM, United States of America (September 21, 2000), Available at Http://www.unhchr.ch/tbs/doc.nsf/cerd.c.351.add.1.en?opendocument (Last Visited: June 26, 2002).

[33]*Id.*

[34]ICERD, *supra* note 9 at Articles 9-14; INITIAL REPORT OF THE UNITED STATES OF AMERICA TO THE UNITED NATIONS COMMITTEE ON THE ELIMINATION OF RACIAL DISCRIMINATION, September 2000, Available at Http://www.state.gov/www/global/human_rights/cerd_report/cerd_index.html (Last Visited: June 26, 2002).

[35]United Nation High Commissioner for Human Rights, FACT SHEET NO. 12: THE COMMITTEE ON THE ELIMINATION OF RACIAL DISCRIMINATION, available at http://www.unhchr.ch/html/menu6/2/fs12.htm (last visited: June 26, 2002).

[36]*Id.*

[37]ICERD, *supra* note 9, at Article 9(1).

[38]*Id.* at Article 9.

[39]*Id.* at Articles 8-14.

[40]*Id.*

[41]Makani Themba-Nixon Editor., *The Persistence of White Privilege and Institutional Racism*, in U.S. POLICY: A REPORT ON UNITED STATES GOVERNMENT COMPLIANCE WITH THE INTERNATIONAL CONVENTION ON THE ELIMINATION OF ALL FORMS OF RACIAL DISCRIMINATION ( 2001), Available at Http://www.arc.org/trji/ (Last Visited: June 26, 2002).

[42]*Id.* at 10-11.

[43]*Id.* at 12-13.

[44]*Id.* at 17-26.

[45]*Id.* at 39-53.

[46]*Id.* at 39-53.

[47]*Id.* at 24-37.

[48]*Id.* at 54-71.

[49]United States Report, *supra* note 34.

[50]United States Commission on Civil Rights, THE HEALTH CARE CHALLENGE II, *supra* note 3 at 52-64.

[51]United States Commission on Civil Rights, THE HEALTH CARE CHALLENGE I, *supra* note 1.

[52]*Id.*
[53]*Id.* at 189.
[54]*Id.*
[55]ICERD, *supra* note 9, at Article 2(1)(A)..
[56]ICERD, *supra* note 9.
[57]United States Commission on Civil Rights, THE HEALTH CARE CHALLENGE II, *supra* note 3 at 275.
[58]*Id.* at 677.
[59]*Id.*
[60]United States Commission on Civil Rights, THE HEALTH CARE CHALLENGE I, *supra* note 1 at 190.
[61]*Id.*
[62]ICERD, *supra* note 9 at Article 2(1)(C)..
[63]United States Commission on Civil Rights, THE HEALTH CARE CHALLENGE II, *supra* note 3 at 275.
[64]ICERD, *supra* note 9 at Article 2(1)(C)..
[65]United States Commission on Civil Rights, THE HEALTH CARE CHALLENGE II, *supra* note 3 at 59.
[66]ICERD, *supra* note 9 at Article 2(1)(D).
[67]ICERD, *supra* note 9.
[68]United States Commission on Civil Rights, THE HEALTH CARE CHALLENGE II, *supra* note 3 at 274-75.
[69]United States Commission on Civil Rights, THE HEALTH CARE CHALLENGE I, *supra* note 1 at 1.
[70]United States Commission on Civil Rights, THE HEALTH CARE CHALLENGE II, *supra* note 3 at 280.
[71]ICERD, *supra* note 9 at Article 5(e)(Iv)..
[72]ICERD, *supra* note 9.
[73]United States Commission on Civil Rights, THE HEALTH CARE CHALLENGE II, *supra* note 3 at 274.
[74]*Id.* at 275-76.
[75]*Id.* at 276.
[76]*Id.*
[77]*Id.*
[78]*Id.* at 276.
[79]*Id.*
[80]*Id.*
[81]*Id.*
[82]*Id.*
[83]DEFINITION OF DISCRIMINATION (Article 1, Paragraph 1): 22/03/93. Cerd General Recommendation. 14 (General Comments).
[84]*Id.*
[85]REPORTS SUBMITTED BY STATES PARTIES UNDER ARTICLE 9 OF THE CONVENTION, *supra* note 32.
[86]Makani Themba-Nixon, THE PERSISTENCE OF WHITE PRIVILEGE AND INSTITUTIONAL RACISM, *supra* note 41
[87]*Id.*at 7-15.
[88]SUMMARY RECORD OF THE 1475TH MEETING: UNITED STATE OF AMERICA 22/08/2001/cerd/c/sr1475 (Summary Record).
[89]CONCLUDING OBSERVATIONS OF THE COMMITTEE ON THE ELIMINATION OF RACIAL DISCRIMINATION: UNITED STATES OF AMERICA 14/08/2001 A/56/18, 380-407 (Concluding Observations/comments) Committee on the Elimination of Racial Discrimination, 59th Session July 30 - August 17, 2001.

## Chapter 8:
### USING REPARATIONS TO REPAIR BLACK HEALTH

[1] W. E. Burghardt Du Bois, BLACK RECONSTRUCTION: An Essay Toward a History of the Past Which Black Folk Played in the Attempt to Reconstruct Democracy in America, 1860-80 703 (1962).

[2] United States Department Of Health & Human Services, SECRETARY'S TASKFORCE REPORT ON MINORITY HEALTH (1986).

[3] Joel Havemann, *A Safety Net Snags on Its Cost: Western Europe's Prized Welfare Programs Follow Citizens from Cradle to Grave. But Tax Rates Are Astronomical by U.S. Standards and Critics Are Gingerly Making Changes*, LOS ANGELES TIMES, April 21, 1992, at A1; John Lucadamo, *Porter, Sullivan Clash at Debate Over Everything But Pension*, CHICAGO TRIBUNE, March 10, 1992; President George Bush, *Remarks of President Bush to the San Diego Rotary Club*, FEDERAL NEWS SERVICE (Feb. 7, 1992); H. Rowley, *Prescription from Canada: Would Universal Health Care Work in this Country?*, CHICAGO TRIBUNE, May 31, 1992; Scott, *Lawmakers Differ on Measures to Reform Health Care*, MEMPHIS BUSINESS JOURNAL, June 1, 1992, 41; George Will, *Revision of Our Health-care System Should Be High on Nations' Agenda*, ATLANTA JOURNAL & CONSTITUTION, Mar. 9, 1992.

[4] Tom Wicker, *Introduction*, in REPORT OF THE NATIONAL ADVISORY COMMISSION ON CIVIL DISORDERS, at VII (1968).

[5] United States. Dept. of Health and Human Services, Healthy people 2010 / U.S. Department of Health and Human Services (2001)

[6] United States. Dept. of Health and Human Services, Healthy people 2010 / U.S. Department of Health and Human Services (2001)

[7] Vernellia R. Randall, *Racist Health Care: Reforming an Unjust Health Care System to Meet the Needs of African-Americans*, 3 Health Matrix: Journal of Law-Medicine 127-194 (Spring 1993).

[8] Disadvantaged Minority Health Improvement Act of 1990, Public Law Number 101-527, Statute 2311.

[9] *Id.* at § 3.

[10] *Id.* at § 4.

[11] *Id .*at § 4.

[12] *Id.* at § 6.

[13] *Id.* at § 8.

[14] *Id.* at § 9.

[15] *Id.* at § 10.

[16] Arkansas, Illinois, Iowa, Missouri, Ohio, Texas.

[17] *Id.*; Office of Minority Health, CHARACTERISTICS OF MINORITY HEALTH ENTITIES BY STATE (Table 1) (Unpublished).

[18] Alabama, Georgia, Hawaii, Indiana, Massachusetts, Oregon, South Carolina and Virginia; Office of Minority Health, *supra* note 15.

[19] Delaware, Michigan, Mississippi and New Jersey, Office of Minority Health, *Characteristics, supra* note 15.

[20] Alabama, et al. *supra* note 16; Office of Minority Health, *supra* note 16.

[22] *Id.* ; Office of Minority Health, *supra* note 15.

[23] Office of Minority Health, *supra* note 15.

[24] Bureau of Labor Statistics & Bureau of the Census, CURRENT POPULATION SURVEY, at Http://www.bls.census.gov/cps/cpsmain.htm (Last Visited: August 8, 2002).

[25] *Id.*

[26] Mary Beth Lipp, *Legislators' Obligation to Support a Living Wage: A Comparative Constitutional Vision of Justice*, 75 SOUTHERN CALIFORNIA LAW REVIEW 475 (January 2002).

[27] Acorn Living Wage Resource Center, THE LIVING WAGE MOVEMENT: BUILDING POWER IN OUR WORKPLACES AND NEIGHBORHOODS, at

Http://livingwagecampaign.org (Last Visited: August 18, 2002); Robert Pollin & Stephanie Luce, THE LIVING WAGE: BUILDING A FAIR ECONOMY 2 (1998).
[28]Peter J. Sammon, The Living Wage Movement, AMERICA, Aug. 26, 2000.
[29]Donna Gareis-Smith, Environmental Racism: The Failure of Equal Protection to Provide a Judicial Remedy and the Potential of Title VI of the 1964 Civil Rights Act, 13 TEMPLE ENVIRONMENTAL LAW & TECHNOLOGY JOURNAL 57, 62 (1994).
[30]Id. at 62.8037; See E.G. Cole, Empowerment as the Key to Environmental Protection, infra note 34 .
[31]Commission for Racial Justice, TOXIC WASTES AND RACE IN THE UNITED STATES: A NATIONAL REPORT ON THE RACIAL AND SOCIO-ECONOMIC CHARACTERISTICS OF COMMUNITIES WITH HAZARDOUS WASTE SITES 13 (1987); Carolyn M. Mitchell, Environmental Racism: Race as a Primary Factor in the Selection of Hazardous Waste Sites, 12 NATIONAL BLACK LAW JOURNAL 176 (1993); United States General Accounting Office, SITING OF HAZARDOUS WASTE LANDFILLS AND THEIR CORRELATION WITH RACIAL AND ECONOMIC STATUS OF SURROUNDING COMMUNITIES (Jun. 1, 1983), Available at Http://www.gao.gov/ (Last Visited: August 8, 2002).
[32]Robert D. Bullard, Environmental Justice: A New Framework for Action, 5 ENVIRONMENTAL LAW NEWS, Number 1, 3 (1996).
[33]Carolyn M. Mitchell, Environmental Racism, supra note 29.
[34]Robert D. Bullard, The Legacy of American Apartheid and Environmental Racism, 9 SAINT JOHN'S JOURNAL OF LEGAL COMMENT 445, 445-48 (1994).
[35]Luke W. Cole, Empowerment as the Key to Environmental Protection: The Need for Environmental Poverty Law, 19 ECOLOGY LAW QUARTERLY 619, 628 (1992).
[36]Vicki Been, Locally Undesirable Land Uses in Minority Neighborhoods: Disproportionate Siting or Market Dynamics?, 103 YALE LAW JOURNAL 1383, 1386 (1994); Robert D. Bullard, Anatomy of Environmental Racism and the Environmental Justice Movement, in CONFRONTING ENVIRONMENTAL RACISM: VOICES FROM THE GRASSROOTS 15, 23 (Robert D. Bullard ed. 1993); Jill E. Evans, Challenging the Racism in Environmental Racism: Redefining the Concept of Intent, 40 ARIZONA LAW REVIEW 219 (Winter, 1998); Kathy Seward Northern, Battery and Beyond: A Tort Law Response to Environmental Racism, 21 WILLIAM & MARY ENVIRONMENTAL LAW & POLICY REVIEW 485, 522 (1997).
[37]Ivette Perfecto, Pesticide Exposure of Farm Workers and The International Connection, in RACE AND THE INCIDENCE OF ENVIRONMENTAL HAZARDS, 180 (Bunyan & Paul Mohai eds. 1992).
[38]A.J. McMichael, et. al., Mortality Among Rubber Workers: Relationship to Specific Jobs, 17 JOURNAL OF OCCUPATIONAL MEDICINE 178, 184 (1976).
[39]J. William Lloyd, Long-term Mortality Study of Steelworkers: Respiratory Cancer in Coke Plant Workers, 13 JOURNAL OF OCCUPATIONAL MEDICINE 53, 55-56 (1971).
[40]Hawley Truax, Minorities at Risk, ENVIRONMENTAL ACTION, January-February, 1990, at 19-20.
[41]Aaron Blaine, Causes of Death Among Laundry and Dry Cleaning Workers, 69 AMERICAN JOURNAL OF PUBLIC HEALTH 508 (1979).
[42]Luke W. Cole, Empowerment as the Key to Environmental Protection, supra note 34.
[43]Id.
[44]Agency for Toxic Substances and Disease Registry, Centers for Disease Control, THE NATURE AND EXTENT OF LEAD POISONING IN CHILDREN IN THE UNITED STATES A REPORT TO CONGRESS (1988); Environmental Equity Workgroup, United States Environmental Protection Agency, ENVIRONMENTAL EQUITY: REDUCING RISK FOR ALL COMMUNITIES 11-12 (1992).
[45]Agency for Toxic Substances and Disease Registry, LEAD POISONING IN CHILDREN IN THE UNITED STATES, supra note 43.
[46]Title III, "Reduction in Underage Tobacco Use", focuses on state laws regarding the sale of tobacco products to minors, provides for a model state law, and requires states to reduce their underage usage of tobacco. Senate 1530, 105th Congress 300-317 (1997).

⁴⁷Tim Collie, *Black Teen-Age Girls Refuse to Follow the Smoking Pack*, Sun-Sentinel (Fort Lauderdale, Florida), January 12, 1998, at 1A, available in 1998 WL 3239427.

⁴⁸*Id.*

⁴⁹*Id.*

⁵⁰*Minority Caucuses Seeking Share of Tobacco Deal Money*, Congress Daily, November 18, 1997, available in 1997 WL 11444004.

⁵¹Minority Caucuses Seeking Share of Tobacco Deal Money, Congress Daily, Nov. 18, 1997, available in 1997 WL 11444004

⁵²Office of Technology Assessment, MEDICAL TECHNOLOGY AND COSTS OF THE MEDICARE PROGRAM 45-61(1984).

⁵³*Id.*

⁵⁴*Medicaid, A Cooperative State-Federal Program, Provides Health Insurance to Eligible Individuals and Families*, 42 UNITED STATES CODE § 1396 (1992); *Medical Technology Assessment: Hearings on House Rule 5496 Before The Subcommittee on Health and The Environment of The Committee on Energy and Commerce*, 98th Congress 2d Session 544 (1984) (Statement of Raymond Dross, Medical Doctor, on Behalf of The Health Insurance Association of America); Office of Technology Assessment, MEDICAL TECHNOLOGY AND COSTS OF THE MEDICARE PROGRAM, *supra* note 50; SOCIAL SECURITY AMENDMENTS OF 1965, PUBLIC LAW NUMBER 89-97, 79 Statute 286 (Codified as Amended in Scattered Sections of 42 United States Code).

⁵⁵Office of Technology Assessment, MEDICAL TECHNOLOGY AND COSTS OF THE MEDICARE PROGRAM, *supra* note 50.

⁵⁶Pamela Short, et. al., *Health Insurance of Minorities in the United States* 1(2) JOURNAL OF HEALTH CARE FOR THE POOR & UNDERSERVD 9-24 (1990).

⁵⁷Karen Davis, et. al., HEALTH CARE FOR AFRICAN AMERICANS: THE PUBLIC SECTOR, HEALTH POLICIES AND BLACK AMERICANS (David Willis ed. 1989) at 225-26; Stephen Long, *Public Versus Employment-Related Health Insurance: Experience and Implications for Black and NonBlack Americans*, in HEALTH POLICIES AND BLACK AMERICANS 200-12, at 203 (David P. Willis ed 1989).

⁵⁸Karen Davis, *Closing the Gap in Health Insurance Coverage for African-Americans* (Unpublished Paper); Stephen D. Long, *Public Versus Employment-Related Health Insurance*, supra note 55 at 203.

⁵⁹*Id.*; Pamela Short, *Health Insurance of Minorities, supra* note 54.

⁶⁰Karen Davis, *Closing the Gap in Health Insurance Coverage for African Americans*, *supra* note 55; Stephen Long, *Public Versus Employment-Related Health Insurance, supra* note 55 at 203; Pamela Short, *Health Insurance of Minorities, supra* note 54.

⁶¹Pamela Short, *Health Insurance of Minorities, supra* note 54.

⁶³*Id.*

⁶⁴*Id.*

⁶⁵Karen Davis, *Closing the Gap in Health Insurance Coverage for African Americans*, *supra* note 55.

⁶⁶*Id.*

⁶⁷*Id.*

⁶⁸*Id.*

⁶⁹*Id.*; Pamela Short, *Health Insurance of Minorities, supra* note 54.

⁷⁰*Id.*

⁷¹*Id.*; United States House of Representative, Committee on Ways and Means, 1991. GREEN BOOK, BACKGROUND MATERIAL AND DATE ON PROGRAMS WITHIN THE JURISDICTION OF THE COMMITTEE ON WAYS AND MEANS, Washington, D.C.: United States Government Printing Office, May 7 (1991).

⁷²Karen Davis, *Closing the Gap in Health Insurance Coverage for African Americans*, *supra* note 55; Pamela Short, *Health Insurance of Minorities, supra* note 54.

⁷³*Id.*

⁷⁴*Id.*

⁷⁵Stephen Long, St *Public Versus Employment-Related Health Insurance, supra* note 55 at 200-12.

[76]*Id.*

[77]*Id.*

[78]Karen Davis & Diane Rowland, *Uninsured and Undeserved: Inequalities in Health Care in the United State,* 61 MILBANK MEMORIAL FUND QUARTERLY 149,155-58 (1983).

[79]Karen Davis, *Closing the Gap in Health Insurance Coverage for African Americans,* *supra* note 55.

[80]*Id.*

[81]Stephen Long, *Public Versus Employment-Related Health Insurance, supra* note 55, at 200-12.

[82]Alan Sager, THE CLOSURE OF HOSPITALS THAT SERVE THE POOR: IMPLICATIONS FOR HEALTH PLANNING, A Statement to the Subcommittee on Health and the Environment, Committee on Energy and Commerce, United States House of Representatives, 2 (April 30, 1982); Mark Schlesinger, *Paying the Price: Medical Care, Minorities, and the Newly Competitive Health Care System,* in HEALTH POLICIES AND BLACK AMERICANS 275-76 (David Willis ed. 1989).

[83]*Bryan v. Koch,* 627 Federal2d 612, 619-20 (1980); *National Association for the Advancement of Colored People v. Wilmington Medical Center,* 657 Federal2d 1322 (1981).

[84]Sager, THE CLOSURE OF HOSPITALS, supra note 80.

[85]Mark Schlesinger, *Paying the Price: Medical Care, Minorities, and the Newly Competitive Health Care System, supra* note 80.

[86]Alan Sager, *The Closure of Hospitals, supra* note 80; Roger Wilkins, *Loss of Hospitals in Central City Said to Cause Array of Problems,* NEW YORK TIMES, September 17, 1979, at D4.

[87]Alan Sager, *The Closure of Hospitals, supra* note 80

[88]Kenneth R. Wing, *The Community Service Obligation of Hill-Burton Health Facilities,* 23 BOSTON COLLEGE LAW REVIEW 577,613- 14 (1982).

[89]42 United States Code § 291 A(1).

[90]*National Association for the Advancement of Colored People v. Wilmington Medical Center., supra* note 81.

[91]*The Crisis of the Disappearing Black Hospitals,* EBONY, March 1992, at 23-28.

[92]Id.

[93]Id.

[94]Id.

[95]Id.

[96]*Id.*

[97]Amanda Husted, *Shortage of Black Dentists Has Ill Effect in Community,* ATLANTA JOURNAL & CONSTITUTION, August 19, 1991, at B3; Woodrow Jones Jr & Mitchell F. Rice, *Black Health Care: An Overview, in Health Care Issues* in BLACK AMERICA: POLICIES, PROBLEMS AND PROSPECTS 3,4 (Woodrow Jones, Jr. & Mitchell F. Rice eds. 1987); United States Department Of Health & Human Services, MINORITY & WOMEN IN THE HEALTH FIELDS, Table 3 (1990).

[98]Woodrow Jones Jr & Mitchell F. Rice, *Black Health Care, supra* note 94; United States Department Of Health & Human Services, *supra* note 94.

[99]Kenneth Reich, *Panel Hears Horrors of Health Care Crisis,* Los Angeles TIMES, January 12,1992, at B1 (reporting that witnesses at public hearing tell of long waits at county-run facilities in minority communities).

[100]Id.

[101]Karen Davis, *Health Care for African Americans, supra* note 55 at 225-26; House of Representatives REPORT NUMBER 804, *supra* note 99.

[102]*Id.*

[103]*Id.*

[104]Woodrow Jones Jr & Mitchell F. Rice, *Black Health Care, supra* note 94 (Quoting John Romano, *Basic Orientation and Education of the Medical Student,* 143 JOURNAL OF THE AMERICAN MEDICAL ASSOCIATION 411 (1950)).

[105]Woodrow Jones, Jr & Mitchell F. Rice, *Black Health Care, supra* note 94.

[106]*Id.*

[107]*Id.*

[108]*Id.*

[109]Max Seham, BLACKS AND AMERICAN MEDICAL CARE 20-21 (1973); United States Department of Health & Human Services, MINORITIES & WOMEN IN THE HEALTH, *supra* note 94; Wilson, Donald, *Minorities and the Medical Profession: A Historical Perspective and Analysis of Current and Future Trends*, 78 JOURNAL OF THE NATIONAL MEDICAL ASSOCIATION,177,178 (1986).

[110]Sidney D. Watson, *Health Care in the Inner City: Asking the Right Question*, 71 NORTH CAROLINA LAW REVIEW 1647 (June, 1993).

[111]Vernellia R. Randall, *Ethnic Americans, Long Term Health Care Providers and the Patient Self-Determination Act*, LONG TERM HEALTH CARE PROVIDERS AND THE PATIENT SELF-DETERMINATION ACT (Marshall Kapp ed. 1994); Henry S. Perkins, *Cultural Differences and Ethical Issues in the Problem of Autopsy Requests*, 87 THE JOURNAL OF TEXAS MEDICINE (1991); Alan Harwood, *Guidelines for Culturally Appropriate Health Care*, in ETHNICITY AND MEDICAL CARE (1981).

[112]Vernellia R. Randall, *Ethnic Americans, Long Term Health Care Providers*, *supra* note 110.

[113]Id.

[114]*Id.*

[115]Alan Harwood, *Guidelines for Culturally Appropriate Health Care*, *supra* note 110.

[116]Alan Harwood, *Mainland Puerto Rican*, in ETHNICITY AND MEDICAL CARE (1981); Stephen J. Kunits & Jerrold E. Levy, *Navajos*, in ETHNICITY AND MEDICAL CARE at 337 (1981); Vernellia R. Randall, *Ethnic Americans, Long Term Health Care Providers*, *supra* note 110; Janet M Shreiber .& John P. Homiak, *Mexican Americans*, in ETHNICITY AND MEDICAL CARE 301 (1981); Gabriel Smilkstein, *The Cycle of Family Function: A Conceptual Model for Family Medicine*, 11 J. FAMILY PRO 223,224 (1980).

[117]Gabriel Smilkstein, *The Cycle of Family Function*, *supra* note 115.

[118]Vernellia R. Randall, *Ethnic Americans, Long Term Health Care Providers*, *supra* note 110.

[119]Janet M. Shreiber & John P. Homiak, *Mexican Americans*, *supra* note 115.

[120]Lorene Cary, *Why It's Not Just Paranoia: An American History of 'Plans' for Blacks*, NEWSWEEK, Apr. 6, 1992, at 23; *Forgotten Americans-A Special Report on Medical Care for Blacks*, 9 AMERICAN HEALTH: FITNESS OF BODY AND MIND 52 (1990); James Jones, *The Tuskegee Legacy: AIDs and the Black Community*, 22 HASTINGS CENTER REPORT 38 (1992); Michael S. Laguerre, *Haitian Americans*, in ETHNICITY AND MEDICAL CARE at 198 (1981); Thomas A. Laveist, *Segregation, Poverty and Empowerment: Health Consequences for African Americans*, 71 MILBANK QUARTERLY 41 (1993); Wendy Mettger & Vicki S. Freimuth, *Is There a Hard-to-Reach Audience?*, 105 PUBLIC HEALTH REPORTS 232 (1990); Laura Uba, *Cultural Barriers to Health Care for Southeast Asian Refugees*, 107 PUBLIC. HEALTH REPORTER 544, 546 (1992).

[121]James Jones, *The Tuskegee Legacy: AIDs and the Black Community*, *supra* note 119.

[122]Wendy Mettger & Vicki S. Freimuth, *Is There a Hard-to-Reach Audience?*, *supra* note 119.

[123]Gustavo M. Quesada, *Language and Communication Barriers for Health Delivery to Minority Group*, 10 SOCIAL SCIENCE & MEDICINE 323, 324 (1976).

[124]*Id.*

[125]*Id.*

[126]Donald Gelfand & Barbara W.K. Yee, *Trends & Forces: Influence of Immigration, Migration, and Acculturation on the Fabric of Aging in America*, 15 GENERATIONS 7 (1991); Susan Pollak, *Melancholia and Depression: From Hippocratic Times to Modem Times*, 22 PSYCHOLOGY TODAY 73 (1988); Charles E. Rosenberg, *Disease in History: Frames and Framers*, 67 MILBANK QUARTERLY 1 (1989); J. Temple & D.P. Burkitt, *Towards a New System of Health: The Challenge of Western Disease*, 18 JOURNAL OF COMMUNITY HEALTH 37 (1993).

[127]Donald Gelfand & Barbara W.K. Yee, *Trends & Forces, supra* note 125.

[128]Gordon Bonnyman, Jr., *Unmasking Jim Crow*, 18 JOURNAL OF HEALTH POLITICS, POLICY AND LAW 871 (1993); David Barton Smith, *The Racial Integration of Health Facilities*, 18 JOURNAL OF HEALTH POLITICS, POLICY & LAW 851 (1993); See e.g., George Annas, et. al., AMERICAN HEALTH CARE LAW 80-81 (1990).

[129]Barbara M. Abed, et . al., *Barriers to Prenatal Care for Low-income Women*, 158 WESTERN JOURNAL OF MEDICINE 493,497 (1993).

[130]*Id.*

[131]Michelle A. Bardack & Susan H. Thompson, *Model Prenatal' Program of Rush Medical College at St. Basils Free Peoples Clinic*, 108 PUBLIC HEALTH REPORT 161, (1993).

[132]Jaime A. Davidson, *Diabetes Care in Minority Groups: Overcoming Barriers to Meet These Patients' Special Needs*, 90 POSTGRADUATE MEDICINE 153, 158 (1991).

[133]*Id.*

[134]*Id.*; Miriam Ross, *Societal/Cultural Views Regarding Death and Dying*, TOPICS IN CLINICAL NURSING 5 (1981).

[135]Eli Ginzburg & Miriam Ostow, *Beyond Universal Health Insurance to Effective Health Care*, 265 JOURNAL OF THE AMERICAN MEDICAL ASSOCIATION 2559 (1991). See e.g., United States Commission on Civil Rights, THE HEALTH CARE CHALLENGE: ACKNOWLEDGING INEQUITY, CONFRONTING DISCRIMINATION, AND ENSURING EQUALITY, VOLUME II, THE ROLE OF FEDERAL CIVIL RIGHTS ENFORCEMENT, 438 Page 902-00063-1 (Sept., 1999).

[136]United States Commission on Civil Rights, THE HEALTH CARE CHALLENGE: ACKNOWLEDGING INEQUITY, CONFRONTING DISCRIMINATION, AND ENSURING EQUALITY, VOLUME I, THE ROLE OF GOVERNMENTAL AND PRIVATE HEALTH CARE PROGRAMS AND INITIATIVES, 287 Page Number 902-00062-2 (Sept., 1999).

[138]*Id.*; Public Law Number. 103-43, 107 Statute 122 (Codified in Scattered Sections Of 8 and 42 United States Code (1994 & Supplement II 1996).

[139]Public Law Number 103-43, 107 Statute 122 (codified in scattered sections of 8 and 42 United States Code (1994 & Supplement II 1996); United States Commission on Civil Rights, THE HEALTH CARE CHALLENGE I, *supra* note 134 at 135.

[140]Derrick A. Bell, Jr, AND WE ARE NOT SAVED: THE ELUSIVE QUEST FOR RACIAL JUSTICE (Basic Books, 1987); Alan D. Freeman, *Legitimizing Racial Discrimination Through Antidiscrimination Law: A Critical Review of Supreme Court Doctrine*, 62 MINNESOTA LAW REVIEW 1049 (1978).

[141]SOCIAL SECURITY AMENDMENTS OF 1965, Public Law Number 89-97, Titles Xviii, 79 Statute 286

[142]*Id.*

[143]20 United States Code §1681-88 (2002) (Limited to Sex Discrimination in Educational Programs).

[144]42 United States Code § 291-2910 (2002).

[145]TITLE VI OF THE 1964 CIVIL RIGHTS ACT, Public Law Number 99-352, 378 252 (Codified at 42 United States Code Section 2000d-200d-4 (1982); Vernellia R. Randall, *Racist Health Care,, supra* note 5; David Barton Smith, *Addressing Racial Inequities in Health Care: Civil Rights Monitoring and Report Cards*, 23 JOURNAL OF HEALTH POLITICS, POLICY & LAW 75 (1998); David Barton Smith, HEALTH CARE DIVIDED: RACE AND HEALING A NATION (1999); Sidney D. Watson, *Reinvigorating Title VI: Defending Health Care Discrimination--It Shouldn't Be So Easy*, 58 FORDHAM LAW REVIEW 939 (1990).

[146]Daniel K. Hampton, *Title VI Challenges by Private Parties to the Location of Health Care Facilities: Toward a Just and Effective Action*, 37 BOSTON COLLEGE LAW REVIEW 517 (1996); Marianne Engelman Lado, *Breaking the Barriers of Access to Health Care: A Discussion of the Role of Civil Rights Litigation and the Relationship Between Burdens of Proof and the Experience of Denial*, 60 BROOKLYN LAW REVIEW 239 (1994); Barbara A. Noah, *Racial Inequities in the Delivery of Health Care*, 35 SAN DIEGO LAW REVIEW 135 (1998).

[147]Title VI of the 1964 Civil Rights Act, Public Law No. 99-352, 378 252 (Codified at 42 United States Code Section 2000d-200d-4 (1982).

[148]TITLE VI OF THE 1964 CIVIL RIGHTS ACT, *supra* note 144.

[149]*Alexander v. Choate*, 469 U.S. 287 (1985).

[150]Terry Smith, *Everyday Indignities: Race, Retaliation and the Promise of Title VII*, 34 COLUMBIA HUMAN RIGHTS LAW REVIEW 529 (2003).

[151]Peggy C. Davis, *Law as Micro-Aggression*, 98 Yale Law Journal 1559, 1576 (1989).

[152]Robert Belton, *Mixed-Motive Cases in Employment Discrimination Law Revisited: A Brief Updated View of the Swamp*, 51 MERCER LAW REVIEW 651, 662-63 (2000); Michael Selmi, *Subtle Discrimination: A Matter of Perspective Rather Than Intent*, 34 COLUMBIA HUMAN RIGHTS LAW REVIEW 657, 667 n.40 (2003).

[153]*Lynn V. Regents of University of California*, 656 Federal2d 1337, 1343 note 5 (California Attorney General 1981).

[154]M.Gregg Bloche, *Race and Discretion in American Medicine*, 1 YALE JOURNAL HEALTH POLICY LAW & ETHICS 95, 95-96 (2001); René Bowser, *Racial Profiling in Health Care: An Institutional Analysis of Medical Treatment Inequities*, 7 MICHIGAN JOURNAL OF RACE & LAW 79, 80-91 (2001); Barbara A. Noah, *Racial Inequities in the Delivery of Health Care*, 35 SAN DIEGO LAW REVIEW 135, 137 (1998); Mary Crossley, *Infected Judgment: Legal Responses to Physician Bias*, 48 VILLANOVA LAW REVIEW 195 (2003).

[155]Marian E. Gornick, VULNERABLE POPULATIONS AND MEDICARE SERVICES: WHY DO INEQUITIES EXIST? 43 (2000).

[156]Jessie Allen, *A Possible Remedy for Unthinking Discrimination*, 61 BROOKLYN LAW REVIEW 1299 (1995).

[157]Jessie Allen, *Unthinking Discrimination*, *supra* note 155.

[158]Ann C. McGinley, *Viva La Evolucion!: Recognizing Unconscious Motive in Title VII*, 9 CORNELL JOURNAL OF LAW & PUBLIC POLICY 415 (2000); Barbara J. Flagg, *Was Blind, But Now I See: White Race Consciousness and the Requirement of Discriminatory Intent*, 91 MICHIGAN LAW REVIEW 953 (1993); Charles Lawrence III, *The Id, The Ego, and Equal Protection: Reckoning with Unconscious Racism*, 39 STANFORD LAW REVIEW 317 (1987); David B. Oppenheimer, *Negligent Discrimination*, 141 UNIVERSITY OF PENNSYLVANIA LAW REVIEW 899, 967-72 (1993); Jessie Allen, *Unthinking Discrimination*, *supra* note 155; Jody David Armour, NEGROPHOBIA AND REASONABLE RACISM: THE HIDDEN COSTS OF BEING BLACK IN AMERICA 68-80 (1997); Martha Chamallas, *The Architecture of Bias: Deep Structures in Tort Law*, 146 UNIVERSITY OF PENNSYLVANIA LAW REVIEW. 463, 466-67 (1998); Sheri Lynn Johnson, *Unconscious Racism and the Criminal Law*, 73 CORNELL LAW REVIEW 1016 (1988).

[159]Charles Lawrence III, *The Id, the Ego, and Equal Protection*, *supra* note 157.

[160]David R. Williams, *Race, Health, And Health Care* 48 SAINT LOUIS UNIVERSITY LAW JOURNAL 13 (Fall 2003); Institute of Medicine, UNEQUAL TREATMENT: CONFRONTING RACIAL AND ETHNIC INEQUITIES IN HEALTH CARE, Committee on Understanding and Eliminating Racial and Ethnic Inequities in Health Care 171-173 (Brian D. Smedley, Adrienne Y. Stith, & Alan R. Nelson eds. 2003).

[161]*Id.*.

[162]*Id.*.

[163]David R. Williams, *Race, Health, And Health Care*, *supra* note 159.

[164]Susan T. Fiske, *Controlling Other People: The Impact of Power on Stereotyping*, 48 AMERICAN PSYCHOLOGIST 621, 627 (1993); Susan T. Fiske & Peter Glick, *Ambivalence and Stereotypes Cause Sexual Harassment: A Theory with Implications for Organizational Change*, JOURNAL OF SOCIOLOGICAL ISSUES 97, 119-112 (Spring 1995); Samuel L. Gaertner et al., *Reducing Intergroup Bias: Elements of Intergroup Cooperation*, 76 JOURNAL OF PERSONALITY AND SOCIAL PSYCHOLOGY 388, 398 (1999).

[165]House of Representatives Document Number 318, 88th Congress, 2d Session (1964); Stan Dorn, et.al., *Anti-Discrimination Provisions and Health Care Access: New Slants on Old Approaches*, 20 CLEARINGHOUSE REVIEW 439, 441 (Special Issue, Summer 1986) at 439- 40; Sidney Watson., *Reinvigorating Title VI*, *supra* note 144.

[166]45 Code of Federal Regulations § 80.3(b)(2) (1991) (Emphasis Added).
[167]45 Code of Federal Regulations Section 80.13(I) (1991).
[168]42 United States Code Annotated Section 2000d-1 (1981); 42 United States Code Annotated 2000d-4 (1981).
[169]45 Code of Federal Regulations Section 80.3(b)(6)(I) (1991).
[170]45 Code of Federal Regulations Section 80.3(b)(I)(Vii)(2) (1991) {Health Education and Welfare)
[171]*Id.*
[172]45 Code of Federal Regulations Section 80.3(b)(1)(I) (1991).
[173]45 Code of Federal Regulations Section 80.3(b)(1)-(3) (1991).
[174]*Id.*
[175]*Alexander v. Sandoval*, 532 United States 275, 280 (2001).
[176]Jessie Allen, *Unthinking Discrimination, supra* note 155.
[177]Sidney Watson, *Reinvigorating Title VI, supra* note 144; Vernellia R. Randall, *Racist Health Care, supra* note5; Marianne Engelman Lado, *Breaking The Barriers Of Access To Health Care, supra* note 145; Daniel K. Hampton, *Title VI Challenge, supra* note 145.
[178]28 Code of Federal Regulations Section 42.406(a) (1992); 45 Code of Federal Regulations Section 80.6(b) (1991).
[179]Sidney Watson, *Health Care in the Inner City, supra* note 109.
[180]*Id.*
[181]45 Code of Federal Regulations Section 80.6(3) (1991), 12 80.3(b) (1991); Sidney Watson, *Health Care in the Inner City, supra* note 109.
[182]Sidney Watson, *Health Care in the Inner City, supra* note 109.
[183]*Id.*
[184]*Lesley v. Chief*, 250 Federal3d 47, 53 (1st Circuit 2001); *Howe v. Hull*, 874 Federal Supplement 779, 789 (Northern District Ohio 1994).
[185]United States Commission on Civil Rights, THE HEALTH CARE CHALLENGE: VOLUME II, *supra* note 134.
[186]*Id.*
[187]*Desnick v. American Broadcasting*, 44 Federal Reports3d 1345, 1352 (1995); Stan Dorn, *Anti-discrimination Provisions and Health Care Access, supra* note 164.
[188]Desnick v. American Broadcasting Companies, Inc.,, *supra* note 192.
[189]Ian Ayres, *Fair Driving: Gender and Race Discrimination in Retail Car Negotiations*, 104 HARVARD LAW REVIEW 817 (1991); Stephen E. Haydons, *A Measure of Our Progress: Testing for Race Discrimination in Public Accommodations*, 44 UNIVERSITY OF CALIFORNIA AT LOS ANGELES LAW REVIEW 1207 (April, 1997).
[190]42 United State Codes § 3604.
[191]Stephen E. Haydons, *A Measure of Our Progress, supra* note 193; *Havens Realty Corporation v. Coleman.* 455 United States 363 (1982).
[192]Michael J. Yelnosky, *Filling an Enforcement Void: Using Testers to Uncover and Remedy Discrimination in Hiring for Lower-Skilled, Entry-Level Jobs*, 26 UNIVERSITY OF MICHIGAN JOURNAL OF LAW REFORM 403 (1993); Alex S. Navarro, *Bona Fide Damages for Tester Plaintiffs: An Economic Approach to Private Enforcement of the Antidiscrimination Statutes*, 81 Georgia Law Journal 2727 (1993).
[193]*Linda R.S. v. Richard D.*, 410 United States 614, 617 note 3 (1973) citing *Hardin v. Kentucky Utilities Company*, 390 United States 1, 6, 88 Supreme Court 651, 654, 19 L.Ed. 2d 787 (1968).
[194]*Alexander v. Sandoval, supra* note 174.
[195]Derek Black, *Picking up the Pieces after Alexander V. Sandoval: Resurrecting a Private Cause of Action for Disparate Impact*, 81 NORTH CAROLINA LAW REVIEW 356 (December, 2002).
[196]*Id.*
[197]*Id.*
[198]*Id.*

[199]David Williams, *Race/Ethnicity and Socioeconomic Status: Measurement and Methodological Issues*, 26(3) INTERNATIONAL JOURNAL OF HEALTH SERVICES 483-505 (1996).

[200]United States Commission on Civil Rights, THE HEALTH CARE CHALLENGE I, *supra* note 135 at 50-52.

[201]David Williams, *Race/Ethnicity and Socioeconomic Status, supra* note 202.

[202]Marianne Engleman Lado, *Unfinished Agenda: the Need for Civil Rights Litigation to Address Race Discrimination and Inequalities in Health Care Delivery*, 6 TEXAS FORUM ON CIVIL LIBERTIES. & CIVIL RIGHTS 1 (Summer 2001); *Madison-Hughes v. Shalala*, 80 Federal3d 1121, at 1123 (6th Circuit 1996); United States Commission on Civil Rights, FEDERAL TITLE VI ENFORCEMENT TO ENSURE NONDISCRIMINATION IN FEDERALLY ASSISTED PROGRAMS 246 (Washington, D.C, 1996), at 246.

[203]United States Commission on Civil Rights, THE HEALTH CARE CHALLENGE I, *supra* note 135 at 50-52.

[204]*Id.*

[205]F. Frost, et. al., *Racial Misclassification of Native Americans in Surveillance Epidemiology and End Results Cancer Registry*, 84 JOURNAL OF NATIONAL CANCER INSTITUTE 957-962 (1992); R.D. Kennedy & R.D. Deapen, *Differences Between Oklahoma and Indian Infant Mortality and Other Races*, 106 PUBLIC HEALTH REPORT 97-99 (1991)8198; David Williams, *Race/Ethnicity and Socioeconomic Status, supra* note 202.

[206]*IJd.*

[207]David Williams, *Race/Ethnicity and Socioeconomic Status, supra* note 202.

[208]*Id.*

[209]United States. Commission on Civil Rights, THE HEALTH CARE CHALLENGE I, *supra* note 135.

[210]David Williams, *Race/Ethnicity and Socioeconomic Status, supra* note 202.

[211]Washington State Department Of Health, DATA REPORT ON PEOPLE OF COLOR 33.

[212]David R. Williams, *Race and Health: Basic Questions, Emerging Directions*, 7 ANNALS OF EPIDEMIOLOGY 322-333 (July 1997).

[213]C. Bagley, *A Plea for Ignoring Race and Including Insured Status in American Research Reports on Social Science and Medicine*, 40 SOCIAL SCIENCE MEDICINE 1017-1019 (1995); David R. Williams, *Race and Health, supra* note 215.

[214]David R. Williams, *Race and Health, supra* note 215.

[215]*Id.*

[216]Vernellia R. Randall, *Racist Health Care, supra* note 5.

[217]David R. Williams, *Race and Health, supra* note 215.

[218]James M. Jones, Prejudice and Racism 352-356 (1997).

[219]David Barton Smith, *Addressing Racial Inequities in Health Care, supra* note 144.

[220]Rene Bowser, *Racial Profiling in Health Care, supra* note 153; H. Jack Geiger, *Race and Health Care: An American Dilemma*, 335 New England Journal of Medicine 815, 816 (1996); David Barton Smith, Race and Healing a Nation, *supra* note 144.

[221]David Barton Smith, *Addressing Racial Inequities in Health Care, supra* note 144.

[222]Alain C. & Carol B. Vorhaus Enthoven, *A Vision of Quality in Health Care Delivery*, Health Affairs, May/June 1997; National Commission on Quality Assurance, Health Plan and Employer Data Information Set (Version 3.0 1998); David Barton Smith, Race and Healing a Nation, *supra* note 144.

[223]Sidney D. Watson, *Book Review Essay Health Care Divided: Race and Healing a Nation David Barton Smith*, 21 Journal of Legal Medicine 601 (December, 2000).

[224]Sidney D. Watson, *Book Review Essay Health Care Divided, supra* note 226.

[225]Stephen E. Haydons, *A Measure of Our Progress, supra* note 193.

[226]*Fair Housing Council Finds Discrimination Against Hispanics in DC*, 66 Number 40 Interpreter Releases 1154 (October 16, 1989).

[227]Macon Dandridge Miller, *Catalysts as Prevailing Parties Under the Equal Access to Justice Act*, 69 University of Chicago Law Review 1347 (Summer 2002).

[228]*Stanton v Southern Berkshire Regional School District*, 197 Federal3d 574, 577 (1st Circuit 1999); *Marbley v Bane*, 57 Federal3d 224, 234 (2nd Circuit 1995); *Baumgartner v Harrisburg Housing Authority*, 21 Federal3d 541, 551 (3rd Circuit 1994); *Environmental Defense Fund, Inc. v Environmental Protection Agency*, 716 Federal2d 915, 919 (DC Circuit 1983).

[229]Jason P. Pogorelec, UNDER WHAT CIRCUMSTANCES DID CONGRESS INTEND TO AWARD PUNITIVE DAMAGES FOR VICTIMS OF UNLAWFUL INTENTIONAL DISCRIMINATION UNDER TITLE VII?, 40 BOSTON COLLEGE LAW REVIEW 1269 (September, 1999).

[230]Jason P. Pogorelec, PUNITIVE DAMAGES FOR VICTIMS, *supra* note 233.

[231]Mathew J. Klaben, *Split-Recovery Statutes: The Interplay of the Takings and Excessive Fines Clauses*, 80 CORNELL LAW REVIEW 104, 105 (1994); Leo M. Stepanian II, *The Feasibility of Full State Extraction of Punitive Damages Awards*, 32 DUQUESNE LAW REVIEW 301, 317 (1994).

[232]*Id.*

[233]Sidney D. Watson, *Reinvigorating Title VI: Defending Shouldn't Be So Easy*, *supra* note 144; David Barton Smith, HEALTH CARE DIVIDED, *supra* note 144; David Barton Smith, ADDRESSING RACIAL INEQUITIES IN HEALTH CARE, *supra* note 144; Vernellia R. Randall, *Racist Health Care*, *supra* note 5.

[234]Barbara A. Noah, *Racial Inequities in the Delivery of Health Care*, *supra* note 145; Daniel K. Hampton, *Title VI Challenges*, *supra* note 145; Barbara Noah, *Racist Health Care?*, 35 SAN DIEGO LAW Review 135 (1998); Marianne Engelman Lado, *Breaking The Barriers Of Access To Health Care*, *supra* note 145.

[235]*Id.*

[236]Elena Nightingale, et al., *Apartheid Medicine: Health and Human Rights in South Africa*, 264 Journal of the American Medical Association 2097, 2102 (1990).

[237]W.E.B. Dubois, BLACK RECONSTRUCTION 703 (1962); Louis L. Knowles & Kenneth Prewitt, INSTITUTIONAL RACISM IN AMERICA 1 (1969).

# Index

Note: Page numbers followed by "c" indicates a chart; page numbers followed by "t" indicates a table; page numbers in *italics* indicate figures; "para." indicates paragraph.

## A

Abortion
    Black's attitudes towards, 126
    Blacks/Whites, rates of, 126t
    divisiveness of, 126
    right-to-life v. pro-choice and, 127
Acquired immune deficiency disease (AIDS), 44
African American organizations, and tobacco money, 97
African Americans. *See* Blacks
Africans
    breaking in periods of, 35
    enslavement of, 35–36
    interior trek of, 32
    middle passage of, 32–34
Afrocentric bioethics, 134
Agassiz, Louis, 125
AHA. *See* American Hospital Association
AIDS. *See* acquired immune deficiency disease
Alabama, and Tuskegee Syphilis Experiment lawsuit, 121
*Alexander v. Sandoval* decision, 171
Allied Research Center, 139
Almshouses, 107
Alvin Ailey American Dance Theater, 97
American Health Foundation, on smoking, 100
American Hospital Association (AHA), 107
*An American Health Dilemma: A Medical History of African Americans and the Problem of Race, 1900 to 2000* (Byrd & Clayton), 31
*An American Health Dilemma: A Medical History of African Americans and the Problems of Race, Beginnings to 1900* (Byrd & Clayton), 31

## B

Barriers
    to health care institutions, 76–80
    to health care providers, 80–81
    to hospitals, 76–80
    to long term care, 81–84
    to physicians, 80–81
    racial, to health care, 64
*Bell v. Buck* decision, 124–125

Disparities. See Health inequities.
Dissatisfaction, definition of, 29
Distributive justice, 21
Distrust. *See* Black's distrust
Dixon, Julian, 97
DMHIA. *See* Disadvantaged Minority Health Improvement Act
Dubois, W. E., 179

**E**

*Ebony* magazine, 95, 97
Education/preventive services, 156–158
Elimination of Racial Discrimination Committee, 145–146
   selected concluding observations
      bringing end to racial discrimination (para. 392), 153
      Committee's concern regarding affirmative action (para. 399), 154
      Committee's concern regarding equal opportunities (para. 398), 153
      Federal Government's obligation (para. 383), 153
      State Party obligations to Convention (para. 393), 153
      state's consistent application of provisions(para. 390), 153
      U.S., periodic reports (para. 380), 153
Emergency Medical Treatment and Active Labor Act, 79
Environmental hazards, eradication of, 159
Epidemics (cholera/small pox/yellow fever), 38
Equality health care council, 176
Ervin, Frank R., 127
*Essence* magazine, 95
Eugenics programs, 127–128
Eurocentric bioethical perspective, 118, 134–135

**F**

Family planning clinics, 124–125
Feagin, Joe, 45
Federal Initiative to Combat Violence. *See* Violence Initiative
Fee-for-service providers
   full risk-shifting, 112
   no risk-sharing, 112
Females, Blacks
   age-adjusted death rates, 51t
   death rates of, 44
   excess deaths, all causes, 52t, 54t, 56t
   excess deaths, selected causes/years, 53t
   life expectancy of, 41, 50t
Females, life expectancy at birth, international comparison, 59t

Whites
    abortion rates of, 126t
    becoming, as cure for *Negritude,* 66
    death rates of, 48t
    and health insurance, 161–162
    middle class, health of, 27
    racist roots of, 156
    self-health descriptions by, 47, 61t
    and smoking, 19, 94, 99–102
    upper class, health of, 27
WHO. *See* World Health Organization
Wicker, Tom, 156
Withholding, definition of, 116
Women
    slaves, as breeders, 131
    Third World, exploitation of, 131
World Health Organization (WHO), 24
World War II, Black labor during, 70

**Y**

Yellow fever epidemic, 38
Young, Margaret B., 96
Young, Whitney, 96

1 Narcicuss Randles (Great-Grandmother)
2 Manlis Randles (Great-Grandfather)
3 Narcicuss's Sister Name Unknown
4 Arlee Hall (Uncle)
5 Mary Pauline Hall (Mother)
6 James Hall (Uncle)
7 Maude McGill Hall Grandmother
8 John Elmer Hall (Uncle)
9 Jesse Hall (Grandfather)
10 Jim McGill (Great-Grandfather)
11 Helen Hall Johnson
12 Teresa Hall Reid
13 Francis Craddock McGill (Great Grandmother)
14 Barbara Hall Bowie (aunt)
15 Tom Randall (Grandfather)
16 Cora Phillips Randall (Grandmother)
17 Brenda Randall Randall (Sister)
18 Vernellia Randall (Author)
19 James Ernest Randall (Brother)
20 James Carey Randall (Uncle)
21 Mary Randall Talley (Aunt)
22 Ora Randall Carey (Aunt)
23 Ernest Randall (Dad)
24 Elmer Randall (Uncle)
25 Arthur Randall (Uncle)
26 Issa Randall (Son)
27 Tshaka Randall (Son)
28 Tonya Dewberry (niece)
29 LeEartha Randall (Sister-in-law)
30 Korrie Nikole Randall (niece)
31 Gina Natasha Randall (niece)
32 Jerry Edward Randall (brother)

# Dying While Black!

Help your friends, family and co-worker understand the crisis in black health and health care by giving them a copy of this book. .

Quantity discounts are available as follows:

| | |
|---|---|
| 2 – 4 books | 15% |
| 5 – 9 books | 20% |
| 10 – 19 books | 25% |
| 20 or more books | 30% |

To get a quantity discount the following is applicable:
- Discounts apply to two or more copies.
- All books must be sent to the same address.
- These discounts apply only to orders placed directly with Seven Principles Press. Please do not ask for a discount at your book store.

To order go to the website:
http://sevenprinciplespress.com.

CPSIA information can be obtained at www.ICGtesting.com
Printed in the USA
BVOW05s0814231115

428156BV00001B/23/P